MEDICINE AT THE PARIS HOSPITAL, 1794–1848

MEDICINE
AT THE
PARIS HOSPITAL

1794-1848

BY ERWIN H. ACKERKNECHT, M.D.

THE JOHNS HOPKINS PRESS, BALTIMORE

Copyright © 1967 by The Johns Hopkins Press
Baltimore, Maryland 21218
Printed in the United States of America

Library of Congress Catalog Card No. 66–23003

To Lilian and Owsei Temkin

PREFACE   The symbol of the doctor from the Middle Ages to the eighteenth century was the urinal. The symbol of the modern doctor is the stethoscope, one of the many contributions the Paris clinical school made to medicine between 1794 and 1848. A history of this school seems a legitimate enterprise.

Since 1948, I have published some twenty papers on different aspects of the history of the Paris school. Yet this book is not a collection of those papers. It is a new book. Only three of its seventeen chapters are drawn from the old papers. Those who want to know more details concerning the problems dealt with in the papers should refer back to them.

The same holds good for the fourteen theses that have been written under my supervision on the history of the specialties in the Paris school. I have used here only a very small part of the material they contain. I would like to take this occasion to thank for their kind cooperation the authors—Drs. G. Bass, B. Bianchetti, F. Ebneter, A. Gadient, G. Geller, E. Häfliger, I. Mantel, P. Fischer, S. Müller, U. Mutzner, J. R. Nyffeler, D. Schneider, P. Weidmann, and B. Wigdorowits—and the librarian of our Zurich Institute, Miss Margaret Curti, who was very helpful in bringing together the material for the theses.

In spite of its great value, I have not discussed in any detail the work of the physiologists, microscopists, chemists, or other French scientists of the period. I did this for the simple reason that I am writing a medical history, and that the philosophy or the prejudices of the Paris clinicians effectively prevented their incorporating the discoveries of other branches of science into medicine.

The footnotes contain only abbreviated titles. Full titles are found in the bibliography at the end of the book. The latter is limited strictly to books quoted in the text; it cannot contain all the material examined. In general, I have tried to offer the essential elements of the story but to keep the book as short as possible. I wanted it to be read, not simply consulted as a kind of handbook.

Many people have helped me during the long years of incubating this book. It is unfortunately impossible to mention them all. I owe special thanks to the American Philosophical Society for financing a research trip to Paris in the summer of 1951; to the librarians of the Paris Academy of Medicine, the Musée de l'Homme, the Paris and Nantes Faculties of Medicine, and the University of Wisconsin Medical School; to the late and much-regretted Dr. Paul Delaunay of Le Mans, with whom I discussed my research problems repeatedly between 1951 and 1956; and to my wife Edith, who showed great patience with the well-known peculiarities of men in the book-producing stage.

The frontispiece is a reproduction of the Charles Méryon etching of 1850, "Le Petit Pont" (Delteil 24), from an original in my collection. It shows the old Hôtel Dieu, which appears so often in this book. The vignettes which open the chapters are all from Honoré Daumier's illustrations for A. F. H. Fabre's collection of satirical poems, *Némésis médicale*, published in Paris in 1840.

For several reasons I like this book better than those I have written previously. I hope that, after perusing it, my readers will feel the same way.

ERWIN H. ACKERKNECHT

Zurich, June, 1966

TABLE OF CONTENTS

INTRODUCTION   When, in 1845, the doctors of France held
their first national assembly, they decided quite appropriately to place a
statue of Bichat by David d'Angers in the courtyard of the Faculty of
Medicine at Paris, Rue de l'École de Médecine. There he still stands in the
beauty and glory of his eternal youth, symbol of the generation that chased
the Diafoirus from French medicine and a symbol of its greatest moments.
There he stands at the spot which, for 110 years, was the center of Parisian
and of French medicine and, for fifty-five years, the center of world medicine
—"the first faculty of the universe," as Monfalcon wrote in 1819.

It is of these fifty-five years that we will speak in the following account.
Their medicine was not our modern "laboratory medicine"; but it was not
ancient "bedside medicine" either. Nor do we deal here with a medical
"transition period," even if one wants to use this basically meaningless
notion. These fifty-five years represent, in spite of their brevity, a whole
epoch in medicine; they saw the rise of a quite specific and unique type of
medicine which, after its central element, we have called "hospital medicine."
Though this school incorporated quite a few elements of, for example,
British, Viennese, and Italian medicine, it also created something new and
original. Many of its protagonists felt that, after 1794, they were only
reviving the Hippocratic tradition, to which French and British medicine
had long been far more attached than had, for example, German medicine.
That this medical tradition had survived so long was not too surprising in
view of the fact that it operated in a world which had changed very little,
technologically, since the days of the sage of Cos.

But in fact, despite all its verbal Hippocratisms and Galenic survivals,
the new medicine that was practiced and taught at Paris was born out of a
political and technological revolution. It was a medicine based on techniques
and concepts unknown to the ancients and their followers—one based on
physical examination by hand and ear, on pathological anatomy, on statistics,
and on the concept of the lesion. The inordinate interest of the period in
pathological anatomy was reflected even in such details as the publication
of the autopsy results of many famous contemporaries (for example, Louis
XVIII, Saint-Simon, Broussais, Gall, and Dupuytren). It was a most characteristic expression of the spirit of this new school when Cruveilhier re-
proached the past for having seen many diseased people, but almost no
diseases, and when Georget said, "You should paint diseases rather than
diseased people."

To study this medicine, famous for its realism and the extreme rapidity
of its rise, to see a school in which medicine and surgery were reunited after

1600 years of separation, and to attend the performances of the virtuosos of diagnostics, whose powers of observation were as great as their technical aids were limited, students and doctors from all over the world streamed into Paris for about six decades. They went almost exclusively to Paris, since the centralism of the Revolution had made Paris the undisputed center of France, medically as well as politically.

We report in the following on only fifty-five years of medical history in one capital city; but what years, politically and medically speaking! And these were years in which, by the way, political and medical changes generally coincided. The new school and the new medicine were children of the Revolution, originating in the tumult, cold, and hunger of the year III (1794). Robespierre was dead, but the Jacobins still ruled. The invaders had been pushed back, and French troops had begun to march into Holland and Spain. Full of utopian fantasies, the Revolution had set out to abolish hospitals, medical schools, and doctors (see Chapters I, II, and IV); instead, it created new hospitals and new and better schools for doctors as well as for veteri-narians and pharmacists.

Its social accomplishments made the Revolution to a certain extent irrever-sible. It gave poor country boys like Dupuytren, Richerand, Duméril, Moreau, and Ribes a chance to study medicine; under its self-styled imperial continuator Napoleon, who liked to use scientists as ministers, they became barons, millionaires, and chevaliers—or at least professors. This rise of gifted poor boys continued with Esquirol, Billard, Béclard, and Georget. The first twenty years of the new medicine, the years of revolution and empire, were dominated by Pinel and Corvisart. At the end of this long war period, medicine showed signs of fatigue, as did the whole nation. Thus the area of Pinel and Corvisart ended, as its successor did later, in a large epidemic—the typhus of 1814.

The Restoration (1814–1830) was, in spite of its official conservatism, an extremely lively period, freer and more productive than the stiff military society of Napoleon. Carbonarism and Saint-Simonism wrestled with Catholic conservatism in a fight for the minds of the young generation. In medicine, the radical Broussais was able to dominate; his royalist adversary, Laennec, resisted, but did not live to see the triumph of his medically equally progressive ideas. In February, 1830, Victor Hugo won the "battle of Hernani." This period ended with the cholera epidemic of 1832, in which their heroism, already displayed during the July Revolution of 1830, made doctors very popular.

The long reign of Louis Philippe (1830–1848), the "bourgeois king," saw the full bloom of middle-class society. In medicine, the so-called eclectics—Andral, Louis, Bouillaud, Piorry, Rostan, Rayer, and Trousseau—dominated the scene. The conquest of Algeria, begun in 1830, was to continuously influence French politics and medicine for well over a century to come.

In 1848, a new medicine, "laboratory medicine," made its appearance in Paris under the leadership of Louis Pasteur, Claude Bernard, and the Société de Biologie. While all the warring factions of the preceding fifty-five years had had a common ground in pathological anatomy, "laboratory medicine" did not. For many decades, it was unable to conquer French medicine, despite the fact that, by 1848, Paris "hospital medicine" had come to a dead end, its momentum spent. There was undoubtedly a connection between the political fate of France in and after 1848 and later medical events. Thus we feel that our periodization from 1794 to 1848 is justifiable from the point of view of medical, as well as political and cultural, history.

Today, these lines of evolution are clearly visible. Yet we should never forget that, at all times, doctors of all possible persuasions were practicing in Paris and that the medicines of the past, present, and future were coexisting there. Therefore, the picture which offered itself to contemporary observers was bound to be a rather chaotic one.

During our period (1794–1848) Paris witnessed not only political and medical triumphs, but an extraordinary flourishing of science and general culture. We can suggest this dynamic background to medical events by mentioning only a few names. Scientific contemporaries of our movement were Laplace, Gay-Lussac, Monge, A. von Humboldt, Cuvier, and Lamarck, and in the social sciences, Guizot, A. Thierry, Michelet, De Tocqueville, Comte, Boucher de Perthes, and Proudhon.

Great names in literature were V. Hugo, Musset, Balzac, Stendhal, Flaubert, and Baudelaire; in their time, they were probably no greater than those of George Sand, Béranger, Casimir Delavigne, E. Sue, or F. Pyat. Rossini, Chopin, Berlioz, and Liszt were the great contemporary musicians. Rahel was the great actress. David and Ingres painted the society in which our doctors found their patients, and Dantan Jeune and Daumier caricatured it. David d'Angers sculpted the great in politics, science, and literature. The fame of Delacroix has survived that of Horace Vernet or Ary Scheffer. Ceasing after 1815 to be the political capital city of the world, Paris became its intellectual capital.

It is to a certain extent possible to relive our period by walking through the cemetery Père Lachaise in Paris. There almost all those who made this period great in politics, in the arts, and in science are reunited in death. Larrey, Dupuytren, Hahnemann, P. Ricord, G. L. Bayle, Béclard, Gall, Raspail, Villermé, and Trousseau sleep there next to Casimir Périer, Thiers, Saint-Simon, Michelet, Balzac, Delacroix, David, Chopin, Rossini, Arago, G. Saint-Hilaire, and Cuvier.

The pre-Haussmann city in which our story starts was still almost medieval. Incredible filth lined the dark, narrow streets, which were often not paved. There were few sewers and poor water supplies. An enormous amount of poverty, hunger, and misery was often, according to Paris custom, concentrated in the upper floors of houses, while the powerful and wealthy lived below. The doctor saw them all. Prisons for debtors still existed. A new technology was beginning to change this world. The 1820's brought gas lighting, and the 1830's railroads (which were opposed by Arago and Thiers). The first railroad accident, in 1842, left an extraordinary impression on medical men like Villermé, P. Ricord, and De Man, as well as on poets like De Vigny. On May 1, 1839, a large exhibition of industrial products opened in Paris. In that same year, Arago announced Daguerre's discovery of photography. Under the Restoration, students and military men were the main exponents of antigovernment activities; under Louis Philippe, an increasing number of strikes pointed toward certain negative aspects of economic growth and middle-class prosperity, which eventually erupted in 1848. They also, as we will see in more detail, created medical problems.

As a whole, this was a period of great medical advances, which have to be seen in their own rhythm as well as influencing and influenced by great scientific, technological, cultural, and economic advances. The medical advances were by no means restricted to diagnostics; they were also observable in therapeutics and preventive medicine. A most characteristic phenomenon was the development of specialties like psychiatry, pediatrics, dermatology, orthopedics, urology, otology, and legal medicine. These specialties were only one of the many contributions of this period that still play an important role in our own medicine.

MEDICINE AT THE PARIS HOSPITAL, 1794–1848

I. PHILOSOPHY

A vast philosophical movement had preceded the great political Revolution of 1789. The beginnings of the medical revolution, daughter of the larger political event, were likewise profoundly influenced by a certain philosophy. The "medicine of observation" was fathered by a "philosophy of observation." Later stages of the Paris school were also formed or reflected by philosophical attitudes.

The best-known philosopher of the medical revolution was Pierre Jean Georges Cabanis. His influence was widespread and lasting. Ten years after Cabanis' death, Rayer dedicated his thesis to him, and Cabanis' name still appeared frequently in the third decade of the nineteenth-century medical literature. Though he does not strike us today as a great philosopher by any means, he put his stamp not only on medical men, but also on writers like Saint-Simon, Comte, B. Constant, Stendhal, Sainte-Beuve, De Vigny, and Flaubert. It seems that it is response to need for explanation rather than profundity that makes a philosopher influential.

Cabanis was one of the most prominent members of a philosophical group called the *idéologues*,[1] which was composed of La Reveillère, Destutt de Tracy, Garat, Gallois, Laromiguière, Thurot, and Fauriel, among others, and which developed the "sensualist" philosophy of Condillac in different ways. Cabanis was by no means the only disciple of Condillac in medicine. Félix Vicq d'Azyr (1748–1794), the very influential but short-lived secretary of the Royal Society of Medicine, was a sensualist too.

Cabanis, born in 1757 in Rognac in southwestern France, son of a jurist father who wrote books on scientific gardening, came to Paris at fourteen and graduated there in medicine in 1783. Turgot introduced him to Mme Helvetius, the widow of the philosopher, at whose salon he met such representatives of the Enlightenment as Condillac, Diderot, D'Alembert, Condorcet, Jefferson, Franklin, Chamfort, Morrillet, D'Holbach, and Roussel.

As the friend and physician of Mirabeau, he was, in spite of his youth, an active participant in the earlier states of the Revolution. He survived the Terror in rural retirement at Auteuil. After the fall of Robespierre, he again came to the foreground. He drafted the proclamation endorsing Napoleon's *coup d'état* of 18 *Brumaire* (November 9, 1799). But General Bonaparte soon discarded his liberal philosophical helpers. Cabanis was thus given back to medicine and philosophy. He published on the reform of hospitals and medical education, on certitude in medicine (1797), on the relations of the physical and the moral in man (1802—his most famous book), on catarrh (1803), and on the revolutions and reform in medicine (1804). He was professor of hygiene, and later professor of medical history and clinical medicine at the École de Santé; member of the Institute; and member of the central hospital administration. He died from apoplexy in 1808. Like many other materialists of his time (Broussais, Georget), he left a spiritualist letter, a kind of deathbed confession, which was published after his death.

Cabanis always had close political connections—for example, his fellow *idéologues* and Napoleon's Minister of the Interior, Chaptal. His wife was the sister of Marshal de Grouchy and Mme Condorcet. He admired Franklin tremendously and would probably have liked to be the Franklin of the French Revolution. But Napoleon was no Washington.

He furthered the careers of his medical fellow *idéologues*—Pinel, Moreau de la Sarthe, Richerand, Alibert, and Pariset—a group to which Sainte-Beuve referred somewhat contemptuously as "les médecins écrivains." Saucerotte has said of the doctors in the Revolution, "Primarily the mediocre physicians went into politics." Cabanis was probably a better practitioner than has been realized; but essentially Saucerotte's statement seems to hold good for him too. He was primarily a philosopher and a politician—but a "good and honest" politician, according to Virey.[2]

Cabanis was a sensualist in the tradition of Locke and Condillac; sense impressions were, to him, the basic psychological events. "When we feel, we are."[3] His whole physiology was a physiology of sense impressions. Hippocrates was, to him, the first sensualist; he had liberated medicine from the philosophers, invented the true method of observation,[4] and was therefore the greatest physician of all time.[5] Observation was, to the sensualist, quite logically the center of medicine. Even man's negative traits, like the embracing of chimeras or having shameful prejudices, were considered a consequence of his "too great sensitivity."[6] Philosophical sensualism, as a product of the Enlightenment, was application-minded and thus, was bound to support certain tendencies in social, educational, and medical reform. In particular, it furthered interest in improved diagnostic procedures and favored pioneering attempts in psychotherapy. Likewise, it was no accident that Pinel, Bayle, Alibert, and their colleagues, emphasized the necessity of "picturing" diseases and that illustrated medical books became far more frequent.

"The true instruction of young doctors is not received from books, but at the sickbed," said Cabanis.[7] That was why, at the beginning of the Revolution, he suggested clinical schools of the sort that his teacher Dubrueil had installed at the navy hospitals of Brest and Toulon.[8]

Like all *idéologues*, Cabanis used the method of "analysis" in approaching a problem. He differentiated four species of analysis.[9] "Analysis," for him, seemed to mean an elaboration of Descartes' famous rule, "Divide difficulties." Cabanis refined sensualism by differentiating three types of "sensations": those produced by the external sense organs, those arising from internal impressions, and those arising in the brain itself.[10] The French interest in cenesthesia seems to go back to him.

The brain, center of all sensory functions, which produced "thought like the liver bile, the parotis saliva,"[11] and the whole nervous system were, for the sensualist, of prime importance. Temperament was a question of the nervous system;[12] the influence of the moral on the physical was ultimately the influence of the cerebral system.[13] Medicine was therefore the basis of the science of man[14]—and so, also, a "moral science."[15] It could participate in perfecting man, in that uninterrupted movement toward amelioration so essential in the philosophy of the Enlightenment.[16] This idea can, by the way, also be found in Descartes' *Discourse on Method*: "The spirit depends so much on the temperament and the arrangement of the bodily organs, that, if it is possible to find means to render man wiser and smarter than he has been so far, I believe they have to be looked for in medicine."

It was held that one should try to improve not only individuals, but the whole human race, as is done with horses.[17] "Crime is often, like madness, only a physical disease."[18] In turn, "man's diseases depend almost always on his own errors or those of society."[19] If, on the one hand, psychological difficulties can be remedied by physical means, "moral" psychological treatment can also do much for physical ailments. "How many people are killed or cured by imagination? Bacon claims that making new plans every day is a means of prolonging life."[20] "One should try immediately to develop a series of rules on how to use the soul for the re-establishment or conservation of health."[21]

Cabanis, still steeped in the classic tradition, was a medical "classicist." His pronouncements on "sympathies"[22] read like those of Fracastoro. He was a climatist in the Hippocratic tradition, siding with Montesquieu and Hallé against Helvetius and Volney. Even the post-Revolutionary Paris school was far more classicist than is usually realized. Till 1832, every inaugural (M.D.) thesis was closed by some aphorisms of Hippocrates, and the theses for the *agrégation* (competitive examinations prerequisite for university faculty positions) were written in Latin. Cabanis himself felt that Galen's influence was still stronger than was publicly admitted; "Medical practice still reflects his long tyranny, even now, when no enlightened person would dare to call himself an adherent of Galen."[23] Only someone for whom medicine was still essentially classical medicine could pretend that "medical practice of all centuries is basically the same."[24] Cabanis retained the four classic tempera-ments, though he emphasized organs rather than humors as their basis, and added two new temperaments—one with predominance of the sensitive system and one based in the motor system. He coined the pre-Adlerian aphorism, "Every one of us has his strong and his feeble organ."[25] This solidistic adaptation of the old doctrine of temperaments began in 1798 with Hallé and Husson (vascular, nervous, muscular temperament) and was continued by Gerdy and Rostan.

Cabanis also had his roots deep in the eighteenth century. Stahl was, to him, the greatest physician since Hippocrates, mainly because he had ex-pelled physics and chemistry from medicine.[26] Cabanis spoke of "fevers" all the time. Occasionally, he correctly prognosticated the paths of future progress: "In order to make great discoveries in anatomy, we should now invent more perfect instruments."[27] But to the son of the eighteenth century, the essential problem was not discovery, but the proper classification of the existing knowledge; find a system, he thought, and in a short while, every-thing will be (almost) perfect. "Yes, I dare to predict: with the true spirit of observation, the philosophical spirit will be reborn in medicine. . . . One will reunite its [science's] dispersed fragments and will form of it a system simple and fertile as the laws of nature."[28] "Twenty-five to thirty years will be sufficient to verify all observations, to repeat all experiments. Then we have only to perfect the practical methods."[29] "We don't need new remedies; we need only a good method of using those we have."[30]

It is significant that his attitude toward pathological anatomy, which was to become the scientific backbone of medicine, was quite ambivalent. On the one hand, he saw its necessity; on the other, he disliked its "exclusiveness."[31]

Though Cabanis was a philosopher, a strong antimetaphysical, anti-theoretical feeling is observable in him. He "does physiology, not meta-physics."[32] "The theoretical part of a science must be simply its classifications and the relations of the facts composing this science. If theory does not severely observe these narrow limits, it produces but empty ghosts."[33] "Better no theory, than one contradicting certain facts."[34]

Cabanis spoke with great bitterness of the detrimental application of other sciences, especially of chemistry and physics, to medicine.[35] There was certainly much to be said for this opinion. Even in 1809, medicine could not be based on the then existing sciences. On the other hand, Cabanis' opinion (shared by his friend Jefferson) that it was doubtful whether Harvey's discovery was of any actual usefulness[36] showed an embarrassing lack of understanding of the value of science.

In his disbelief in the usefulness of the auxiliary sciences, Cabanis consoled himself with the idea that primary causes (which, with him very much resembled all causes) not only could never be known,[37] but did not need to be known.[38] *Experience was sufficient.* It was, for example, useless to know the nature of quinine, antimony, or mercury.[39] The study of nature was, in general, that of facts, not causes.[40] He felt that the traditional medical literature reflected reality only very imperfectly.[41] Cabanis thus showed very strong elements of skeptical empiricism.

Revolutions are paradoxical by nature and very often end up accomplishing the opposite of what they set out to do. Our medical revolution was no exception to this rule. This revolution, which wanted to abolish hospitals, improved them[42] and made them the center of medicine; this revolution, which wanted to abolish official medical teaching,[43] created a new, particularly vigorous type of it; this revolution, which dreamed of abolishing medicine, opened a new medical era. All this reminds us somewhat of the Russian Revolution of 1917, which set out to "abolish the state."

Much of Cabanis' writing, especially his *On the Degree of Certitude in Medicine* of 1797, can only be fully understood when seen as a defense of medicine against these attempts to abolish it and against the accusations that it was "superstition" or "charlatanism"—accusations proffered by Rousseau, by the Jacobin "Know-Nothings," and by their erstwhile pupil Napoleon, and occasionally supported even by political doctors such as M. A. Baudot, F. Bousquet, and Guillemardet. Cabanis' efforts at defense were very necessary; official medical teaching was, after all, abolished between 1792 and 1794 and medical licensing, from 1792 to 1803. Fodéré speaks in 1793 of the "proscription" of internal medicine in the army.[44] Twenty years later, Corvisart, continuously needled by his imperial master, still felt obliged to come out vigorously in defense of medicine. And Rostan still fought this battle in 1864.

Cabanis argued against the abolition of medicine as follows: "Suffering man wants relief . . . therefore a universal faith in medicine. . . . Destroying medicine, one would not destroy her, but only deliver a greater number of defenseless victims into the hands of daring ignorance."[45] "Scurvy, venereal disease, malaria [and] dropsy are deadly, if they are not treated."[46] Cabanis also dreamed of a time when teaching would be free, but he knew that, in his time, the government had to organize it.[47] His fight for improved hospitals, which filled his whole career, was also ultimately directed toward the abolition of hospitals.

Some other contributions of Cabanis might at least be mentioned. Today he might be particularly appreciated for his semanticism[48] and for his psychosomatic orientation. Our fathers might have been more impressed by his evolutionist ideas[49] or by his clear differentiation between geno- and phenotype[50] under the names of "natural" and "acquired" temperament. Some passages on the secretion of ovaries and testicles into the blood make him one of the precursors of the idea of internal secretion.[51]

As the school developed, some of the philosophical tendencies of Cabanis survived. Above all, his leanings toward *skeptical empiricism* were more and more accepted and cultivated. It was no accident that the word "positive" was used more and more often in medical literature. Fodéré, for instance, published a *"physiologie positive"* in 1808. Rostan propagated *"des idées positives"* in 1826. Lallemand did the same in 1830, as did Bouillaud in 1836. The word "philosophy" tended to become rarer and rarer in medical titles. Philosophical remarks were no longer systematic, but accidental. The article "Philosophie" by Bricheteau, the mouthpiece of Pinel, in the *Dictionnaire des sciences médicales* (1820, 41:296), was the last of its kind in a medical dictionary. Subsequently, when the word "philosophy" was used, it was said that philosophy had become a branch of physiology.[52]

A German observer, Casper, reported in 1822 that the whole Paris school, above all Pinel, was "sensualist." Pinel resembled his fellow *idéologue* Cabanis in his admiration for Hippocrates, for observation, and for experience. He was against "getting lost in reasoning on objects inaccessible to human understanding," and against vain theories;[53] he did not "produce vain discussions of hypotheses."[54] He wanted statistics to be used as much as possible (which was not surprising in an ex-mathematician) and did so himself.[55] His disciple and collaborator Rostan repeated the old sensualist credo that one is instructed only through the senses: "The knowledge of causes is impossible and unimportant."[56] Pinel's most famous pupil, Bichat, another sensualist, felt that "knowledge of primary causes is almost always impossible,"[57] and opposed the use of microscopy, chemistry, and physics in medicine. But Bichat was far less opposed to theorizing than were the typical Paris clinicians of his time, and he was a fervent advocate of animal experimentation. In his hostility toward chemistry, Bichat echoed the traditions of the Montpellier school.

Pinel's competitor Corvisart, another Hippocratist, called his only book "a work of pure practice founded on observation and experience."[58] In his view, the senses were the faithful guides of observation and experience, and needed only a special medical education. Theories usually disappeared at the sickbed.[59] He had painted the following sentence on the wall of his lecture room: "Never do something important following pure hypothesis or simple opinion." Corvisart's pupil, the Hippocratist G. L. Bayle, claimed that he did not know the most important part of the laws that governed the human body in health and disease. He added piously that he had never been able to penetrate the secrets which the Almighty had reserved for Himself. Bayle limited himself to the examination of facts.[60] He used statistical methods. Corvisart and Bayle continued the defense of certitude in medicine, partly with the arguments of Cabanis.

Their pupil, the famous Laennec, a staunch Hippocratist, waved the flag of observation (Ars medica tota in observationibus was his motto) and limited himself to studying anatomical lesions in the dead, diagnosing them in the living, and giving remedies the value of which experience had confirmed.[61] No wonder that theories were to him only aids to memory—"scaffolds."[62] In his course of 1822, he even went so far as to say that only facts constituted science.[63] He held that the cause of pulmonary tuberculosis could not be found.[64] Laennec was very strongly opposed to medical microscopy in his treatise, and even more so in his course—a point of view (or prejudice) also found in the Encyclopédie and in Bichat, Cabanis, Blainville, and Trousseau (1:175). (Antimicroscopism has been traced back to Locke and Sydenham by D. E. Wolfe.) Peisse attacked microscopy as late as 1854 (1:175).

Chomel, the influential professor of internal pathology and physician of the Hôtel Dieu, was opposed to any systematic ideas. He deemed it impossible to know the causes of diseases or the effects of remedies, and called all discussions of insoluble questions unprofitable and dangerous.[65]

Probably nobody went farther along these lines than P. C. A. Louis, the "inventor" of the numerical method and, according to Henle, the greatest empiricist. Louis no longer referred to Hippocrates. His famous book on typhoid fever started with a Rousseau quotation: "I know that the truth is in the things and not in my mind which judges them. The less I put of my own into these judgments, the surer I am to approach the truth."[66] Louis, the great admirer of observation, and the founder of the Société d'Observation Médicale, became its great systematizer; systematic examinations and systematic autopsies were systematically analyzed through statistics. They were to him the solution of the contradictory position that one was opposed to theories, but needed a synthesis. Louis was by no means the first Paris clinician to use statistics, but he was the first to make them the basis of medicine. All earlier, "imprecise" medical literature thus became, to him, automatically worthless.

Louis abstained from formulating hypotheses. "True science is but a summary of facts [which] are of no value if they are not enumerated."[67]

> Statistics are the fundamental and only bases of all medical studies. The general facts are the laws of science; these general facts are but the collection of particular facts that have been distinguished, compared, and classified. None of these operations can be precise if one does not count the facts. So far we have not counted, or we have counted badly. All the authors' assertions that are only the result of poor induction, without statistics, or numerical analysis, or are based on remembered facts, can only be considered to be provisional.[68]

Louis hoped that statistics would provide him with that *methodus medendi* already adumbrated by Sydenham. For Louis, therapeutics could not be derived from pathology, anatomy, or physiology.[69] He disliked animal experimentation. Peisse showed that, under these circumstances, he often replaced animal with human experimentation. Aversion to animal experimentation was also expressed by Cuvier, Gall, Fodéré, Chaussier, Royer-Collard the elder, and Georget, and even the physiologist Adelon.[70] Louis' American pupil O. W. Holmes felt that science was taught primarily for mnemonic reasons.

Though in the next, the "eclectic," generation of Bouillaud and Rayer, the radical empiricism of Laennec and Louis and the skepticism of Corvisart and Andral lost ground, they remained strong enough among clinicians to provoke an attack by Claude Bernard in his *Introduction* of 1865. Much of this book can be understood only with this background in view.

The question arises: is the above a *post festum* construct, or did there really exist around 1830 a group of influential clinicians having a consistent philosophy on these issues, that is, on the role of theories, the character of science, the impossibility of knowing causality, the uselessness of certain sciences, and techniques for medicine, and the central role of statistics?

We felt greatly relieved in finding in Bouillaud's *Philosophie médicale* (1836) a whole chapter devoted to the "enemies of theories and systems in medicine."[71] This chapter constituted a contemporary attack on Laennec, Bayle, Louis, and Chomel, exactly on account of their "antitheorism." Bouillaud, a rather independent pupil of Broussais, a friend of Lallemand, a horrible therapist, but an excellent clinician and scientist, was philosophically far more advanced than his adversaries. He had no use for Chomel, but admired Laennec greatly as a clinician; he shared Louis' enthusiasm for the numerical method, yet did not adopt his somewhat primitive fears of theories and basic sciences. These fears, it must be admitted, are excusable, when we remember the miserable theorizing of the preceding century.

On most issues, Bouillaud was the exact opposite of the "classic" group, which took up the arguments used repeatedly by former radical empiricists in medical history (see Ackerknecht 1949). He was for reasoning in connection with observation and experimentation,[72] and even for certain research into causes. He saw the limitations of pathological anatomy and, in opposition to Bichat, advocated the use of physics and chemistry.[73] He likewise advocated animal experimentation and the use of the microscope. Hippocrates was no god to him. He poked fun at extreme sensualism. "An idiot," said Bouillaud, "can have his five senses highly developed." . . . (1836, 129)

That a consistent philosophy did exist behind the casual remarks of Laennec and Louis is further borne out in An Essay on the Philosophy of Medicine, a book by Louis' well-known American pupil, Elisha Bartlett. Bartlett, professor in many medical schools and the subject of an excellent essay by William Osler, was the author of a remarkable book on fevers in the United States and of a variation on Cabanis' essay regarding certainty in medicine. Summarizing his thought in a number of "theses," he gave a very concise form to the basic tenets of his medical philosophy. His theses were as follows: All science consists in ascertained facts; these facts can be ascertained only by observation or experience; all science is absolutely independent of hypothesis; a class of facts cannot be deduced from another class of facts; histology cannot be deduced from anatomy, nor physiology from anatomy, nor pathology from physiology, nor etiology nor therapeutics from pathology; causes are, in general, not attainable. Bartlett opposed the use of chemistry and animal experimentation. The best generalization was the numerical method. It is no exaggeration to say that each one of these theses can be found in the writings of the Paris clinicians, who were Bartlett's teachers. Many of these ideas were also repeated in Raige-Delorme's article on medicine in the Dictionnaire de médecine (1839, 19:194ff.).

Trousseau, the last of the great classic clinicians, believed that "from the day a young man wants to be a doctor, he must visit the hospitals."[74] Likewise, he would "profoundly regret the time the student would lose in acquiring too extensive chemical knowledge."[75] Though this pupil of Bretonneau was not at all opposed to hypotheses,[76] he thought little of science. "Science renders the mind lazy. Please, a little less science and a little more art, gentlemen."[77] He also rejected the numerical method.[78]

As early as 1798, Alibert had claimed that "the accessory sciences have not conquered medicine, medicine has conquered the accessory sciences."[79] It was typical that he said "accessory sciences" where we would say "basic sciences." No wonder that, as a result of this philosophy, Pasteur, Claude Bernard, Bichat, Magendie, Flourens, Paul Bert, Brown-Séquard, Donné, Davaine, and Duchenne were never professors in a French medical school or faculty. They were not suited to being "accessory" scientists. "Clinicism," as Abraham Flexner has baptized this particular form of myopia, had become the law in France. Radical empiricism had for a while played a very positive role in the rebirth of medicine, but it has led, eventually, to a dead end.

Since our study stops around 1848, the stormy appearances of medical positivism and experimentalism, as well as of the idealist reaction during the following decades, are beyond our self-imposed limits.[80]

II. THE HOSPITALS

The fact that Paris in 1794 possessed and had developed *hospitals*—the workshops of the new medicine—was no less important than philosophy for its emergence. "It is generally recognized that the true advances which medicine has made lately must almost all be attributed to those doctors who practice or observe in the hospital."[1] Or in the less benevolent formulation of Wunderlich, "The hospital is the backdrop of all medical thinking; all is applied in the hospital; all can be confirmed only there or in the autopsy room."[2]

Actually it was only in the hospital that the three pillars of the new medicine—physical examination, autopsy, and statistics—could be developed. It was no accident that the very extensive English and German medical travel literature of the period[3] centered around descriptions of the Paris hospitals. Never before—with one exception—had medicine been based in such a way on hospitals. The twelve beds of Boerhaave's clinic cannot be compared with the 20,341 persons residing in forty-eight Paris hospitals in 1788.[4] The exception, Vienna, was seriously handicapped in the elaboration of a new medicine by absolutism and traditionalism. On account of the strategic role of the hospital in the medicine of this period, I have called the latter "hospital medicine," thus differentiating it from the preceding "library" and "bedside" medicine and from the subsequent "laboratory medicine."[5]

For the leaders of the new school, from Cabanis, Pinel, and Corvisart, to Alibert, G. L. Bayle, and Laennec, to Rostan and Bouillaud,[6] it was axiomatic that the hospital was the center of teaching, and of research as well. We might add that a hospital position was also essential politically. A position in the hospital hierarchy was more important than one in the university hierarchy. Best were, of course, simultaneous positions in both. The hospital was a doctor's fortress, his bailiwick, his ward. Though Bichat and Louis were never professors, their hospital positions enabled them to exert a tremendous influence on coming generations. It would not have worked the other way around. Pariset, in his purple prose, called the hospitals the "observatories" of the new medicine; in a certain sense, he might also have called them its factories.

The last decades of the eighteenth century and the first of the nineteenth saw important transformations, enlargements, reforms, and improvements of the Paris hospital system. These were essentially a consequence of the tremendous influx of uprooted and penniless boys and girls from the country and of the beginnings of the Industrial Revolution. Some of these changes

15

in the hospitals came before the political Revolution of 1789, others during and after it. They facilitated the medical revolution and were facilitated by it.

It is well known that the situation in the hospitals in Paris and the prov-inces before the Revolution was most unsatisfactory. One need but remember the famous reports of J. Howard or Tenon (1788). We quote from the latter:[7]

> The general policy of the Hôtel Dieu—policy caused by the lack of space —is to put as many beds as possible into one room and to put four, five, or six people into one bed. We have seen the dead mixed with the living there. We have seen rooms so narrow that the air stagnates and is not renewed and that light enters only feebly and charged with vapors. We have seen convalescents together with the sick, the dying, and the dead, forced to go barefoot to the bridge in summer and winter when they want fresh air. We have seen a room for convalescents on the third floor, which could be reached only via the smallpox ward. The ward for the insane is next to the one for the unfortunate postoperative patients, who cannot hope for rest in this neighborhood which is full of outcries day and night.
>
> Often we saw contagious and noncontagious diseases in the same wards, women with syphilis and some with fever. The operation ward where they trephine, cut the stone, and amputate members contains those who are being operated upon, those who will be operated upon, and those who have already been operated upon.
>
> The operations are performed in the center of the room. One sees the preparations, one hears the cries of the sufferer. The one who will be operated upon tomorrow sees his future sufferings. The one who has passed through this ordeal is shaken by these cries of anguish. He under-goes these emotions in the midst of inflammation and purulence. Thus his recovery and life are endangered. The St. Joseph ward is destined for pregnant women. Legitimate spouses and whores, healthy and sick women are all together. Three or four are in the same bed, exposed to insomnia, contagion, and the danger of hurting their children. The delivered women are also four or more in one bed at different periods after delivery. It is nauseating to think how they infect each other. Most of them die or leave diseased. A thousand particular and accidental causes are added every day to the general and constant causes of air corruption, and force us to conclude that the Hôtel Dieu is the most unhealthy and most uncomfort-able of all hospitals, and that of nine patients two die.

The situation was so disastrous, the delusions about what a free economy could automatically accomplish outside hospitals so rife, and the wishes of politicians to control the aid money so strong that serious reformers like De Chamousset or Dupont de Nemours asked for the abolition of the hospitals. In 1817, Coste still examined some of the arguments against hospitals at great length in his extensive article in the *Dictionnaire des sciences Médicales* (21:367–544). The antihospital trend was so powerful that Raige-Delorme in 1837 and Boisseau in 1888 (Dechambre's *Dictionnaire*) felt obliged to defend hospitals as institutions!

Meanwhile, things had worked out quite differently. The Revolution, which had set out to abolish the hospitals,[8] strengthened them and made them the core of medicine. Improvement of the hospital situation was obtained during the last years of the old regime and the first years of the new mainly through application of five methods:

1. Improvement and enlargement of old hospitals (for example, the Hôtel Dieu, the Charité.

2. Separation of the medical institutions (hospitals) from the philanthropic ones (for orphans, old people, and so on; differentiated from the former as "hospices" after 1808) and prisons (for example, the Pitié, Charenton, Salpêtrière). While the latter lost its prison division in 1795, one subsisted at Bicêtre till 1836, as every reader of *Les misérables* knows.

3. Erection of new, smaller hospitals. Between 1775 and 1785, as many hospitals were founded as in the preceding 130 years: 1775 Clinique de Perfectionnement; 1778 Necker; 1780 Cochin; 1784 Beaujon; 1785 Venereal Diseases; 1781 Maison de Santé.

4. Transformation of confiscated monasteries into hospitals (for example, St. Antoine, Vâl de Grace, Maternité).

5. Government ownership of hospitals and centralization of their administration, which allowed much larger hospitals than private foundations could support.

The mortality statistics leave no doubt as to the improvement of the situation through these measures and through improved medical knowledge. Meding[9] reported the following mortality rates in the general hospitals:

> 1805–14: one out of 5.35
> 1815–24: one out of 5.82
> 1825–34: one out of 8.00
> 1835–44: one out of 9.59
> 1850:   one out of 11.03

The same evolution was confirmed by other Parisian data and by the travel reports of foreigners.[10]

The Comité de Mendicité of the Constituent Assembly, composed, among others, of the able Duke de La Rochefoucauld-Liancourt, the doctors Thouret and Guillotin, and the later terrorists, Barrère and Prieur, and the Comité d'Assistance Publique of the Legislative Assembly tried in vain to reform the hospitals. The dreaded Convention (1792–1795) was more successful. It opened St. Antoine, Val de Grâce, and the Maternité, and decided on November 15, 1793, that every patient should have his own bed.

The reforms continued during the Directory and Consulate. A great many of them were due to Antoine Claude Chaptal (1755–1832). This friend of Pinel and Cabanis, a doctor and chemist-manufacturer from Montpellier, was Napoleon's Minister of the Interior from 1800 to 1804.[11] Among other things, he is credited with creating the Conseil General des Hôpitaux (1801) of which, after 1817, he became a very active member;[12] the central bureau of admissions for the Paris hospitals; the *internat* and the *externat* in the hospitals (1802); and architectural improvements at the Hôtel Dieu.[13] He was also instrumental in improving public health (vaccination, schools for midwives) and regularizing the practice of medicine. It is not surprising that numerous medical books in the first decades of the nineteenth century were dedicated to him (for example, those of Barthez, Double, Dumas, Berthe, and Fodéré). He was the protector of, for example, Bretonneau. The extreme economic liberalism of the following decades was less favorable to hospital expansion than the Convention era had been.

The growth of Paris hospitals in our period cannot be measured statistically, since every author selects his material and uses different criteria. Since in the early years more than one patient occupied one bed, figures on beds are not comparable. In 1788, Tenon speaks of twenty-eight hospitals harboring 6,236 persons and of 14,105 in twenty hospice-like accommodations. Coste names, for 1817, twelve hospitals harboring a total of 5,400 and ten hospices accommodating 9,400 persons altogether.[14] But these are not the same hospitals and hospices, and it is quite uncertain whether the second list is as comprehensive as the first. Casper admittedly leaving out certain categories, mentions twelve hospitals and twelve hospices with a total of 15,000 persons in 1822. Muehry gives the same figures in 1836.[15] In 1853, Meding reports nine general and eight special hospitals and ten hospices with a total of 17,903 inmates. According to Bouchardat,[16] Paris hospitals received 37,743 patients in 1807; 41,000 in 1817; 53,000 in 1827, and 83,643 in 1852. Even these deficient statistics, combined with the study of the evolution of individual hospitals,[17] show a continuous and vigorous increase of Paris hospital facilities during the period under discussion.

Unlike British hospitals, Paris hospitals, "*das gottgeheiligte Riesenwerk*" ("this saintly giant structure"), as a German visitor exclaimed enthusiastically,[18] were state property after 1790 and strongly centralized under the general council of hospitals (1801) and later, after 1849, under the Assistance Publique. They had a central bureau of admissions, a central pharmacy, a central wine cellar, and a central bakery. In 1802, the internship, with central competitive examinations, was established in Paris hospitals; up until that time, only the lowly apprentice surgeons had lived in these places of horror.[19] After the Revolution, surgeons and physicians enjoyed the same rights outside and inside the hospitals. Strengthening the position of the surgeons within medicine meant automatically shifting emphasis toward their bailiwick —the hospital—and furthering the study of pathological anatomy. Conversely, giving the hospitals a larger place in medical education meant elevating the position of the surgeons and improving the hospitals. The founding of several specialized hospitals was another characteristic feature of the new Paris hospital system.

The Berlin professor Casper reported in 1822 that it was an honor to be attached to certain hospitals, that the service was in the hands of nuns, that visits were made too early in the morning, and that Paris hospitals were no "palaces" like those in London. But he commented favorably on their operating rooms, baths, and kitchens. He found Paris hospitals too cold. This complaint is also found in Ratier.[20] An official report of 1838 speaks still of 5-degree-centigrade temperatures in the Hôtel Dieu.[21] Bretonneau observed 3 degrees centigrade in the Tours hospital in 1825, and Otterburg considered the cold in the hospitals a cause of death.[22] Raige-Delorme regarded temperatures not lower than 10 and not higher than 15 degrees centigrade as desirable.[23] Meding found temperatures satisfactory in 1853. It was perhaps due to the cold that bed curtains, often criticized by foreigners,[24] but defended by the French,[25] lasted till the end of the century. Casper (1822) still found wooden beds prevailing, when London hospitals had mostly iron beds and the first iron beds in Paris had been put up in 1799 (Hôpital des Cliniques). Hospital physicians were by no means always satisfied with their situation. For example, we read of protest meetings in 1838.[26]

Some notes on the history of some of the Paris hospitals might help in visualizing the evolution after the Revolution.[27] The *Hôtel Dieu* had existed since at least 829. It had burned down in 1772 but had been rebuilt. With what effect we have seen above. One of the main problems remained, overcrowding.[28] The revolutionaries not only changed the name of the institution (to Hospice de l'Humanité), but decongested it by creating several new general hospitals and special institutions—for example, those for the insane, for children, for pregnant women, and for the treatment of venereal diseases. These improvements were continued after 1801. The number of beds (about 1,400) remained unchanged, but there was now only one patient per bed.

The staff improved very much, the products of competitive examinations having replaced the results of protection. The sexes and surgical and medical cases were separated. In 1804, Menuret described a much improved situation. Comparative mortality statistics show the Hôtel Dieu still behind the Charité in 1817 (1:4. vs. 1:7.7), but outdistancing her in 1822 (1:6.8 vs. 1:53).[29] Casper explains the high mortality rate by pointing out the many serious accidents handled in this centrally located institution. The hospital was famous above all for its surgeons: Desault, who started clinical teaching against strong resistance,[30] Bichat, Dupuytren, Roux, Jobert, and even Récamier, who, though officially a clinician, was more important as a surgeon. Only when Chomel succeeded him did internal medicine pick up. With Louis, Rostan, and later, with Trousseau, it excelled. In 1877, the old Hôtel Dieu was torn down. Where it once stood, we can now admire an ugly monument of Charlemagne.

The Pitié, situated opposite the Jardin des Plantes, was an orphan asylum till 1809. It was torn down in 1912. For a long time, it was administered by the Duke de La Rochefoucauld-Liancourt, famous for his promotion of vaccination and his efforts toward prison and hospital reform. For a while (1813–1839), it was, under the influence of Serres, a center for the study of nervous diseases. Serres later on turned to comparative anatomy. Later physicians of the Pitié were Louis and Piorry. No less brilliant were its surgeons: Béclard, Lisfranc, Gerdy, and Velpeau.

The Charité (called "l'Hospice de l'Unité" during the Revolution), founded by the Brothers of Charity in 1607 and located on the Rue St. Pères, was limited to men until the Revolution. It was regarded as the best hospital in Paris. Here Desbois de Rochefort started clinical teaching. It was famous for its lithotomists. After the Revolution, it was greatly expanded. Its surgeons—Boyer, Roux, and Velpeau—remained remarkable, but now its clinicians had even greater renown. Corvisart, G. L. Bayle, Laennec, Chomel, Leroux, Fouquier, Lerminier, Andral, Rayer, Bouillaud, Cruveilhier, and Piorry taught and worked here. It specialized in diseases of the chest and lead poisoning. Most of it was torn down in 1934 and replaced by the new Faculty of Medicine, but the old lecture room of Corvisart still stands.

St. Antoine was transformed by the Convention from a monastery, located in the notorious faubourg of the same name, into a hospital in January, 1795. Medically, it never attracted much attention though Rayer and Velpeau worked there for a while. Casper, in 1812, called it the friendliest hospital in Paris, and mentioned the many fractures treated there.

The Necker on the Rue de Sèvres, founded by the wife of the famous

Geneva banker and French statesman, is above all famous because Laennec discovered mediate auscultation there in 1816. Starting with Civiale, it became a center for urology.

St. Louis, an ancient plague house in the Faubourg du Temple, was built under Henri IV in 1607. After the Revolution, it was transformed into a hospital taking care mainly of skin diseases. It was the first to receive gas-lights. Its dermatologists, from Alibert, Biett, and Cazenave to Sabouraud, were justly famous. Richerand, and after him Jules Cloquet and Malgaigne, acted as surgeons there.

Hôpital du Midi was a convent in the Faubourg St. Jacques which became a hospital for venereal diseases in 1784. After the period of the Culleriers and Bertin, Ricord made the institution world famous.

Enfants Malades, the first children's hospital in the world, was opened in 1802 in an old orphan asylum on the Rue de Sèvres. Guersant, Jadelot, and Trousseau were among its physicians. Its orthopedist was Jules Guérin.

The *Maternité*, the old monastery of Port Royal, the former stronghold of Jansenism, was transformed into a maternity hospital in 1795. J. L. Baudeloque, A. Dubois, and Chaussier were active there.

The *Salpêtrière* was opened in 1656, under the misleading name "Hôpital Général," as a prison for beggars, paupers, and incurables, among whom there were quite a few insane. It was restricted to females. After elimination of its prison aspects in 1795, it became a mixed institution for sick, incurable, and insane women. In the foreword to the second edition of his *Médecine clinique* (1804), Pinel listed recent improvements in the institution. In 1822, it harbored 3,900 incurables, 800 insane people, and 360 sick people. Beginning with Pinel, its physicians were famous, mostly as psychiatrists; we mention here only Esquirol, Georget, Lallemand, Rostan, Ferrus, Falret, and Baillarger. It reached new heights with Charcot and his pupils. The parallel institution for men was *Bicêtre*.

The *Val de Grâce*, formerly a monastery founded by Ann of Austria in 1645, became a large military hospital in 1793. Percy, Larrey, Desgenettes, Broussais, Bégin, and later Villemin and Laveran worked there.

What were the main diseases treated in these hospitals and, consequently, the main objects of scientific research? The American observer F. C. Stewart[31] names the following: phthisis; pneumonia; typhoid fever; cancer, especially of the uterus; eruptive fevers, especially smallpox; puerperal peritonitis; and heart disease. In the old: apoplexy, cancer, and diseases of the urinary tract. In children: pneumonia, phthisis, sclerosis,[32] and meningitis. This list is very much confirmed by contemporary clinic reports from the Hôtel Dieu

21

and the Charité.[33] They bring out, in addition, a surprising prevalence of malaria, rheumatism, lead poisoning, and syphilis. In April, 1794, Pinel had 104 cases of scurvy at Bicêtre (*Nosographie* 3:310). Corvisart mentions *hydropisies* (hydrops) during the famine of 1793. In spite of all "therapeutic skepticism," Paris experienced in 1828 an epidemic of "acrodynia" (mercury poisoning). During epidemics, numerous cases of cholera or "grippe" were admitted. These are, of course, only the diseases which were diagnosed. Others like diphtheria or nephritis were undoubtedly frequently present, but disappeared in some omnibus classification and were generally diagnosed, if at all, only toward the end of the period. It is in full concordance with these admission data that the medical literature of the period centers around phthisis, pneumonia, typhoid fever, vaccination, cholera, and heart, brain, and bladder disease. That puerperal fever and cancer found less discussants was perhaps due to their therapeutic hopelessness.

The Paris hospital of our period was, in its conception and organization, no longer a medieval receptacle of all miseries. It had eventually become a medical institution and thus served as the cradle of a new medicine.

III. ANTECEDENTS

Paris medicine at the beginning of the nineteenth century certainly represented a revolutionary break with the past. But just as there is no traditionalist movement that does not contain some new elements, so there is no revolutionary movement that does not have some roots in the past, that does not continue certain traditions. J. B. Regnault, a physician who returned to France in 1814 after an involuntary absence of twenty-two years, showed quite ably how much recent progress was a continuation of pre-Revolutionary trends.

The Leipzig clinician C. A. Wunderlich, who knew Paris medicine very well from his own experience, wrote, "*Actually the whole new trend of French medicine has come out of the surgical school.*"[1] Temkin substantiated this idea a few years ago in his essay, "The Role of Surgery in the Rise of Modern Medical Thought." Pinel, Bichat, Broussais, Laennec, and Bouillaud all expressly stated that they handled the data of internal medicine like surgeons.[2] Of the leaders of the new internal medicine, Bichat, Récamier, Landré-Beauvais, Laennec, Broussais, and Cruveilhier were all trained as surgeons.[3] Due to the Academy of Surgery, France was the first country in which surgery had started its triumphal social and scientific comeback in the eighteenth century. While French medicine was ridiculed, her surgery was famous. The names of, for example, J. L. Petit, Le Dran, Quesnay, and Desault were and still are great names. Though eventually even the Academy of Surgery had been infected with the dry rot of the *ancien régime*,[4] the times of greatness were close enough to provide a living tradition. Surgeons are by definition localists and anatomists. Anatomists turn easily to the study of pathological anatomy. French surgeon-anatomists were prominent in the eighteenth century. French medical men at the end of that century could inherit these surgeons' localism, their interest in anatomy, and their budding study of pathological anatomy. As a matter of fact, even later important basic ideas, like irritation and neohumoralism, came out of the surgical camp (Dupuytren and Velpeau).

Another important factor in strengthening the surgical point of view in French medicine was *military service*. Military medicine was then to a large extent surgery. France was involved in war from 1792 to 1815. Consequently, a very high percentage of its leading practitioners—not to speak of the rank and file of medical men—served for often lengthy periods in the armies of the Republic and the Empire. We give here (omitting, of course, the great military doctors like Desgenettes, Larrey, and Percy) a certainly incomplete,

25

but not insignificant, list of such temporary military medical men: Amussat, G. L. Bayle, Baumès, Béclard, Bertin, Bichat, Bourdois, Burdin, Broussais, A. Dubois, C. L. Dumas, Desormeaux, Dutrochet, Ferrus, Foy, Gaultier de Claubry, Gerdy, Gouraud, Guilbert, Husson, Jadelot, C. Lachaise, Laennec, Lagneau, Lallemand, Landré-Beauvais, Legallois, Lerminier, Lisfranc, May-grier, Moreau de la Sarthe, Négrier, Ollivier, J. A. F. Ozanam, Pariset, Pelletan, Piorry, Récamier, Réveillé-Parise, Roux, A. Royer-Collard, Sarlandière, Sanson, Sue, Trélat, and Villermé. Common military service also created loyalties that later played a role in unexpected places.

Another French antecedent of our movement was the *Montpellier* tradi-tion. All through the eighteenth century, Montpellier had been a far livelier school than the group of sad pedants on the Rue de la Bucherie in Paris. At Montpellier, medicine and surgery had never separated to the extent that they had in Paris. The most popular Paris physicians, including those at court,[5] were Montpellier graduates; among them, were Chirac, who established a localist tradition, and Bordeu and Barthez, who so profoundly influenced Bichat. Portal, Pinel, Desgenettes, Chaptal, Guillaume Laennec (the uncle of the inventor of the stethoscope), and Double, all well-known admirers of Hippocrates, were Montpellier graduates. Though Paris had its own Hippocratist tradition, there is no doubt that Hippocratism and vitalism in Paris—whatever their merits— were often derived from Montpellier.

A Montpellier graduate whose influence was strongly felt long before as well as long after the Revolution was *Antoine Portal* (1742–1832), known to medical historians for his extensive history of anatomy and surgery (1770) and as founder of the Academy of Medicine (1820). This ambitious man—a strange sight when, dying at ninety, he still wore the fashion of his youth— managed for over fifty years to be the physician of those in power, though governments changed rather frequently between 1780 and 1830. He also held two professorships of anatomy, one at the Collège de France and one at the Jardin du Roi, for over fifty years. In this function he exhibited, as an admirer of Morgagni, a strong interest in pathological anatomy. At the same time, he was one of the few physicians able to palpate the abdomen (he also mentions[6] as "*tateurs*" Duverney, Winslow, Ferrein, and A. Petit). If we add to this interest in pathological anatomy and physical diagnosis his work in surgery and his aversion toward generalizations, we have, long before the medical revolution, a classic representative of the great revolutionary Paris clinical school. As a matter of fact, some of his earlier books, like his 1792 treatise of phthisis, compare very favorably with the "classic" productions of the school. The same could be said of the book on heart disease published in 1749 by J. B. Senac (1693–1770), the physician of Louis XV and the protector of Portal.

After 1776, the progressive forces in Paris medicine were no longer obliged to submit to the fossil Faculty; they had an organization of their own, the *Royal Society of Medicine.* Among its members were Vicq d'Azyr, Lorry, Poissonier-Desperrières, Thouret, A. L. Jussieux, Bucquet, Hallé, Tessier, Doublet, Mahon, Fourcroy, Barbeu du Bourg, and Chambon. We will encounter some of these men among the first professors of the new Medical School founded in 1794. The most powerful personality of the Royal Society was undoubtedly its permanent secretary *Félix Vicq d'Azyr* (1748–1794). He preached the unity of surgery and medicine and the basic importance of anatomy[7] and clinical observation. His memoir on medical reform, submitted to the National Assembly in 1790, was actually the blueprint for the new School of 1794. Only a premature death prevented his being its first director. On account of his sympathies with the Royal Society, *Louis Desbois de Rochefort* (1750–1786) was removed from the ranks of the old Faculty. He did not write books, but he did do something at least as important. Becoming a staff physician at the Charité in 1780, he was the first in Paris to institute clinical teaching. He was also an advocate of pathological anatomy. His tradition was continued by his pupil, friend, and successor, J. N. Corvisart.

Even among leading military physicians, medical reformers could be found. *Jean François Coste* (1741–1819), a protégé of Voltaire, chief physician of the French forces in the American Revolutionary War (later Napoleon's Grande Armée), and mayor of Versailles during the Revolution, claimed in 1775 adherence to Hippocratism; skepticism toward physics, chemistry, anatomy, and botany; and the necessity of teaching hospitals, of two years of internship, and of general education for the physician.[8]

Though the antecedents of the new school were primarily French, foreign antecedents were by no means absent. The first to mention here are *Great Britain* and *Vienna.* Edinburgh was then probably the leading medical center internationally. Cabanis' enthusiasm for Edinburgh and for Vienna was well known.[9] The same feelings were found in Pinel; he placed the beginning of the modern clinic there.[10] He translated Cullen of Edinburgh and the transactions of the London Royal Society himself. The case histories in his *Médecine clinique* follow the Edinburgh pattern. The Paris Medical Society of 1793 was an imitation of the Edinburgh Society, The work of John Hunter was well known. Coste reported extensively on British hospitals.[11] Laennec's uncle studied there, and Roux and Billard made study trips across the

Channel as soon as the political situation allowed. Broussais cursed J. Brown, but he was unthinkable without him.

While Pinel translated Cullen, Corvisart translated Auenbrugger and Stoll! Pinel was equally enthusiastic about the Vienna school,[12] and Coste reported even more extensively on Vienna hospitals than on British ones. Paris, inspired by the first Vienna school, was to be a source of inspiration for the second one.

Italian authors were also of considerable influence. The writings of Baglivi, edited by Pinel, were a factor in strengthening localist tendencies. The admirers of Morgagni were numerous, from Portal to Bichat. Before the Revolution, Desgenettes traveled in Italy, where he met Cotugno, Mascagni, and Fontana. Many physicians, including Broussais, went to Italy with the French armies and were strongly influenced by the Italian Brunonians— Rasori,[13] Tomasini, Bufalini, Brera, and colleagues. It was in this form that Brunonism flourished in France. These teachings were also imported into France by the numerous Italian refugees of the Restoration period, such as Fossati and Rognetta. Rasori's imprint was clearly visible on both Broussais and Laennec.

Compared to these impressions, the German contribution was insignificant. Cabanis and Pinel might praise Stahl, but he had little influence on their actions. Strasbourg channeled French ideas into Germany and German ideas into France. It was no accident that medical microscopy was cultivated officially there earlier than elsewhere in France. The Swiss physiologist A. von Haller also left his mark on some French physicians (Casper named Housset, Delamare, and Fabre)—above all, on Bichat. These were some of the elements which entered the complex new creation of 1794.

IV. THE SCHOOL

We have shown the antecedents of the new medicine. But in order to be born, it needed a new school and a new way of teaching; this was to become the root of both its success and its later stagnation. A new approach can only be victorious when it is supported by the official teaching—when its researchers become the teachers of the young generation. The new teaching and the new school were made possible only through the Revolution. This was one of the rare points on which royalists, Bonapartists, liberals, and radicals all agreed;[1] that the new teaching was an accomplishment of the Revolution.

It is true that clinical instruction had been introduced in the Charité by Desbois de Rochefort in 1780 and continued by his successor Corvisart in 1788. In 1787, the surgeon Desault had, against the opposition of the nuns,[2] instituted clinical teaching at the Hôtel Dieu. But these men were outsiders. The teaching of the Medical Faculty, proud to be *antiquarum tenax*, proceeded unchanged since the Middle Ages, as was graphically described by Richerand.[3] There were only lecture courses in Latin, commenting upon Hippocrates, Galen, or an Arab author. The five professors were annually chosen by lottery from among the doctors of Paris. Small wonder that the products of this Faculty were such excellent props for Molière's comedies. The teaching at the College of Surgery was almost as poor. Surgeons were primarily apprentice-trained. Titles could be bought. The Royal Society of Medicine stated in 1789, "We must say that in the whole kingdom not a single school exists where the basic principles of the healing art are taught in their totality" (D'Irsay 2:22). The Paris Faculty had not graduated a doctor since 1785 or a licentiate since 1790. The Faculty, which was removed by the law of August 18, 1790, suppressing all teaching corporations, was only a corpse.

For several years, no attempt was made to reorganize the medical teaching. In government circles it had been thought sufficient to establish "freedom of teaching"; "free enterprise" would take care of the rest. But "free enterprise" did nothing of the kind. And the war was raging in its second year; more than 900 medical officers in the army had already been killed. The practical need for trained personnel became extremely urgent. Thus, on November 27, 1794, Fourcroy submitted a report to the Convention which contained the following passages:[4]

> Everywhere, men of murderous empiricism and rash ignorance are trapping the credulous in pain. . . . For five years, the most difficult of arts

has had no more teachers, and the schools which preserved it have been closed. . . .

It is not sufficient to give lessons and public courses on all branches of science. The old method did not give a complete course and was limited to words. . . . Once the lesson was finished, its contents vanished from the students' memory. In the École de Santé [the new Paris Medical School], manipulation will be united with theoretical precepts. The students will do chemical exercises, dissections, operations, and bandaging. *Little read-ing, much seeing, and much doing will be the foundation of the new teaching which your committee suggests. Practicing the art, observing at the bedside, all that was missing, will now be the principal part of instruction.* Three hospitals: "Humanité" for external, "Unité" for internal, and that of the School for rare diseases will offer to the students, who have learned the theory, the most useful part of their apprenticeship, the complement of all others. Without this, knowledge is but the source of clever speculations, but almost always useless for humanity. . . .

Your intention to revive useful science and to further its progress makes it necessary that the professors and their associates have only this function and are not distracted by other occupations. Therefore, their salaries must be sufficient for their needs, and they must not be obliged to do additional work in order to subsist. Men who have devoted twenty years of their lives to acquiring knowledge and to learning to transmit it must be treated by their country in a way that no domestic worries torment them. . . .

Medicine and surgery are two branches of the same science. To study them separately means to abandon theory to delirious imagination and practice to blind routine. To reunite them and to melt them together means to enlighten them mutually and to further their progress. . . .

On the basis of this report, the Convention promulgated on December 4, 1794 (14 *Frimaire*, the year III), a law instituting three new medical schools (*écoles de santé*) at Paris, Montpellier, and Strasbourg. The faculty of the new Paris Medical School held its first meeting on December 20, 1794. A magnificent building was available: the former Academy of Surgery (now Ancienne Faculté, Rue de l'École de Médecine). Entrance examinations were held January 25, 1795, and the students were distributed into three classes, whereupon instruction began.

The Fourcroy report designated as the core of the new law the practical character of instruction—the preponderance and immediacy of clinical teaching. The new Paris student did not begin with theoretical instruction. From the first day on, he was trained on the wards.[5] This was the way to become a practitioner, to acquire the famous *coup d'oeil*.[6] This was the type of teaching proposed by Cabanis, whose dictum, "*On lit trop au lieu d'observer*" ("One reads too much instead of observing"),[7] very much re-sembled Fourcroy's "*Peu lire, beaucoup voir, beaucoup faire*" ("Read little, see much, do much"). This was the famous "clinical" teaching which Pinel, after tracing its antecedents, proudly attributed to Corvisart and himself.[8] This new way was to be, to later protagonists of the School, the only possible way. The other practical branch to be cultivated assiduously was dissection. Five hundred cadavers were at the disposal of the School in its first year.

The report emphasizes the full-time character of the future professors. While the new arrangements were adequate to emancipate the professor financially from the students, they were not sufficiently generous to make the professors limit their activities exclusively to the duties connected with their chairs. In addition to private practice, there was the system of *cumul*, that is, the possibility of holding several teaching jobs simultaneously (the creator of the law himself held at least three chairs in different schools), an evil which has vitiated the French system up to this day. The same is true of *permutation*, the professor's priority in obtaining a vacant chair within the same faculty when he wants to quit his own. This practice was by no means rare—for example, out of the nineteen holders of the chair of surgical pathology between 1795 and 1895, twelve left it by *permutation*.

The other great message of the report was the reunification of medicine and surgery, which meant the rehabilitation of the latter and the strengthening of its influence. This was indeed an event of great historical and international importance. It was the closing hour of medical medievalism.

Significant traits of the new law which its authors found unnecessary to discuss in detail, since they corresponded simply to the spirit of the times, were the use of the *concours*, that is, a public competitive examination, for filling various positions—an expression of its democratic trends—and the use of the French language, an expression of nationalistic aspirations. A *national* law for medical teaching was an absolute novelty compared with the independence of the old faculties. On the one hand, it announced the new and rigid centralism in France; on the other, it opened the way for useful innovations such as a *national* licensing system, after a period when, for example, Montpellier or Reims graduates could not practice in Paris. The new office of a permanent dean illustrated the tendency towards centralized bureaucratization.

Antoine François Fourcroy (1755–1809), the father of the law of 1794, is one of the most remarkable figures in French science of the period.[9] This son of an impoverished nobleman was enabled to study medicine through Vicq d'Azyr's protection. He translated Ramazzini. The old Faculty tried in vain to block his career on account of his protector. He started his teaching activities in 1782 with private courses on materia medica. His ability as a chemist brought him the chair of this discipline at the Jardin du Roi in 1784 and gained him the friendship of Lavoisier. He became one of the protagonists of the new chemistry. His analyses of urinary calculi, milk, blood, and other substances, were of great medical importance. He must have been one of the best speakers and teachers in Paris in his time. Medical travel books are full of praise for him. In 1792, he became a member of the Convention and devoted himself to the organization of higher education, a role he continued to play under Napoleon as a Director of Public Education. He was a first-rate organizer and administrator. Not only the École de Santé, where he became professor of medical chemistry and pharmacy, but the new École de Mines, the incomparable École Polytechnique, and many other educational innova-tions are also due to him. Though politically rather adaptable, he lost the favor of his emperor and died from a stroke, full of sorrow, in 1809. He was succeeded in his chair by his pupil Vauquelin. His attitude during the Terror has been much criticized. Fourcroy apparently did nothing to save Lavoisier, but he also seems innocent of the accusation of having worked against his friend and rival. He did intervene in favor of scientists like Darcet, Desault, and Chaptal. Whatever the weakness of his character, his merits as a chemist, teacher, and reorganizer of French higher education remain outstanding.[10]

For assistance in the preparation of the new law, Fourcroy called from Dijon *François Chaussier* (1746–1828), who was particularly interested in problems of education and had a good reputation in anatomy and legal medicine. Chaussier remained influential in the new Faculty. As its first professor of anatomy and physiology, he was apparently a mediocre teacher;[11] to improve his income, he wrote many student theses (as Stahl, Linné, Richter, Schroeder, J. P. Frank, and Pinel had done before him). In 1804, he became a physician of the Maternité and professor of chemistry at the École Polytechnique. He was retired at the notorious "reorganization" of 1822 on account of his liberal past. His burial in 1828 was civil, without benefit of a clergyman.

Fourcroy's collaborator in the selection of the professors of the École was its first dean, *Michel Auguste Thouret* (born in 1748), who held this job to the time of his death in 1810. Thouret had been a member of the rebellious Royal Society of Medicine before the Revolution; he had acquired fame as a critic of "animal magnetism" (hypnotism) and as an administrator. In the latter function, he had liquidated the notorious Cemetery of the Innocents in the center of Paris and had been assistant to his father-in-law Colombier, the inspector general of hospitals and prisons. He had been a member of the

Constitutional Assembly, lost his job in 1792, and his brother, a Girondist, was guillotined in 1794. After *Thermidor*, he became director of the School, and, with Cousin and Cabanis, a member of the committee directing Paris hospitals. He later became a member of the Conseil de Salubrité (Health Council), of the Tribunal, and director of the Mont de Pitié. He did not vote for Napoleon's *coup d'état* elevation to imperial rank. His teaching was limited to lectures on Hippocrates and rare cases. He was one of the leading proponents of smallpox vaccination. He was the father of the law of the year XI (1803) regulating medical practice. He furthered the careers of Alibert, Husson, Desgenettes, L. Valentin, and especially of Dupuytren, but also of the latter's competitors Roux and Marjolin. Wardenburg's accusation that he had not sufficient energy and vision[12] is not confirmed by the facts or by other critics. Starting a new school with quite disparate elements was a very difficult task, and he acquitted himself of it quite honorably.

While the old Paris Faculty had had only six chairs and the College of Surgery ten, the law of 1794 foresaw the following twelve chairs, each one provided with a chairholder and an adjunct professor:

1. Anatomy and physiology	(Chaussier and A. Dubois)
2. Medical chemistry and pharmacy	(Fourcroy and Deyeux)
3. Medical physics and hygiene	(J. N. Hallé and Pinel)
4. External pathology	(Chopart and Percy)
5. Internal pathology	(Doublet and Bourdier)
6. Medical natural history	(Peyrilhe and Richard)
7. Surgical operations	(Sabatier and Boyer)
8. External clinic	(Desault and Boyer)
9. Internal clinic	(Corvisart and Leclerc)
10. Advanced clinic	(Pelletan and Lallement)
11. Obstetrics	(A. Le Roy and Baudelocque)
12. Legal medicine and history of medicine	(Lassus and Mahon)

The adjunct professors soon became quite independent. The dean (Thouret), the librarian (Pierre Sue), and the curator of the collection (Thillaye, Jr.) held professorial rank.[13] Further practical instruction was provided through the outpatient consultations given at the hospital. Of the twenty-seven professors, nine were former members of the old Faculty: Hallé, Thouret, Doublet, LeRoy, Bourdier, Corvisart, Leclerc, Mahon, and Fourcroy. Most of these had been members of the Royal Society. Twelve of the new professors (Chaussier, Dubois, Pelletan, Chopart, Percy, Peyrilhe, Sabatier, Desault, Baudelocque, Lallement, Lassus, Boyer, and Sue) had been connected with the College of Surgery. That some of them were and re mained "*des illustres inconnus*" ("illustrious unknowns") is not surprising. Even the best faculty recruits some members out of this family. What is really surprising is the great number of extremely able men, many of whom are still remembered, who formed the teaching body of the new School.

The School of the year III (1794) was a creation of relatively young men. Fourcroy, Corvisart, and Chaptal were thirty-nine years old, Cabanis thirty-seven, Hallé and Percy forty, Desgenettes thirty-two, A. Dubois thirty-eight, and A. Boyer thirty-seven.

The duration of the studies was fixed at three years. The twelve courses were either "permanent" (the clinical ones) or "nonpermanent" (filling only one semester). Vacations were not envisaged! Roll call and periodic written and oral exams underlined the school character of the instruction. The bachelor's degree was required as a condition for admission only after 1808.

Every district of the Republic was to delegate one student, "*Élève de la Patrie*," who would be state-supported. Three hundred "*élèves*" were to go to Paris, 150 to Montpellier, and 100 to Strasbourg. Among the first students of the Paris École were Alibert, Bichat, G. L. Bayle, Bretonneau, Duméril, Dupuytren, Guersant, Husson, Landré-Beauvais, Legallois, Moreau de la Sarthe, Pariset, Récamier, Richerand, Ribes, and Savigny. After three years, free students were admitted and enrollment rose very rapidly: in the year VI (1797–1798), 896; the year VIII (1799–1800), 1,190; and the year X (1801–1802), 1,390. Most of the students were living very close to destitution, as indicated by the letters of Bichat, Bretonneau, and others. Wardenburg reported in 1797 that they all wore wooden shoes.[14] Competition among them was stiff. By 1825, the number of students had risen to 2,000. About 300 graduated every year.

The structure of the School reflected the utilitarian attitude of eighteenth-century philosophy and Jacobin distrust of the "aristocratic" man of science.[15] The École de Santé was a special school, designed primarily to train practitioners like the École Polytechnique or the Conservatoire des Arts et Métiérs, also founded in 1794. Scientists were relegated into safely secluded "wildlife preserves" such as the Museum (founded in 1793) and the Collège de France, which were primarily research institutions. The latter, which also took a few select students, was the only teaching institution of the *ancien régime* that had survived. With Corvisart (named in 1794), Hallé (1801), Laennec (1822), Récamier (1826), and Magendie (1831) occupying its chair at various times, it certainly provided additional high-caliber instruction.

The structure of the School remained practically unchanged till 1870. When Casper analyzed it in the 1820's, he felt as earlier German travelers (for example, Haindorf), had—that it lacked freedom and that surgery was too powerful. He also felt that the students were not active enough in the clinics. (Where he came from they were not active at all!) Abraham Flexner has dubbed the French type of medical education the "clinical type" (as opposed to the "university type" and the "proprietary type") and defined the Paris Faculty as composed of "hospital staffs engaged in teaching." This clinical system would, in the long run, not prove to be as "natural" and faultless as its authors had thought; but it would take decades for its short-comings to become visible. For the time being, its success was tremendous; Duméril could rightly exclaim in the somewhat flowery style of the period in his annual address of 1816, "Why should I not feel a noble pride when every day I see more clearly that this amphitheater is becoming for us what the school of the city of Ptolemy was to the ancient world, when I see our students from one single family, when I see united without distinction of rank or country the sons of Albion and the sons of Iberia, young men coming from the banks of the Ganges or the banks of the Neva, or sent by the two Americas!" (*Progrès Medicale Suppl.* 1938, 15:8) Cuvier and Regnault regarded the new teaching methods as the most important contribution of French medicine of the period.

Though there were no important changes till the 1870's, continuous minor attempts at improvement were made. In 1795, the position of *chef des travaux anatomiques* (head of anatomical studies) was created, to be filled by *concours* (public competition). With this bitter *concours* of 1799 between Duméril and Dupuytren began the series of Homeric battles that filled the annals of the School during the first half of the century.[16] Professorial chairs too (and later the *agrégation*) were filled by *concours* unless obtained by *permutation*. Only during the Restoration (1815–1830) were chairs filled by royal decree. The *concours* was abolished in 1852.

In 1796, the name of the School was changed to "École de Médecine." The establishment of medical schools for the military at the Val de Grâce in Paris and at Lille, Metz, Strasbourg, and Toulon in the same year added considerably to the educational facilities available.

In 1797, a dissection school was created as an accessory of the Medical School for an elite of 120 students, selected by public competition. This step underlined the importance of anatomy in the School's thinking. The prize in this division was the famous bronze medal, uniting the portraits of Fernel and Paré and bearing the significant inscription, "*La médecine rendu à son unité primitive.*"[17] It was awarded for the first time in 1800, at a solemn session opening the scholastic year. The old Faculty had had many such celebrations.

The new now felt the need for something similar. At the first gathering of this sort (1800), Thouret stated:[18]

> The most important creation of the School is the clinical teaching. Limited first to three hospitals, which were insufficient for the crowd following its lessons, the School has now obtained the doubling of the internal and external clinic. Three new clinics have been instituted: for vaccination, for the treatment of syphilis, and for the practice of obstetrics.

He furthermore praised the fact that legal medicine, the history of medicine, hygiene, physics, animal chemistry, and natural history, all disciplines that were neglected by the old Faculty, were taught in the new School.

In 1802, the positions of "intern" and "extern" were created at the Paris hospitals. They were accessible only to the winners of a *concours*. The historical role and the success of this new attempt at selecting an elite and giving it better training are well known. There was hardly an outstanding man in French medicine after 1802 who had not been an intern.[19] The title *"ancien interne des hôpitaux de Paris"* still has enough magic to be put on French doctors' shingles. The institution has been imitated in other countries.

The abuses that had brought about the founding of the School had by no means disappeared. Again state councillor Fourcroy, now serving the First Consul Napoleon, raised his voice. In a report to the legislative body of 7 Germinal, the year XI (1803), he declared:[20]

> Since the decree of August 18, 1792, which abolished faculties and learned corporations, no regular graduations of physicians or surgeons have taken place. Those who have learned their art are put on the same level with those who have not the slightest notion of it. The life of our citizens is in the hands of men who are as ignorant as they are greedy. The most dangerous empiricism, the most shameless charlatanism are everywhere exploiting credulity and good faith. No proof of skill or knowledge is necessary. Those who during the last seven and one-half years studied in the three medical schools instituted through the law of 14 *Frimaire*, the year III [1794] are barely able to have officially stated that they have acquired knowledge and to be distinguished from the so-called curers one sees everywhere. The cities and the country are infested with charlatans who distribute poisons and death with an audacity which the old laws cannot stop. The most murderous practices have replaced the art of midwifery. Bonesetters and quacks misuse the title of *officier de santé* [health officer] to cover up their ignorance and greed.

On the basis of this report, the legislative body adopted on 19 *Ventôse*, the year XI (March 11, 1803), a law to regulate the practice of medicine. It was no longer admissible to practice without examination. Those who had not been examined so far had to take within six months an examination to qualify either as a doctor of medicine or an *officier de santé.*

The latter category of cheap general practitioners (before the Revolution this role had been played by the surgeons) existed in spite of all pro- testations, till 1892. According to the new law, an *officier de santé* had to show proof of either six years of apprentice training, five years of hospital training, or three years in a medical school. He could practice only in the province where he had been trained and examined. Midwives had to be trained and examined too. Every member of the healing professions had to register.

In many provincial hospitals, some kind of unofficial instruction had been provided. Some of these institutions that had trained health officers or pre- pared students for one of the medical schools were now officially recognized as offering "practical courses"; they were later designated "secondary schools." This status was obtained in 1806 by the hospitals of Besançon, Amiens, Poitiers, and Grenoble, and in 1808 by those of Nantes, Rennes, Caen, and Marseille. By 1820, eighteen such "secondary schools" existed.

In 1803, Napoleon increased the duration of medical studies to four years, halved professorial salaries, and made the professors wear uniforms. In 1808, the old designation of Faculty of Medicine was reintroduced, and a bachelor's degree became the condition for admission into a medical school. In 1813, the position of *chef de clinique* was created as an adjunct to that of clinical professor.

Toward the end of the Empire, instruction declined.[21] F. Dubois d'Amiens tells[22] that in his student days, that is, around 1812, the professors were very famous (A. Dubois, Boyer, Pelletan, Desgenettes, Chaussier) but that the teaching was far superior in the 1840's. The eternal wars (several professors were with the armies)[23] and the narrow, militaristic, utilitarian outlook of Napoleon had a similar effect on, for example, the École Polytechnique.[24] After the wars, things improved.

In 1814, the Bourbons and their followers, who had "learned nothing and forgotten nothing," came back with the armies of the allies. Since the School was a product of the Revolution, and the majority of its professors and students no partisans of the old monarchy, an attack was almost inevitable. It was led by Father Elysée, the first surgeon of Louis XVIII, who tried to separate medicine and surgery again. Hallé, whose authority was great with everybody, opposed this in a famous address of November 4, 1815.[25] Desormeaux, Dupuytren, Le Roux, Richerand, Royer-Collard, and Prunelle held the same opinion.[26] The supporters of the separation—Sédillot, Naquart, and Lugol—were of considerably less eminence, and the attempt failed.

The new Grand Master of the University, Father Freyssinous, was more successful in 1822 with a second attack. On November 18, at the annual opening ceremony, the students, who did not like renewed church domina- tion of the university, booed and hissed the director, Father Nicolle, during an oration by the liberal Desgenettes; the Faculty was dissolved within three days, and the students sent away. It was reopened in March, 1823, but the following eleven professors, suspected of liberal or Bonapartist leanings, were retired: De Jussieux, Vauquelin, A. Dubois, Pelletan, Deyeux, Pinel, Desgenettes, Chaussier, Lallement, Leroux, and Moreau de la Sarthe. They were replaced by ten royalists, all nonentities except Laennec. The reorganized faculty consisted of twenty-three professors, instead of twelve professors and twelve adjunct professors. The latter position was abolished. Of the twenty-three professors, fifteen gave theoretical instruction and eight clinical instruction; that is, two chairs of internal medicine, one of surgery, and one in the obstetrical clinic were newly created.

A fourth clinical chair in surgery was added in 1829, one for general pathology and therapy in 1831, and one for pathological anatomy in 1835. As a reservoir for replacements, the position of *Professeur agrégé* (assistant pro- fessor) was established in 1823. Thirty-six *agrégés* were to exist, with twenty- four actively engaged in lecturing, and twelve waiting for three years before beginning to lecture. The *agrégés* were to be selected by public competition. The first *concours* for these positions took place in November, 1823. The victors were Andral, Rochoux, Duges, Velpeau, and Cruveilhier in medicine; Lisfranc, Jules Cloquet, Baudelocque, and P. Dubois in surgery; Bouvier, Gerdy, and Devergie in the "accessory sciences." A positive achievement of the Restoration was the founding of the Academy of Medicine, of which we will say more later, on December 20, 1820.

The Revolution of 1830 reinstalled those professors who had been dis- missed in 1823 and dismissed the royalists who had replaced them to the extent that members of both groups were still alive. The Paris hospital system created, in 1830, an additional dissection center for its interns and externs—the amphitheater of the hospitals at Clamart.

During the fifty-four years of its existence which we are studying here, the School had five deans. We have already discussed the first, M. Thouret. His successor in 1810 was J. J. Leroux des Tillets, also an ex-member of the old Faculty. Politically quite active at the beginning of the Revolution, he had later concentrated completely on his medical duties, first as adjunct to and later as successor of Corvisart at the Charité. Rather colorless as a dean, he was a competent clinician and teacher and a great orator. He devoted much time to purely literary exercises. Belonging like his predecessor, Thouret, to the Corvisart-Pinel generation, he was purged in 1822. He was rehabilitated in 1830 and died from cholera in 1832. He is also remembered as co-editor, with Boyer and Corvisart, of the *Journal de médecine, chirurgie et pharmacie*.

Leroux was followed by A. J. Landré-Beauvais (1772–1840). First a disciple of Desault and a military surgeon, he became one of the first pupils at the École de Santé and later the close collaborator of Pinel at the Salpêtrière, where he taught semiotics from 1799 till 1807. His lectures appeared as a book in 1809. His thesis of 1800 on "asthenic gout" (now called rheumatoid arthritis) was a real contribution. He had an extensive *praxis aurea*. Like his codisciple and friend, Esquirol, he was politically conservative but personally of a moderate and benevolent disposition, which was reflected in his activities as dean. In 1830, he returned without regret to private life.

In 1830, old Antoine Dubois (1756–1837) became dean for a short while. It was a shrewd move to install this pupil of Desault and participant in the Egyptian expedition; he was an immensely popular teacher, surgeon, and obstetrician. He said "thou" to everybody, helped the "King of Rome" into this world, and "placed" one son and five sons-in-law in good positions.

He was soon (1831) followed by Matthew Orfila (1787–1853). Spanish-born Orfila, a protégé of Vauquelin, was not only an excellent scientist (see the chapter on legal medicine) and a great teacher, teaching at the School for thirty-four years, but also a successful speculator on the stock market and an outstanding administrator, perhaps the most successful dean the Faculty ever had. Sachaile, who in general was a rather stern judge of his colleagues, said: "He has done what we deemed impossible: he has made of a place, which since its creation seemed but an office where students paid and received their titles and but a sinecure for the professors, a real school where teachers and pupils are equally zealous. . . ."[27] Corlieu states: "He strengthened discipline in the school, had the Hôpital des Cliniques and new dissection rooms built, established the new botanical garden at the Luxembourg, and created the Museum of Pathological Anatomy with the money left by Dupuytren for a chair which was paid by the state. He created the Museum of Normal Anatomy which bears his name."[28] He also increased professors' salaries from 400 francs per year to 1,500 francs. But Orfila was also a not-too-scrupulous politician, manipulating the *concours* and serving those in power. He thus made many enemies—some quite voluble ones like A. F. H. Fabre, the editor of the *Gazette des hôpitaux* (*La lancette française*), who published, in 1836, a satirical poem (illustrated by Daumier) entitled "L'Orfiliade." Thus the Revolution of 1848 swept Orfila away.

Since this is the history of a group that called itself the "clinical school," discussion of its clinicians will fill the better part of the following chapters. Only some of the "accessory scientists" will be mentioned here. Hardly one of them was a man of significant scientific stature; those were kept outside the medical schools or preferred to stay outside. Yet among these not-so-eminent scientists were quite a few who were extremely popular and really excellent teachers—and in the life of a school, this is very important too.

A. M. C. Duméril (1774–1860) was primarily a zoologist. He had a chair at the Museum, but he taught anatomy at the School for thirty-two years, and then internal pathology for another thirty years. He played a role in the Academies, but he was not a dramatic teacher; as a matter of fact, he stuttered.[29] He was apparently a very reasonable eclectic. Among his pupils were Rayer, Serres, Jules Cloquet, and Piorry; Bretonneau was his friend.

One of the most popular teachers of the school was Pierre-Augustin Béclard of Angers (1785–1825). A young surgeon, a son-in-law of A. Dubois who preferred science to practice, he held the chair of anatomy for only seven years—not long enough to leave a large scientific legacy, but long enough to win the love, respect, and devotion of his students. Two thousand of them accompanied his coffin to the Père Lachaise. His successor Cruveilhier will be dealt with later, as a pathological anatomist.

The surgeon Gilbert Breschet (1784–1845) won the *concours* for the chair of anatomy in 1836 against poor Bosc, who died a pauper at the Hôtel Dieu. Breschet was a mediocre teacher, but an influential man. A number of valuable scientific studies were published under his name, especially in embryology and physiology. Unfortunately, his use of foreign publications and of younger collaborators as open or silent partners (for example, Bogros and Kuess) was so common as to inspire certain doubts about his actual accomplishments.

P. H. Bérard (1791–1858), a surgeon and protégé of Béclard, won the competition for the chair of physiology in 1831. He never made an important scientific contribution, but he was a very successful teacher for twenty-seven years. He was dean from 1848 to 1852 and, later, inspector general of higher education.

A rather typical "accessory scientist" was N. P. Adelon (1750–1864), a son-in-law of Sabatier and protégé of Chaussier. He wrote a voluminous book on what others had found in physiology and occupied the chair of legal medicine for thirty-five years (1826–1861), thus blocking it for much abler men. He was a poor teacher, but a learned and honest man. For a long time, he was one of the two assistant deans of the École. The popular hygienists Hallé and Desgenettes will be dealt with later.

With the botanist Antoine-Laurent de Jussieu (1748–1836), professor from 1804 till the *coup d'état* of 1822, and Jean Baptiste Dumas (1800–1884), the teacher of Pasteur and collaborator of Haussman, professor of organic chemistry from 1838 till 1852, the Faculty had, for once, two quite exceptional scientists and able teachers in its ranks.

Surgical pathology also counted among the theoretical chairs. It was held from 1807 to 1818 by Anthelme Richerand (1779–1840), who taught at the School for thirty-three years altogether. One of the early pupils at the School and a protégé of Cabanis and Fourcroy, he had a vertiginous career and was quite influential in his time due to his intelligence and his brilliant and poisonous pen. His physiology text, a compilation that he wrote at twenty-one, was translated seventeen times. His *Nosographie et thérapeutique chirurgicales* (*Surgical Nosography and Therapeutics*) was world famous. He jumped on every bandwagon; he was surgeon of the Hôpital St. Louis at twenty-one, and a professor at twenty-eight, but he was never satisfied. With pathological envy and hatred, he pursued those, alive or dead, who, in his mind, obscured his fame—for example, Bichat, Desault, Roux, Magendie, Broc, and Dupuytren. The latter resembled him as to competitiveness but was far more substantial as a scientist. Richerand was a poor speaker and poor surgeon. Chaussier used to allude, in class, to his plagiarisms. Sainte-Beuve called him a charlatan. C. Daremberg put his work into the *littérature médicophilosophique* category, with that of Pomme, Alibert, Moreau, Virey, and Réveillé-Parise—a categorization that did not imply any compliments.[30]

His successor, J. N. Marjolin (1780–1850), who held the chair from 1818 to 1850, was the exact opposite. Marjolin had a hard time under Dupuytren, but nothing could spoil his honest and warmhearted disposition. An industrious but undistinguished writer, he excelled as a practical surgeon and a teacher and enjoyed unusual popularity in these fields.

Private teaching was frequent at the time of the old Faculty. It continued through and after the Revolution. While it proved absolutely insufficient to replace official teaching, it was a highly valuable and ever growing addition to it. As a matter of fact, teaching in the specialties existed only as private instruction up to the 1870's, when chairs of psychiatry, pediatrics, ophthalmology, dermatology, neurology, and urology were eventually created. Private courses allowed more detailed studies and more personal contacts; through them, pedagogic talents could become manifest, develop, and gain a reputation. The facilities of the École Pratique were at the disposal of private teachers. Unorthodox opinions could be defended. Candidates for a professorial career could be kept alive. Maygrier (himself a very successful teacher of anatomy) reported, in 1810, twenty-one private courses;[31] among the teachers were many who later gained official positions or scientific fame—for example, Dupuytren, Roux, Capuron, Alibert, Jadelot, Récamier, Nysten, and Marjolin. In 1831, Horn gave a list of forty private courses.[32] Muehry mentions more than sixty courses in 1836. He found the private clinical lectures and visits of Louis, Piorry, Lugol, Biett, Ricord, Breschet, Magendie, Récamier, Bailly, Civiale, Rayer, and Larrey particularly remarkable.[33] The *Archives générales* of 1838 (p. 2) list Ferrus, Cazenave, Malgaigne, and Donné, among others, as private teachers.

In 1841, Otterburg mentions Amussat, Blandin, Broc, Cazenave, Devergie, Donné, Ferrus, Sabatier, Malgaigne, Raciborski, Ricord, and Sichel.[34] Stewart (1843, 140) mentions over forty courses and lists as instructors Chassaignac, Maisonneuve, Denonvilliers, Bouchardat, Foville, Barthez, Rilliet, Longet, Civiale, Leroy d'Etoilles, Menière, Gibert, and Barth. A similar list is found in Gardner (1848). In 1853, Meding names more than 100 teachers, among whom we find Wurtz, C. Robin, Gerhardt, Auzias-Turenne, Baillarger, C. Bernard, Bouchut, P. Broca, Falret, Follin, Jobert, and Valleix.[35]

We remember that Bichat, Gall, Broussais, Gerdy, Laennec, and many others were engaged for long periods in private teaching.[36] Patriotic Stewart, who strangely enough thought better of medical practice at home in the United States than in Paris, nevertheless declared in 1843 that there was no better place on earth than Paris for studying medicine. He particularly recommended instruction in anatomy, diagnosis, obstetrics, pathological anatomy, dermatology, pediatrics, botany, ophthalmology, chemistry, surgical operations, orthopedics, urology, and comparative anatomy.[37]

Some medical education was also dispensed by institutions like the Musée Français, which was founded in 1781 and continued its activities as the Lycée, Lycée Republicain, and Athénée until 1849. A review of the teaching resources of Paris in the first half of the nineteenth century makes it easy to understand why, for several decades, it became the Mecca of medical students from all over the world.

V. PINEL AND BICHAT

The fifty-five years in the life of the Paris School that are the subject of this book can be subdivided into four periods according to the then-dominant clinical orientation. There can be no doubt that the prevailing influence during the first of these four periods, which reaches from 1794 to 1816, was that of Philippe Pinel. This might come as a surprise to some, since today Pinel is remembered only as a psychiatrist. We will deal with this other important aspect of his personality later, in the appropriate chapter.

As much as we today might admire Pinel's greatness as a psychiatrist, we cannot overlook the fact that, to his contemporaries, he was known through his *Nosographie philosophique* of 1798 and his courses (1795–1822), primarily as the great teacher and systematizer of internal medicine (as was the case with Griesinger sixty years later). Rostan was right in saying, in 1826, that Pinel's hospital and fortress, the Salpêtrière, was the cradle of the medical revolution. The traveler Wardenburg praised Pinel highly in 1797, as did Poumiès de la Siboutie, looking back as an old man. Raige-Delorme wrote in a historical survey in 1839, "We still believe that the foundations which he chose are the only possible ones for the building of pathology. However, that might be, Pinel had an immense influence on his period."[1]

Philippe Pinel, born April 20, 1745, into a medical family, came from St. Paul, a village near Castres in southern France.[2] Destined originally to become a priest, he changed to mathematics and medicine. From 1767 to 1774, he studied at Toulouse and, from 1774 to 1776, at Montpellier. He made a living by tutoring, ghostwriting doctoral theses, and writing articles, mostly on hygiene. A treatise on hygiene that he prepared has never been published. At Montpellier, he befriended Chaptal, on whom he performed a kind of psychotherapy. In 1778, he went to Paris and continued this calm and studious existence[3] there for another ten years, since he still felt insufficiently prepared to practice. He met Cabanis, and Cabanis brought him into the salon of Mme Helvetius, the meeting place of the *idéologues*, where he encountered Benjamin Franklin. This seems to have inspired him for a while with plans to emigrate to the United States.

After 1783, through the tragedy of a friend, he became increasingly interested in mental diseases. Recommended by Thouret and Cabanis, he was made, on August 25, 1793, a physician at the Bicêtre, where he unchained the insane. A moderate revolutionary, he helped his friend Condorcet and other victims of persecution during the Terror. In 1794, he became a professor at the new École de Santé, first of hygiene, then of internal pathology. In May, 1795, he changed from Bicêtre to the Salpêtrière. In 1822, he was purged by the reactionary Restoration government. He died on October 26, 1826. He published a great deal. His main books were the *Nosographie philosophique* of 1798, the *Medicophilosophical Treatise on Mental Alienation* of 1801, and his *Clinical Medicine* of 1802.

Pinel was full of boundless admiration for Hippocrates. The name was quoted over and over again in his writings. One of the essential things to teach a student, he thought, was how to study Hippocrates; only thus could he learn to observe.[4] Still, Pinel's Hippocratism was quite problematic. His Sydenhamian idea of classifying diseases was certainly not Hippocratic. He was an antihumoralist,[5] and a "solidist almost without restriction."[6] To Cuvier, he was above all a localist propagating the notion of the lesion.[7] While he believed in crises,[8] he was quite skeptical as to the so-called "epidemic constitution,"[9] since the same metereological conditions were accompanied by different diseases in different years.[10] Perhaps his most genuine Hippocratic trait was his fight for expectant[11] medicine versus active or "perturbing" medicine.

Pinel was an *idéologue*—a philosopher of the eighteenth century and a member of the last circle of philosophers of the Enlightenment. It is no accident that his books often bear the word "philosophical" in their titles. To the *idéologue*, "observation" was, of course, the watchword; according to him, medical studies had to start in the hospital.[12] Pinel can rightly claim to have been one of the originators of clinical instruction. He was opposed to "vain theories." He used, as an instrument of medical thought, "analysis" (this slogan too is repeated *ad nauseam*) that proceeded from the simple to the complex, that is, in medicine, from symptoms to simple diseases to complicated diseases.[13] In addition, he was a mathematician and a comparative anatomist. Thus classification would have been important to him even if it had not been the scientific craze of his century. As a mathematician, he also used statistics ("*le calcul des probabilités*") as much as possible.[14] He was the actual father of the numerical method in medicine.

Pinel was a sincere admirer of Morgagni. "To pay special attention to the *nécrologe* (autopsy record) is a basic goal of the hospital physician."[15] Through Fourcroy, he became strongly interested in the chemistry of disease. But both these influences had only a limited bearing on his work, which was primarily that of classification.

Classification was, during the eighteenth century, a central concern in science, especially in botany and in medicine. In the latter field, Pinel was preceded by Boissier de Sauvages (1732), Linné (1764), Cullen and Macbride (1772), Vitet (1778), and E. Darwin (1796). He was followed by Baumès and Richerand (1801), Tourdes (1802), Tourtelle (1805), and Alibert (1817). His goal was expressed in the following statements:

> Toward the beginning of the last century an iatromathematician posed this general problem: *if you face a disease, find the remedy.* This was more an expression of pretentiousness than of enlightenment of wisdom. . . . A judicious study of authors, a close scrutiny of the phenomena of disease. . . . teach us to limit ourselves to the following problem which is more circumscribed and measured: *if you face a disease, determine its true char-acter and its rank in a nosological table.*[16]
>
> The historical exposition of the totality and the sequence of symptoms is the only true source of knowledge concerning the progression and the distinctive features of fevers.[17]

It is extremely typical that he is against those who "see diseased people without seeing diseases" ("*voir des malades sans voir des maladies*").[18]

Pinel differentiated five classes of diseases: fevers, phlegmasias (inflamma-tions), hemorrhages, neuroses, and organic lesions. The fevers were sub-divided into six orders: angiotenic, meningogastric, adenomeningeal, adynamic, ataxic, and adenonervous. These corresponded to the inflammatory, bilious, mucous, putrid, malignant, and pestilential fevers of ancient authors. The change of name did not imply better insight. These six orders were subdivided into eighteen genera and numerous species, which it is unneces-sary to enumerate here, all the more since none of them correspond to the disease units of today.

The phlegmasias had five orders: those of the skin (with fifteen genera, including variola and measles), those of the mucous membranes, those of the serous membranes, those of the connective tissue and parenchymatous organs, and those of the muscular, fibrous, and synovial tissues. Class number three, hemorrhages, had only three orders and six genera. The fourth class, that of the neuroses, was very comprehensive and went from deafness to hysteria. The last class, organic lesions, embraced general diseases like scurvy, cancer, and syphilis, as well as heart disease, hydrops, kidney stone, uterine tumors, and intestinal worms. His disciple Schwilgué inserted numerous case histories into the third edition of his *Nosographie*. Pinel's book *Clinical Medicine* consisted essentially of case histories, written up by his pupil Esquirol and illustrating the first three classes of his system.

The goal of Pinel's nosography was to "paint disease." He failed not only because he was not a very gifted "painter," that is, observer and writer—his tremendous learning was in this respect rather a handicap—but because the utopian idea of a systematic classification of disease was a handicap in itself. We have progressed considerably since we gave it up. As "colors," he had mostly only symptoms at his disposal. We know now that they are not suffi' cient to do a real "portrait." The consequence was that reality and Pinel's classification of it were rather far apart, farther probably than in the case of most of our own concepts. Worst in this respect was, of course, his first class, "essential fevers"—one-third of his book! It is legitimate that it has been criticized most severely. Many of our present units, such as typhoid fever, malaria, or diphtheria, occur in several of his subdivisions and cannot be identified with any one of them. The hemorrhages, overestimation of which he inherited from his revered Stahl, were again symptoms elevated to the rank of disease units. The neuroses did not fit in with his intention of collecting only "functional diseases," and they thus became a terrible hodgepodge.

His best chapters are those where anatomical considerations were added to symptomatological ones, that is, those on phlegmasias and organic lesions. He could rightly claim to have inspired Bichat in the field of diseases of the mucous and serous membranes.[19] He showed a definite clinical flair, for example, in his differentiation of the rheumatisms, his observation that scarlet fever was often transmitted by people suffering from simple angina, and in his statement that the mucus of mucous fever was a product, not a cause, of the disease.[20] "Psychosomatic thought," that is, realization of the importance of psychological factors in the causation and cure of disease, is encountered very frequently in his work.[21] Pinel also started the geriatrics movement at the Salpêtrière.[22] Not the least of his merits were his therapeutic Hippocratism and his skepticism, which we will discuss later. Remarkable also were his pioneer efforts in the fields of variolation and vaccination. Thus Pinel's book had more to recommend it than just the absence of a better book.

To us, the work of Pinel, born in 1745, is but a transition from the medicine of the eighteenth century to that of the nineteenth. To his students of 1794, it was extremely useful and had enough new aspects to fire their enthusiasm. If we add that its author possessed not only great intellectual powers, but extraordinary goodness and fairness, we can understand why, for thirty years, he enjoyed tremendous popularity with patients, students, and colleagues. Free from envy, he never attacked anybody. He was never too proud to learn from others; for example, he took percussion from Corvisart, stethoscopy from Laennec, Corvisart's results on heart disease, and those of Alibert on skin diseases, always giving proper acknowledgment of his sources! It is no accident that, among his case histories, there are so many of students. He seems to have been their doctor, and their father, as well as their teacher.

No wonder that so many followed his classes and clinics, though the short, wiry man was no orator. No wonder that so many wrote their theses with him and that so many, like Bricheteau, Landré-Beauvais, and Schwilgué, worked under him for many years, elaborating his ideas. No wonder that men who grew out of the role of pupils and became great men in their own right—Esquirol, Bichat, Broussais—attached themselves to him. Rostan, without equaling them, was also able to develop a rather vigorous position of his own while continuing, to a certain extent, in the Pinelian tradition.

Thus the leading name of the first period of the Paris school was Pinel. If one realizes that, among many others, no lesser men than Laennec, Bayle, Récamier, Broussais, Béclard, Cruveilhier, Richerand, Roux, Dupuytren, and Alibert later claimed Bichat as a teacher and an inspiration, there can be little doubt that the next period would have borne the same name of "the first born of the young Republican school of Paris" if the gods had not, supposedly, loved him. He died in 1802, in his thirty-first year.

Marie-François-Xavier Bichat was born November 14, 1771, at Thoirette, the son of a physician. He began his medical studies in 1791 at Lyon under the surgeon M. A. Petit. In 1793, he moved to Paris, where Desault, the great surgeon and anatomist of the Hôtel Dieu, soon befriended him and took him into his house. After Desault's premature death in 1795, Bichat collected and edited his works, which appeared in 1798. In the same period, while moving away from practical surgery, he began to give very successful private courses in anatomy, surgery, and physiology (Wardenburg mentions him in 1797 as a teacher of anatomy and a surgeon) and founded the Société Médicale d'Émulation with some friends. In 1799, he became, through Chaptal, a physician at the Hôtel Dieu (or the "Grand Hôpital de l'Humanité," as it was then called). During the next year, while continuously teaching, doing research, and taking care of hospital patients, he wrote his first great books—the *Traité des membranes* (*Treatise on Membranes*) and *Recherches physiologiques sur la vie et la mort* (*Physiological Studies on Life and Death*). In 1801, his *Anatomie générale* and the first volumes of his *Anatomie descriptive* appeared. His pace became more and more hectic. He supposedly autopsied 600 corpses during the winter of 1801–1802. He gave a course on pathological anatomy. He experimented with drugs. He started a course on materia medica, but never finished it.[23] He died after a few days of acute illness, probably from tuberculosis meningitis, in the arms of his friends Roux, Esparron, and

Mme Desault, on July 22, 1802. The efforts of his physicians Corvisart and Lepreux to save him had been in vain.

Corvisart wrote to Napoleon (then still First Consul): "Bichat just died at thirty. He fell on a battleground which demands courage too and counts more than one victim. He has enriched medical science. Nobody at his age has done so much so well."

Napoleon ordered that a monument be erected in the hall of the Hôtel Dieu, with the following inscription: "This monument, dedicated to the memory of citizens Desault and Bichat, is testimony to the gratitude of their contemporaries for the services that the former rendered to French surgery as its restorer, and that the latter rendered to French medicine, which he enriched by several works whose realm he would have extended, if pitiless death had not struck him in his thirty-first year."[24]

Bichat's intellectual superiority needs no special emphasis. But the amazing fact has to be underlined that this bold theorist, this ruthless experimenter,[25] this tireless worker, was simultaneously a modest, peaceful, sincere, generous, and warmhearted human being. No wonder he was loved and mourned as few medical teachers before or after him. Hardly a Paris student was absent from his burial. The men of the preceding generation—Corvisart, Lepreux, Hallé, Thouret, Pinel, and Leroux—expressed their bereavement with such sincerity, such sorrow, and such affection for the departed that an echo of it still lingers on.

The life and work of Bichat were only begun. It seems necessary to describe his scientific ideas in some detail, since a benevolent mythology has long ago replaced a precise knowledge of them. His first book, the *Treatise on Membranes* of 1800, deals with the mucous, serous, fibrous, composite, and accidental membranes. He credits Pinel with suggesting to him the basic idea of seeing these membranes, on the one hand, as independent elements of organs, and, on the other, as systems with common traits. He omits mention of Bordeu, author of *Recherches sur le tissu muqueux ou l'organe cellulaire*, and refers to his other principal spiritual godfather, Haller, only critically. He gives detailed anatomical descriptions but unfortunately refuses to use the microscope.[26] He discusses the "vital forces" (sensibility and contractility) of membranes, commenting interestingly on the change of sensibility through habit.[27]

For all his speculative inclinations, Bichat was an experimenter, not an armchair physiologist like Barthez and many others. His descriptions of function are often based on experiments such as those on transfusion of arterial blood, air absorption by the intestine, or air embolism.[28] His chapters on pathology consist mostly of question marks, symbols of his honesty. But he makes the important statement: "The affection of an organ is not neces-sarily the consequence of an affection of its serous membrane and vice versa. . . . The life of serous membranes is thus entirely isolated from that of their corresponding organs."[29] Thus the way is opened to replace, for example, the vague notion of "carditis" by the far more specific pericarditis, myocarditis, or endocarditis, "brain inflammation" by meningitis or encephalitis, and so on. The imaginary "exhaling system" makes its appearance in these pages, and the old notion of "sympathy" is used extensively. The notion of sympathy plays a great role with Bichat, perhaps because it allows him to explain phenomena otherwise not accessible to his pronounced localism-solidism. Detailed discussions of the arachnoid and synovial membranes close the book. The surgeon becomes evident in the detailed classification and description of joints. Many of the ideas of the *Membranes* return more fully developed in Bichat's later works.

The *Physiological Studies on Life and Death* begin with Bichat's famous tautological definition of life ("the total of functions which resist death") and his basic physiological contribution: the subdivision of the vital process in man into "animal life" and "organic life" (which also exists in plants); into functions of action and functions of relation; and into those parts of the animal that are internal (heart, lungs, and so on) and those that are external (for example, the limbs). Animal life (voluntary movement) is symmetrical and intermittent, organic life (digestion, circulation, etc.) asymmetrical and continuous. Animal life is formed by habit, whereas organic life is not. Understanding depends on animal life (sensation); passions depend on organic life and, in turn, act upon it. The nerves of organic life form a center in the epigastrium, but it is not comparable in development to the brain, the center of animal life. Vital forces are different in the two systems and change accord-ing to tissues. He differentiates between animal and organic sensibility. It is impossible to calculate in physiology, he asserts, and the laws of physics and chemistry are not applicable in physiology. He observes the development of organic life in the fetus (a mere plant!—which makes the death of the baby in childbirth preferable to that of the mother) and after the "revolution"of birth. Animal life stops before organic life. Man dies piecemeal.

Life depends essentially on the function of Bordeu's "tripod"—lungs, heart, and brain. The second part of Bichat's study consists mostly of de-scriptions of a series of experiments concerning the effects of the death of the heart on the brain, the lungs, and other organs; the death of the lungs on the brain and the heart; and the death of the brain on the lungs, the heart, and so on. Bichat observes that the essential part of the brain is the brain stem. Air embolism is "brain death." Sudden death from passion is "heart death." In most diseases, death starts in the lungs. Stimulation of the nerves of the heart in decapitated people, he notes, is without effect.

Physiology at Bichat's time did not yet exclude the observation of social factors and influences. He regards the superiority of the right side as a "social convention." Society strongly influences the development of the organs of animal life. Due to society, we are unlike animals and do not die a natural death. Was it for these sociological excursions that Saint-Simon, Schopenhauer, and Comte—the latter made him a saint in his new religion— liked Bichat so much?

General Anatomy Applied to Physiology and to Medicine is Bichat's most substantial and most ambitious work. It starts with 100 pages of "general considerations." Its first sentence is a manifesto of extreme vitalism. "In nature there are two classes of beings, two classes of properties, two classes of sciences. The beings are organic and inorganic, the properties vital and nonvital, the sciences physiological and physical." What gravity, elasticity, and the like are to the latter, the vital properties (sensibility, contractility) are to the former.

He gives the subdivision of his five vital properties in further differentiating animal sensibility into the external and the internal (1:xvi). Therapeutics must re-establish these properties (xvii). He foresees the possibility of fever therapy (xx). "One cannot foresee, predict or calculate the phenomena of vital functions; we have concerning them only approximations, which are most of the time uncertain" (xxvi). Inert bodies have neither a pathology nor sympathies, nor do they need medicaments. He enumerates the classic vitalist arguments as to differences between the animate and the inanimate. Bichat brings eighteenth-century vitalism—he had never studied at Montpellier, but he was strongly influenced by Bordeu and Barthez—to a climax. The development of vitalism during the eighteenth century is a necessary corollary to the tremendous development of physics, which accentuated the vast gulf between living and nonliving things. With Fracastorius, for example, in an age of most rudimentary physics, everything was still considered animate.[30]

Bichat's discussion of vital properties in their relation to solid organs and fluids shows him as a determined solidist. "Since the vital properties are essentially located in the solids, organs, and . . . the phenomena of disease are but changes of vital properties, it is obvious that pathological phenomena reside essentially in the solid organs" (xlv). The fluids carry noxious substances to and from the organs. At this occasion, he gives a case history of "gray blood," which might very well be one of leukemia (lv). Bichat subdivides diseases (xlix ff.) into (1) those of animal life and organic life; (2) sympathetic and direct diseases; (3) diseases with and without tissue change; (4) chronic and acute diseases; and (5) those where the whole system is affected, and those where this is not the case.

After these preliminaries, he eventually tackles his subject: the organization of animals. All animals are composed of organs, the "little machines in the great machine" which is the whole being. The organs, in turn, are formed by tissues, which generate them in the way in which the simple chemical elements (oxygen, carbon, nitrogen, etc.) associate to form chemical compounds (lxvi). These anatomical "elements" are the following:

1.	cellular	12.	fibro-cartilaginous
2.	nervous, of animal life	13.	muscular, of animal life
3.	nervous, or organic life	14.	muscular, or organic life
4.	arterial	15.	mucous
5.	venous	16.	serous
6.	exhalant	17.	synovial
7.	absorbent	18.	glandular
8.	osseous	19.	dermoid
9.	medullary	20.	epidermoid
10.	cartilaginous	21.	pilous
11.	fibrous		

This splitting up of organs into tissues is Bichat's application of the sensualists' idea of "analysis," as Laín Entralgo showed many years ago. It netted Bichat the title of "father of histology."

The vital properties take a different character in each tissue (lxxiv). Consequently, different tissues in the same organ are affected separately (lxxvii), as he shows with many examples (arachinitis, not "inflammation of the brain"; retinitis or conjunctivitis, not "inflammation of the eye"; pericarditis, not "inflammation of the heart"). The sympathies too do not go from organ to organ, but from tissue to tissue (lxxxi). Pathological anatomy, which clarifies this situation, is the science of the future.

It seems to me that we have entered an epoch where pathological anatomy must make a new effort. This science is not only that of the organic changes which arrive slowly or as consequences in chronic diseases. It consists of the study of all possible alterations of our bodies whenever we examine their diseases. With the exception of certain fevers and nervous diseases, almost everything in pathology is in its domain. . . . Medicine was for a long time excluded from the exact sciences. She will have the right to belong to them, at least for diagnostics, when rigorous observation is everywhere combined with examination of organ changes. . . . What is the value of observation, if one does not know the seat of the disease? You can take notes for twenty years from morning to evening at the sickbed on the diseases of the heart, lung, and stomach, and you will reap nothing but confusion. The symptoms, correspond- ing to nothing, will offer but incoherent phenomena. Open a few corpses, and immediately this obscurity, which observation alone would never have re- moved, will disappear (xciii).

This is by no means the central theme of the book, but *this actually became the center of Bichat's legacy!* The lengthy introduction closes with a classifi- cation of functions, that is, of physiology. Comparison of the "table of physiology" published in *General Anatomy* with a student notebook of L. J. Jusserandot on a course of eighty-six lectures by Bichat on physiology in 1801–1802, the year X (Zurich Institute Collection), shows that Bichat fol- lowed this table faithfully in his own teaching.

He begins his descriptive work with the systems common to all organs, among them the "cellular tissue" of Haller, our present "connective tissue." (The expression "cellular" has absolutely nothing to do with the cellular theory.[31]) He subdivides it into cellular tissue outside, inside, and inde- pendent of organs. He offers innumerable interesting details on, for example, fatty degeneration (1:74) or the formation of connective tissue in scars. (Bichat was, after all, a surgeon!) He, like Virchow later,[32] considered this tissue the source of all tumors (1:129). In his description of the nervous sys- tem of animal life, he tries through experiments (the whole book abounds in experiments) to minimize its role (1:238). The differentiation between "red-blooded" and "black-blooded" vascular systems sounds rather artificial. Here we encounter, all of a sudden, a quite humoralist statement (2:14). Arteriosclerosis, observed by Bichat in seven out of ten people over seventy, is discussed in detail (2:63 ff.). Since the changes due to old age are noticed in all tissues, the book is also an early contribution to gerontology. The other end of the life cycle, the "revolution" of birth (2:231), is also considered. Air embolism is again an important subject (2:231). Inflammation and gangrene start in the solid organs, that is, in the capillary system. The "exhalant system," a nonexistent continuation of the capillaries believed in by Bichat and most of his contemporaries, including Pinel, is faithfully described (2:400 ff.). Bichat's description of the absorbent (our lymphatic) system is more nearly correct than those of many of his successors.

The last two volumes are devoted to those tissues that can be found only in certain formations: the osseous, medullar, cartilaginous, fibrous, and fibrocartilaginous—all particularly familiar to the surgeon. The two muscular systems, and the mucous, serous, glandular, dermoid, epidermoid, and pilous tissues follow. These weighty volumes end with the philosophical question of why we are not shocked by such an unnatural sight as a man without a beard (4:507).

Bichat was far more a medical revolutionary than were Pinel and Corvisart. Bichat wanted, for example, to do away with the 4,000-year-old classification *a capite ad calcem*, still dear to Morgagni (lxxxix). *He was no Hippocratist.* "Accessory sciences" were essential sciences to him. He was above all a surgeon-anatomist and a physiologist-scientist. Though his name became its symbol and banner, he actually had relatively little in common with the past and the future of the Paris school of 1800.

In order to appreciate Bichat's unique position within the Paris school it suffices to look at his program as outlined in the preface of his *General Anatomy*: "Analyze with precision the properties of living tissues; show that each physiological phenomenon ultimately derives from these properties; that each pathological phenomenon depends on their augmentation, diminution, or alteration; that each therapeutic phenomenon should effect their return to their natural type, from which they have deviated" (vii).

Of course, he too had predecessors. He was even accused by Regnault and others of not mentioning them (for example, Barthez and Haller) often enough.[33] Cabanis accused him, probably unjustly, of plagiarism.[34] Actually, Bichat had great originality. Out of small suggestions in Haller, Bordeu, and Pinel, he developed and constructed an imposing system of ultravitalist tissue anatomy, tissue physiology, and tissue pathology. His physiology (except for the organic-life–animal-life division) proved to be a dead end and a failure. He did not become the Newton of physiology, as he had hoped and tried to be. Still his work remains a magnificent fresco. *And his tissue anatomy, upon which modern histology was founded, was indeed a great step forward in biology.* But his histology was so tied up with vitalism that it became usable only after elimination of these latter elements. He distrusted "overgeneralization" (xxiv; lii) very much, and yet he became its victim. Raige-Delorme[35] says, not without justification, "Bichat, while advancing science, made it deviate." Pathological anatomy, the field in which he had not yet had time to work much, was paradoxically enough the one where his influence and his tendencies toward tissue studies, solidism, and localism were felt most immediately, most strongly, and most usefully.

P. J. Roux, his friend and disciple, continued his course, finished his *Anatomie descriptive*, and—a queer form of devotion—kept Bichat's alcohol-preserved head with him for forty-three years. Roux became, as is known, a famous surgeon, but neither he nor anybody else could replace Bichat, though the latter had had innumerable gifted pupils.[36] Haindorf[37] thought astutely in 1813 that Dupuytren would eventually succeed Bichat. An anatomist, physiologist, and pathologist of the first order, Dupuytren would probably have had the necessary talent, but his ambitious character made him prefer the career of a dictator of surgery. Laennec continued the work of Bichat only in pathological anatomy, and Magendie only in experimental physiology. We will see in the next chapter what kind of continuation his self-styled successor Broussais provided.

Pinel's long reign from 1795 till 1816 did not witness the rise of another star of Bichat's magnitude. These were years of war; but it is the presence of so many good studies, rather than the absence of any great ones, that should be emphasized. Essentially it was a period of monographs: Fodéré on goiter, the year VIII (1799–1800); Alibert on skin diseases; and Corvisart on heart diseases, 1806; Broussais on chronic inflammations, 1808; G. L. Bayle on phthisis, 1810; Riobé and Rochoux on apoplexy, 1812; M. A. Petit and Serres on "enteromesenteric fever"; and Orfila on poisons, 1813. Petit, Lallemand, and Bayle even considered it desirable to write only monographs.[38] But the hard fact remained that monographs could never replace general books in effectiveness.

Very few general books appeared other than those of Pinel and Bichat. Prost's *Medicine Enlightened by Autopsies* (1804) had excellent autopsy records, but was utterly confused. The author, a pupil of Bichat and Bayle but influenced by *Naturphilosophie* (Schelling's notorious application of romantic philosophy to science and medicine), abandoned medicine early for psychiatry. Barbier (*Therapeutic Hygiene*, 1811) tried with limited success to continue Bichat's work in the therapeutic field. The *General Semiology* of Double (1811) is an interesting book for historians. This inveterate Hippocratist said some very pertinent things to the Hippocrates philologists of his day, but he understood the importance of pathological anatomy far less even than did Portal, who was thirty-five years older; the latter's *General Anatomy* (1803) was unfortunately one of his weakest productions. Bichat was dead, Pinel was growing old (he was seventy in 1815), and a vacuum was beginning to be felt more and more. It was soon filled in a most dramatic fashion.

VI. BROUSSAIS

The great change came in 1816. The old concentration on symptoms and essentialism was replaced with astonishing speed by a new orientation toward lesions and localism. It was introduced by a man now almost forgotten: François Joseph Victor Broussais, the inventor of "physiological medicine." He therewith became the leader of Paris medicine for the next two decades.

Broussais was born in 1772, the son of a surgeon in St. Malo. He was thus a Breton—the countryman of his rival Laennec and of two other explosive figures of his period, Chateaubriand and Lamennais. From 1792 to 1794, he served enthusiastically in the Revolutionary army against the "chouans," the royalist insurgents of the west. On Christmas Eve of 1795, his parents were murdered by political enemies, an event which influenced him to the end of his life. The lines he wrote to his wife on this occasion reflect his personality rather well:[1] "*Cherre amie la seulle qui me reste au monde mon tender pere, ma respectable mere, j'apprens dans l'instant leur massacre. Des monstres les chouans je suis suffoque. . . .*" ("Dear friend, the only one left to me, I have just learned that my loving father, my worthy mother have been murdered. What monsters those *Chouans*[!] I suffocate. . . .")

After a hasty education as a surgeon, he served from 1795 to 1798 in the navy, mostly on buccaneering boats. In 1798 he went to Paris to study medicine in the newly opened École de Santé. Although he heard Cabanis, Corvisart, Chaussier, and Hallé, his main teachers were apparently Bichat and Pinel. In 1803, he graduated with a thesis on "hectic fevers," written entirely in the spirit of Pinel.

From 1803 to 1814, he served as a physician in Napoleon's armies in Holland, Germany, Austria, Italy, and especially Spain.[2] Army life threw him together with such influential figures as Larrey, Desgenettes, and the generals Foy and Soult. With remarkable energy, Broussais continued to collect clinical observations and autopsy records during his peregrinations. He published them in 1808 in his *Histoire des phlegmasies ou inflammations chroniques*. Here he dealt primarily with inflammations of the lung and the gastrointestinal system, which he regarded as the main cause of death and which he subdivided, as a faithful pupil of Bichat, into inflammations of the tissues involved. He was able to explain many "fevers" on this anatomical basis. Scientifically speaking, this book, still undogmatic, is a quite respectable contribution and Broussais' best work. It was praised by Pinel, Chaussier, and Desgenettes, but it did not find the general response its author had hoped for. The pathological descriptions suffer from what Laennec called "brevity and incertitude of details"[3] and especially from Broussais' unwillingness to separate pneumonia and tuberculous phthisis. As a protégé of Desgenettes, Broussais became, in 1815, second professor at the Val de Grâce, the Paris military hospital and medical school, and in 1820, chief physician. Solidly entrenched in this hospital, he could now start his conquest of Paris medicine.

Broussais' teaching immediately attracted a large number of students, not only on account of his oratorical superiority over the mostly aged teachers of the Faculty (the Faculty became even less attractive after the purge of 1822), but especially on account of what he said. The Broussais of the *Phlegmasies*, the respectful pupil of Pinel and Bichat, had evolved into a new Broussais—the great reformer of medicine, who opposed his own new system to the whole medical past. A new messiah of medicine had appeared. In 1816, he brought his message to a larger public through his *Examen de la doctrine médicale généralement adoptée*.

The book was a bombshell and marked a dramatic turning point in the history of French medicine. Broussais' attack was primarily directed against Pinel, whose *Nosographie philosophique* had for twenty years dominated Paris medical thought. Broussais "within ten years made Pinel's *Nosographie* age by a century."[4] Pinel's approach in creating disease entities from symptoms was condemned as arbitrary construction, as "ontology." Diseases had to be explained by the lesions of organs. Such an approach would do away with Pinel's "essential fevers," which took up one-third of his work, and show them (and most other diseases) to be inflammations, especially of the gastrointestinal tract. As Muehry said: "There is the actual breeding place of his ideas."[5] Treatment therefore had to be energetically "antiphlogistic" (local bleeding by leeches and low diet). The whole new doctrine was dubbed "physiological medicine."

"Never has a systematist conquered such a powerful party in such a short time."[6] Students flocked in such numbers to Broussais' lectures that he had to change to larger lecture halls twice. The impact of Broussais on French medical practice in the following two decades is graphically illustrated by French exportation and importation figures for leeches:[7]

Year	Importation	Exportation
1820	—	1,157,920
1823	320,000	1,188,855
1827	33,634,494	196,950
1833	41,654,300	868,650
1834	21,885,465	868,650

Female fashion showed the influence of Broussais through leech-like formations, and even cooking was modified by the theories of "physiological
medicine."[8]

Broussais found enthusiastic translators and followers in Germany, the
United States, Belgium, Holland, Spain, and other countries. Sociologists like
Comte were profoundly impressed by him.[9] Broussais became a leading practitioner, treating such celebrities as Benjamin Constant, Casimir Perier,
Manuel, Saint-Simon, E. de Girardin, Hyde de Neuville, and the liberal
generals Foy and Lamarque. It was no accident that Broussais was (together
with Récamier and Magendie) one of the three big consultants in Balzac's
Peau de chagrin. Even such an inveterate enemy of Broussais as Trousseau
had to admit, in 1861:

> Thirty to forty years ago, we seemed to have quite lost sight of the tradi-
> tions of past centuries. Broussais had made a *tabula rasa* of everything said
> prior to his day, and pretended to have re-established medicine on new
> foundations. . . . Endowed with a great talent for exposition, and in-
> fluenced by an impetuous mind and a profound conviction of the soundness
> of his views, he proclaimed that no treatment except the antiphlogistic
> was right; his pupils "swore by their master's word" and spread his
> opinions everywhere, till they became accepted, without any modifica-
> tions, by so large a number of physicians that for a long time they domi-
> nated medicine.[10]

An obvious proof of Broussais' strength is the fact that he found favorable
judgment even from outstanding representatives of a generation that had
been brought up by his adversaries and was very differently oriented in its
own work. Both A. Bouchardat and J. Béclard gave favorable opinions of his
contribution in their *Reports on the Progress of Hygiene* (Paris 1867) and
Medicine in France (Paris 1867), respectively, while Rochard regarded his
influence as wholly negative.[11] In 1867, the great Charcot recognized the
passage from symptom to lesion and the appreciation of disease, not as an
independent unit, but as a change in function, as the two cornerstones of
modern medicine—and attributed both advances to Broussais.[12] Bouchut
started his discussion of Broussais with a characteristic sentence: "Broussais,
who was born in St. Malo in 1772 and died in 1838, made as much noise as
one man possibly can during one lifetime";[13] but he recognized that Broussais'
work contained an element of real progress[14] and that he was "an important
chief of modern pathological anatomy."[15] Claude Bernard was critical of
Broussais,[16] yet recent publications have confirmed the extent to which he
was dependent on Broussais' armamentarium in his own fight against Hippocratism and skepticism.[17]

Wunderlich openly admitted his indebtedness to Broussais in the fields of irritation and sympathies[18] and of antiontology and antinosology.[19] Virchow praised Broussais' localism.[20] As a matter of fact, Broussais' influence on Virchow was much more extensive than that; it is easily perceived in Virchow's concepts of pathological physiology, antiontology, irritation, and phthisis. There is certain justification for Bouchut's claim that much of Virchow's work as a microscopic extension and confirmation of Broussaisian ideas.[21]

Broussais' appearance brought about a twenty-year period of intensive internal warfare in French medicine. Due to his position at the Val de Grâce, Broussais could immediately gather around him a group of able young military physicians and surgeons who defended him and developed and applied his ideas in articles, pamphlets, and books. Almost all of them, in the course of time, filled leading positions in the French army's medical corps. Probably the most outstanding were L. J. Bégin, F. G. Boisseau, J. B. A. Coutanceau, J. Desruelles, N. Damiron, M. J. Ducamp, J. C. Gasc, J. M. A. Goupil, R. H. J. Scoutetten, and J. B. M. Treille.[22]

Broussais was no less successful in attracting able young civilian doctors like C. E. S. Gaultier de Claubry, M. D. E. H. Chauffard, C. Londe, J. B. Monfalcon, L. C. Roche, and, above all, C. F. Lallemand and J. B. Bouillaud.

Broussais' attraction was not limited to the younger generation. He won over older clinicians like Capuron and H. M. Husson, enjoyed the support of Desgenettes and of the patriarch of French physiology, Chaussier, and was admired by outstanding surgeons like Marjolin and Richerand.

The full measure of his success is shown by the fact that his influence was felt even in the work of such nonpartisans (some of whom later became adversaries) as Andral, Piorry, Rayer, Dupuytren, Cruveilhier, A. L. Bayle, Marc, Larrey, and Guersant the elder.

The opposition against him consisted first of representatives of the old generation, like Hallé, who said, "The mere scent of his style shows the arrogance of the sectarian."[23] Other adversaries were J. P. T. Barras, Fouquier, Fodéré, [24] Fodera, L. Castel, Virey, and Macquart.

It was relatively easy for Broussais and his pupils to deal with those more or less following Pinel and the past. The real danger arose out of a group of brilliant young men who were no longer followers of Pinel and who, less through polemics than through extensive work in pathological anatomy a study that Broussais himself had demanded and stimulated, disproved his claims by bringing forward new facts. Of this group, we may mention Laennec, P. C. A. Louis, Billard, Calmeil, Chomel, Dance, Dardonville,

Georget, J. B. de Laroque, Ollivier d'Angers, C. R. Prus, and Rostan. These men, many of whom, like Laennec, Billard, Dance, Georget, Ollivier, and Prus, died prematurely, became representatives of the "anatomic-pathological" school that eventually replaced both the "nosologists" and "physiologists" and was, in turn, replaced by the "eclectics" and the "experimentalists."

One of the most effective blows against Broussais was delt by two young doctors, A. Miquel and J. B. Bousquet, in 1824. Broussais had somewhat rashly claimed that, due to the excellence of his method, he lost only one in 30 patients. Miquel and Bousquet produced statistics from the Val de Grâce to show that between 1815 and 1819, he had actually lost one in twelve patients.[25] Another very successful adversary was Barras, who, an accomplished neurotic himself, demonstrated the nervous character of many "gastroenterites."[26]

In order to emphasize the effect of Broussais' revolution in 1816, we have deviated somewhat from strict chronological sequence. We now turn back to our systematic survey of his life.

In 1821, Broussais published a second and very much extended edition of his *Examen*, now called *Examen des doctrines médicales et des systemes de nosologie*. Now the whole past of medicine was "weighed in the balance and found wanting." In Broussais' eyes, Hippocrates was an old fatalist. His successors were no better, not even the "methodists," although, or perhaps because, they were reminiscent of the "physiological doctrine." The Middle Ages were despicable anyway. Paracelsus was a reformer, but an ontologist who fought artificial disease entities with poisonous "stimulants." He ridiculed all the patient accumulation of clinical and pathological data during the seventeenth and eighteenth centuries as ontology. Only Bordeu and Cabanis received some approval. Brown and his Italian followers Rasori, Tommasini, and Geromini were particularly condemnable since, in many ways, they had preceded Broussais. After an execution of German, English, and Spanish medicine, Pinel was again taken apart. But now a new enemy had arisen—the anatomic-pathological school of Laennec and Bayle. Broussais' third edition of 1829–1834, swollen to over 2,200 pages, devoted about one-third of this space (680 pages) to denouncing this new school (Laennec, Bayle, Louis, Gendrin, Rostan, etc.), while discussion of Pinel occupied only one-tenth. This illustrates the change of fronts that Broussaisism underwent between 1816 and 1834. Broussais felt particularly menaced by the "eclectics" like Andral, who adopted valid data and methods whether they came from him or from the anatomic pathologists. Broussais' giant pamphlet has a certain sinister fascination—the author succeeds all too well in bringing out the nonsensical aspects of the medical past.

In 1822, Broussais started a fighting journal, *Les annales de la médecine physiologique*, which appeared for twelve years. In the same year appeared his *Traité de physiologie appliquée à la pathologie*, which did not contain any new ideas. Due to the poverty of the physiology on which the author tried to base this pathology, the book revealed the weakness of his doctrine and was criticized even by such a faithful pupil as C. Londe.[27]

In 1823, Broussais became a member of the newly founded Académie de Médecine. In 1824, he anonymously published his *Catéchisme de la médecine physiologique*, a crude piece of propaganda that shocked even Gaultier de Claubry.[28]

These years also brought dissension between Broussais and his followers Bégin,[29] Boisseau, Guerin de Mamers, Maillot, Tanchou, and Bouillaud.[30] This friction was often due to the authoritarian habits of the master and to an increasing indifference on the part of the students toward the no-longer-so-new doctrine. Then, with a strong political instinct, Broussais entered a new field that was bound to win back those who had begun to hesitate and to gain him new supporters.[31]

In 1826, in his *De l'irritation et de la folie*, he opened the fight against a new ontology in the field of philosophy and psychology—that of the "spiritualists" and "psychologists," the foreign-influenced "eclectic" philosophers like Cousin and Damiron. He defended the materialistic legacy of Cabanis, the Revolutionary patriot, against the idealistic reaction of the 1820's. The book was essentially a courageous reaffirmation of Cabinis' ideas on the "*rapports du physique et du moral*." "The words 'reason, ego, conscience' express only the results of the action of the brain's nervous matter."[32] As to the second part of the book, the application of the irritation theory of physiological medicine to the field of mental diseases, even Broussais' faithful apologist Paul Reis found it "more clever than based on reality."[33]

The Revolution of 1830 brought the political and personal friends of Broussais into power. Under these conditions, accession to the official medical Faculty from which he had been barred for such a long time could no longer be denied him. The new government, which repaired the injustices committed by the Restoration government in the notorious purge of the Paris Medical Faculty in 1822, created a chair of general pathology and therapeutics for him. His lectures from this chair were published in five volumes. He also became a member of the Académie des Sciences Morales et Politiques. In 1832, he was one of the founders of the Société de Phrénologie, along with

Andral, Bérard, Bouillaud, Falret, Rostan, Ferrus, and F. Voisin.[34] This being the year of the first great cholera pandemic, he published a monograph on the subject from the point of view of "physiological medicine" and sided with the anticontagionist majority of the Paris profession.[35] His inability to either explain or treat cholera properly apparently contributed a great deal to the subsequent decline of his reputation.

Broussais' entrance into the Faculté at the age of fifty-nine was the climax of his career but also the beginning of a rather rapid decline. The students no longer followed him. His doctrine had lost its momentum, and weaknesses had become obvious. Then too, listening to Broussais was no longer considered a sign of political rebellion. The time of the great personalities struggling under the oppressive rule of the Restoration government was gone; the era of the great spiritual conflicts was over. Laennec was dead. Armand Carrel had been killed in a duel. Chateaubriand and Lamennais were isolated. And in the shadow of the fat bourgeois king, Louis Philippe, everything seemed to settle down to normal. According to Reis, Broussais gave way to Chomel, Andral, Rostan, Piorry, and Trousseau,[36] that is, to eclectics with an anatomic-pathological orientation. Lee[37] reported in 1834, "The number of practitioners who adhere to purely expectant measures in the treatment of disease is now extremely limited. The number of exclusive Broussaisists is also very small, although many of the profession still incline to the principles of that doctrine."

Oliver Wendell Holmes has left a classic description of Broussais in his declining years (1834):[38]

> Broussais was in those days like an old volcano, which has pretty nearly used up its fire and brimstone, but is still boiling and bubbling in its interior, and now and then sends up a spurt of lava and a volley of pebbles. . . . Old theories and old men who cling to them must take themselves out of the way as the new generation with its fresh thoughts and altered habits of mind comes forward to take the place of that which is dying out. This was a truth which the fiery old theorist found it very hard to learn, and harder to bear, as it was forced upon him. For the hour of his lecture was succeeded by that of a younger and far more popular professor (Gabriel Andral). As his lecture drew towards its close, the benches, thinly sprinkled with students, began to fill up; the doors creaked open and banged back oftener and oftener, until at last the sound grew almost continuous, and the voice of the lecturer became a leonine growl as he strove in vain to be heard over the noise of doors and footsteps.

Broussais enjoyed a final resurgence of popularity, when, in 1836, he organized a course on phrenology, to which he had gradually become converted.[39] More than 1,000 students attended his course, and a gold medal was minted in his honor.

He died rather suddenly in 1838. The autopsy confirmed Amussat's diagnosis of cancer of the rectum. It seems that during his last illness, treated by the homeopath Frapart, Broussais experimented with homeopathic remedies, and the report seems plausible that the man to whom "doctrines were only instruments of warfare"[40] planned to take up this heresy.[41] Broussais had often been accused of being a politician. In one respect, he certainly did not correspond to the pattern. He died poor. At his funeral, students carried his coffin from the Val de Grâce to the École de Médecine, the Institut, and the Napoleon Monument at the Place Vendôme; and from there to the cemetery Père Lachaise.[42] In 1844, his body was brought back to the Val de Grâce and buried beneath a monument erected in his honor by public subscription in 1841.

Broussais embodied his system in 468 propositions that opened the second edition of the *Examen*. Fortunately, they can be summarized in a much more restricted space. His point of departure was "anti-ontological." The old disease pictures, based on symptoms, were *"des romans"* ("novels"). The symptomatologists mistakenly took the effect for the cause. He started with a theory of life. Life was possible only through external or internal stimuli or irritation. The main stimulus was oxygen. These stimuli produced contractions or "vital erections" in different organs; these were felt through sensibility. The processes were those of "vital," not ordinary, chemistry.

In the case of disease, certain organs were overstimulated (pathological irritation). Such stimuli or disease causes could be the modifiers (especially cold air); the "ingesta" (food, drugs, and "miasmata" [noxious substances in the atmosphere] that were swallowed); and the "percepta" ("moral" or psychological influences). Psychogenic body disease was thus by no means excluded from the system. Though in theory Broussais admitted the possibility of both overstimulation and understimulation, he always observed overstimulation (irritation) in practice.

Irritation was always a local phenomenon that turned into general inflammation, which could, in turn, be observed in the form of anatomical lesions. Fever was only a symptom of inflammation. "Essential fevers" were therefore nonexistent; they could always be reduced to local lesions. Anatomical lesions had to be studied according to tissues. But one further step had to be taken. Anatomical lesions were, claimed Broussais, evidence of an irregularity in function.

To understand the disturbance in function was, according to him, the main goal of pathology. "The nature of diseases thus depends, for the physician, on a noticeable physiological change in the organs."[43] Therefore, his doctrine was "physiological," not anatomic-pathological and narrowly localist. It was "physiological" because it did not regard disease as a foreign element, as the ontologists did, but simply as a change in function.

If one organ was irritated, irritation would spread by "sympathy" (that is, by the way of the nervous system) to other organs, which would in turn experience irritation, inflammation, and irregularity of function. Broussais denied the existence of specific diseases. Smallpox and syphilis were simply inflammations; cancer and tuberculosis were the aftermaths of inflammations; and phthisis was only a chronic pneumonia or pleurisy.

Most diseases either started or ended as gastroenteritis, a disease that, so far, had been badly neglected. (We must not forget that Broussais autopsied a great number of typhoid cases.) It was "the destiny of the stomach always to be irritated." There was a particularly close relation between the stomach and the brain. "The knowledge of gastritis and gastroenteritis is the key of pathology."[44] Drugs practically had to be discarded, since they almost always irritated the stomach. As Broussais' system developed, gastroenteritis became more and more the sole disease to be treated, not only in the "ataxic" and "adynamic" fevers, but also in conditions such as variola, measles, scrofula, hypochondriasis, hepatitis, and the like. His system was also applied to venereal disease by Richond[45] and accepted by Cullerier the younger, the most influential Paris venereologist of the period.[46] Mercury was thus discarded in favor of leeches in the treatment of syphilis.

To somehow square the facts with his gastroenteritis doctrine, Broussais had to use a lot of what he would call, in others, "sophisms" and "subtilities." To begin with, he had to recant his own previous observations, in which he had noted numerous acute diseases without the presence of gastroenteritis.[47] The postmortem absence of redness no longer proved the absence of inflammation. The notions of subinflammation and of gastroenteritis without symptoms had to be introduced. Symptomless irritation, he explained, could produce sympathetic inflammations with fulminant pain, and so on and so on. One of the minor by-products of the assumption that gastroenteritis was the universal disease was that arsenic poisoning often went undiagnosed.

In order to explain malaria, Broussais had to invent a "periodic gastroenteritis." This disease, which insisted on yielding to the condemned specific, quinine, rather than to leeches, and scurvy, where even Broussais did not dare to claim inflammation, were particularly popular examples in counter-arguments against his doctrine.[48]

Broussais' therapeutics were logically derived from his "physiological" premises. Since disease was an overstimulation—an inflammation, mostly of the stomach—it had to be fought by inflammation-reducing, "antiphlogis-tic" means, that is, the generous application of leeches, mostly on the ab-domen, and a very strict diet consisting mostly of "emollient and acidulous" liquids. Whether the condition was typhoid fever or syphilis, variola or worms, tuberculosis or mental disease, leeches on the stomach were the appropriate therapeutic answer. Leeches apparently had become popular during the Revolution when not enough surgeons were available for venesec-tions.[49] Broussais "rationalized" this procedure through his localism.

Broussais energetically condemned the Hippocratic idea of the *vis medicatrix nature* which served as an excuse to the "skeptico-fatalists," the "timid ones," around and after Pinel. His "fearless" treatment was, according to him, rewarded by marvelous successes. "I have made phthisis very rare," he boasted.[50] Cancer was dying out under his hands.[51] He cured general paresis. These quackish claims of curing the incurable remind one very much of Paracelsus, with whom Laennec actually compared Broussais.

It is not difficult to see that Broussais was indebted to numerous predeces-sors for the elements of his doctrine. "Contractility" was a legacy from Haller's physiology. The stimulation theory of life and disease stemmed from the Scotch reformer John Brown. But with Brown the overwhelming majority of diseases were "asthenias," that is, there was too little irritation, instead of too much; treatment consequently consisted of stimulation ("murderous" according to Broussais). Bérard of Montpellier made a pun on the double meaning of *retourné*, saying: "*La médecine physiologique n'est que le Brownisme retourné.*" ("Physiological medicine is only Brownism returned [or, turned around].") Actually it was more, since Brown had lacked the notion of local disease. The Italian Brownists (Rasori and Tommasini, for example) pre-ceded Broussais in almost everything, but they treated with dangerous contrastimulants (high doses of tartar emetic and the like). In his ideas of local inflammations of tissues and sympathies, Broussais was immediately preceded by John Hunter, Bichat, Marandel (the mouthpiece of Dupuytren), and Pinel. The central role of gastroenteritis could already be found in Rega, Bordeu, and Pujol de Castres in the eighteenth century and even more so in Broussais' immediate predecessors Prost, F. A. Petit, Serres, Caffin of Saumur, Tommasini, and Edward Miller. Bleeding and fasting were old therapeutic procedures. Portal wrote and taught on "*physiologie pathologique*"

70

in 1800. To show that the great reformer was not quite as original as he pretended to be is no longer as important for us as it was for those involved in immediate polemics with him. Anyhow, he could always demonstrate that the particular combination of the elements of his doctrine was all his own. Broussais pretended to continue the work of Bichat, and Monfalcon[52] and C. Daremberg[53] have supported this claim. It is true that both tried to unite physiology and pathology. But Bichat completely lacked the sinister dogmatism and the extensive ignorance of physiology that his erstwhile pupil possessed.

Time has taken care of Broussais' system to such an extent that no detailed refutation is any longer needed. Today, we can see very well where Broussais was right when he fought the ontology of his time and how progressive his physiological concept of disease was. But the main difficulty with the ontology of his time was not that it was ontology but that is was a *false* ontology. In spite of all logical reservations, the experiences of bacteriology have shown that the "ontology" and specificity of disease are to a certain extent realities. Broussais' fight against the first acquisitions of a new *realistic* ontology (like the tuberculosis of Laennec, the *dothiénentérie* of Bretonneau, or the typhoid fever of P. Louis) was reactionary.

His speculative theories of life, disease, and disease causes seem to have hampered rather than furthered the conquest of reality, and we therefore incline rather toward his anatomic-pathological adversaries (Bayle, Laennec, Chomel, Louis), who felt that to have no theories was preferable to having theories of this type.[54]

Broussais' localism and antiessentialism represented great progress, and his intent to go "physiologically" beyond pathological anatomy was judicious. Unfortunately, it remained largely unrealized, since his physiology was of the type dubbed "romantic" by Magendie[55] and condemned as "systematic physiology" by Corvisart,[56] who contrasted it to the sounder "physiology of observation." Broussais' system was closer to the drawing-room or arm-chair physiology that had become fashionable under the influence of Cabanis and Richerand, had been dear to Saint-Simon and Comte, and had produced such treatises as the *Physiologie du mariage* of Balzac, the *Physiologie du goût* of Brillat-Savarin, and the *Physiologie des passions* of Alibert. It was a physiology without experiments. Critical insight into the limitations of pathological anatomy (an insight shared by Bayle and Laennec) and the desire to go beyond them did not make a pathological physiologist. The reformer remained essentially, for better or for worse, an anatomist like his whole generation. His interest in physiology even had an adverse effect on this science in

France. It brought about, as a reaction, a dislike for and a suspicion of physiology[57] which Claude Bernard complained about in his famous *Report* of 1867.

The theory of sympathies is now long outdated; the monism of gastroenteritis (with all due allowance to the prevalence of typhoid fever) was never more than a fantasy. Broussais' therapeutics are today repulsive, though a look at those of his contemporaries and predecessors (even those of Laennec, Louis, and Bretonneau), few of whom had the courage of a purely expectant attitude and all of whom lacked almost entirely our modern therapeutic armamentarium, does not allow us to single him out for special blame.

Broussais was an extremely logical thinker. This made for immediate success, and would have been a lasting asset in many other fields. In young medical science, however, where most of the realities were unknown and the few that were known were unlikely to fall into logical patterns, this very virtue proved to be one of the main sources of his failure.

As a whole, the Broussaisian movement strikes us today as belonging to that type of locomotion that has been characterized as "one step forward, two steps backward." The main problem for us is no longer to pinpoint the intrinsic weaknesses of this doctrine, which have long been obvious, but to explain the surprising fact that it was so enthusiastically received in its time.

Though we cannot hope to fully explain Broussais' success, it nevertheless seems possible to contribute several elements of an answer to this problem. The impact of Broussais on his time is perhaps more easily understood when we realize what the Paris school had to offer in 1815, the year before the beginning of Broussais' "revolution" and the year in which, according to Leroy (2:92), the nineteenth century really began. The long war had retarded development on all fronts. Broussais was to ride in on that wave of economic and intellectual prosperity that peace brought to France in 1815. The Revolution had brought about profound changes in organization and teaching by suppressing the old Faculty and opening the new École de Santé in 1795. But the decisive break with the past in the field of medical theory had not yet taken place.

At his premature death in 1802, Bichat left a new anatomy. But he had had no time to apply it to pathology or in the clinic. The central figure of the Paris school in 1815 was Pinel, and his *Nosography* was still its bible. Pinel was certainly sensitive to new problems. He had given the idea of tissue localization in disease to Bichat and had received it back with rich interest. But Pinel was far too much a bookman and a naturalist to carry through the medical revolution. "Essential fevers" still filled one-third of his *Nosographie*, not to speak of other shortcomings of his work, which exhibited relatively little sense of actual clinical and anatomical observation. His "timid" treat-ment was certainly preferable to what was to follow, but it is rather obvious that Pinel was no match for an aggressive modernist. The other *idéologues* of the Paris Faculty of this time—Richerand, Alibert, Pariset, and Moreau de la Sarthe, whom Sainte-Beuve called *"les médecins littéraires,"* were of even less consequence.

The most prominent clinician after Pinel was N. Corvisart. His classic book on heart diseases appeared in 1806; we still value it very highly today, but we can easily see why, though it influenced a few select students like Bayle and Laennec, it did not become a guide for the perplexed of the period. It was a specialized monograph, intentionally abstaining from the discussion of general medical ideas, skeptical as to the possibility of attaining knowledge of such, and even more skeptical as to therapeutic possibilities. Skepticism of this sort might be very honest and sometimes fertile; but it does not make revolutions or move masses. Besides, Corvisart retired from teaching in 1805. The same skepticism pervaded the remarkable book on phthisis (1810) written by Corvisart's pupil and Laennec's older friend and collaborator, G. L. Bayle. Bayle's admirable effort too was a specialized monograph and marred by an all too faithful application of Pinel's species idea (Bayle had originally been an entomologist). Bayle died in 1816.

P. A. Prost's *Médecine éclairée par l'observation et l'Ouverture des corps* of 1804 resembled, in many aspects, Broussais' *Phlegmasies*, published in 1808. As a matter of fact, Prost's autopsy records were far better than those of Broussais. Prost was very much inclined—even more than Broussais was at that time—to attribute general disease to inflammations of the intestinal mucosa (to the extent that, in his opinion, intestinal parasites produced mental disease). On the other hand, when he tried to develop generalities purely out of observed facts, he became extremely confused.

The works of Pinel, Corvisart, Bayle, and Prost were practically all that was available when Broussais started his revolution. Most of the works which, today, represent the Paris school to us in all its glory appeared later and were written by men younger than Broussais. (Laennec's book appeared in 1819, Rostan's in 1820, Cruveilhier's in 1821, Louis' in 1825, Bretonneau's in 1826, and Andral's in 1829.) Under these circumstances, it is quite under-standable that J. B. Regnault, an *émigré* physician returning to France in 1815, recorded the numerous recent discoveries in detail and then asked what was so terribly new about this new school. Pathological anatomy had been cultivated in Paris before 1795, and many earlier, now forgotten works (like Portal's 1792 book on phthisis) compared favorably with the books of the day. It is interesting that Regnault complained about the skepticism of the current leaders, and ended with the hope for a new medical messiah. "Let us hope that a genius will soon arise who will be capable of embracing all that has been done so far with a single glance, so that he may form an edifice which will withstand the onslaught of time and to which the works of posterity can be added without structural changes."[58]

Broussais was this leader who first broke openly and radically with the past and erected a systematic edifice that seemed, to his contemporaries, destined to last.

To us, Broussais appears primarily as the rather ridiculous prophet of gastroenteritis. To many of his contemporaries, Broussais was primarily the proponent of certain general ideas and only secondarily the defender of opinions concerned with details. Today, we tend to overlook these general ideas in Broussais because they have become commonplace to us. To his contemporaries, they were new, very important, and very progressive; and they made him very popular. As Valleix remarked after Broussais' death, as long as the polemic turned only around general opinions, his success was beyond doubt. Only when it came to details did he have to retreat, and eventually observation and experimentation "killed" him.[59]

Broussais' general ideas were his antiessentialism and antiontology—in general, his wholesale cleaning out of long dead notions like the "regular crisis," the "epidemic constitution," "ataxic" and "putrid" fevers, and the like (in this respect he was far more radical than his great opponent, Laennec); his physiological concept of disease; his physiological concept of mental processes, following Cabanis; and his localism, which looked primarily for the tissue lesion instead of the symptom. (Like Bichat, whose heir he was, he wanted to be a physiologist, but was understood primarily as an anatomist.) These were the "very great services" which he rendered even in the eyes of very critical observers.[60] According to Dezeimeris,[61] "pathological anatomy . . . renovated medicine through Broussais." This brought him the sympathies of Andral and Rayer, and later of Charcot and Virchow. Charles Daremberg[62] stated that, while nothing remained of Brown, such accomplishments would give Broussais "the imperishable right to occupy one of the most elevated positions in the history of medicine."

The negative aspect of Broussais' teaching was that it was based on in-sufficient or mistaken observations and pressed into the rigid frame of an "eternal, immovable"[63] system. This systematic and simplifying aspect which is so repulsive to us today (especially in theory—even today systems find their admirers among scientists) proved psychologically rather attractive at the time of Broussais' appearance, when many people were still conditioned to systems and so many were looking for certainty in a chaotic world. Philosophically, Broussais seemed on sounder ground than his adversaries (mostly skeptical empiricists) when he pleaded for the necessity of theories in the advancement of science,[64] reminding people that, even to Hippocrates, experience was fallacious—that facts in themselves were nothing and that, in general, the observer only perceived those facts which fitted into his own theories.[65]

Today, Broussais' therapeutics probably appear as the worst aspect of his doctrine. Not so around 1820, when they were seen against the background of preceding therapeutics, which was far from rosy. In fact, his therapeutics won him many supporters. Even many of his critics appreciated his throwing out the ugly mess of little-understood drugs, most of them ineffective and many toxic, which had been used until that time.[66] Here again he opened up new avenues. People had been used to radical bleedings since the seventeenth century. Thus his leeching orgies shocked them much less than they shook us. As a matter of fact, all his opponents, except the archskeptic Magendie, bled their patients at that time. The therapeutics of many of them, like, for example, Chomel[67] were very similar to Broussais', in spite of all theoretical differences. His underlying therapeutic principle, that of directing therapeutics toward the affected organ rather than against symptoms seemed praiseworthy. He was an early adherent of vaccination and other progressive hygienic measures. His positive attitude toward therapeutics and his sincere optimism were, unlike the honest hopelessness of Corvisart or Bayle, highly attractive to patients and pupils alike.

In his writings, Broussais sometimes warned against too schematic bleeding. (for example, 1829, Proposition cccxlvi); and at the bedside, he seems to have been even more realistic and adaptable to the situation—far better than his theories and the practices of most of his followers. On the whole, Broussais must have been an able clinician. We have some doubts when devoted pupils (like Begin, Reis, and Montegre) testify to the diagnostic and therapeutic wonders they saw him do at the bedside; but when such devoted enemies of his as Velpeau and Trousseau tell of the same experiences,[68] we are rather convinced. After all, there must have been something in Broussais beyond his own indigestible writings which made him attract, on a whole, an abler group of pupils than either Pinel or Laennec did. In his interesting postmortem, Valleix was willing to grant Broussais many titles, but not that of a profound observer,[69] because he had revoked his own observations in favor of his system. Things are not as simple as that. Broussais was a very contradictory person, not only in the primitive meaning of contradicting himself logically, but in the sense of complexity, which is a characteristic of all and especially of eminent humans. Thus the mind of a good clinician-observer and that of a blind dogmatist where obviously able to dwell in the same skull.

Numerous as the factors in the medical field were which contributed to Broussais' rapid success, it would be wrong to limit our search for such factors to medicine. There seems little doubt that even outside medicine, Broussais' very much corresponded to certain leanings of his time, to its "climate of opinion," its *Zeitgeist*, probably more than any one of his medical contemporaries did. An attempt to characterize this fact has resulted in Broussais being called a "romantic."[70] Magendie probably had Broussais in mind when he spoke up against "romantic physiology."[71] A case can indeed be made for calling some aspects of Broussais romantic—in the manner of the romantic poets, his style, his exaggerated nationalism, and his exaggerated individualism both appealed to and stimulated intense admiration from the disturbed youth of his time.

Yet in one essential area, the political field, this type of analysis completely fails. And just here seems to lie one of the clues to the Broussais problem. The romantics of the 1820's were royalist reactionaries. The few who eventually turned to the left, like Victor Hugo and Lamartine, did so only two decades later. Broussais had been a liberal since his earliest youth; his political leanings were one of the most important elements of his personality—and of his success.[72] Most of the medical students of the 1820's hated the Bourbons, brought back by Cossacks and Prussians; hated their caste society, which would not accept them as equals; and hated the Jesuits, who again ran the universities. Many of these students went to prison for the Carbonari before they went on the barricades in 1830. To them Broussais was often the incarnation of medical progress, because this old soldier of the Revolution, this fierce rebel against the king's Faculty, this outspoken materialist, was the living symbol of their dreams of freedom and justice. How could a man who was so right in politics, a field obviously easy for everybody to understand, not be right in the somewhat more complex field of medicine?

Broussais was an ideal representative of the opposition of the Restoration period, which united liberals and Bonapartists, since he himself was as much a Napoleonic as a liberal symbol. He had all the mannerisms of the old Napoleonic soldier, the *grognard*. Talking of his medical experiences, Broussais could not help evoking the glorious past when, for more than ten years, he had followed the victorious armies of Napoleon all over Europe. He reminisced with gusto whenever an occasion offered itself, and sometimes even when the occasion was not very obvious. The *Examen* contains, for instance, a medically rather unmotivated long chapter on the last illness of Napoleon, who died, of course, from gastroenteritis, due to the ignorance and ill will of his British physicians. Broussais' continuing hostility toward British medicine was always hostility against those who had conquered and exiled his idol. All this was sweet music to the young and to the many war veterans who were starting or finishing their medical educations—the veterans who had been heroes and were now supposed to be ashamed of it; who, once riding all over Europe on the waves of the revolutionary sea with the "Marseillaise" in their ears, were disgusted with the little pool into which their lives had receded and where only the croaking of the Bourbon frogs could be heard. The extent to which Broussais was a Napoleonic symbol is evidenced by the fact that, even on the way to his final resting place, the funeral cortege halted at the foot of the Napoleon Monument in the Place Vendôme.[73]

The army was still the army of Bonaparte, run by his marshals, and still very powerful in politics. This army quite naturally took Broussais under its wing, gave him protection, gave him patients and pupils, and made his medical revolution relatively safe. The army medical corps was so Broussaisian[74] that a non-Broussaisian like Tourdes was a great exception worthy of comment.[75] Broussais' simple method appealed to the mind of the professional army doctor, just as "methodism" had appealed to those called upon to treat the masses on the Latifundia of imperial Rome.

The political constellation helped Broussais gain mass influence; and he was not a man not to make good use of this situation. Broussais knew all the tricks in the politician's books. His repetitiousness, so tiresome to the present-day scientific reader, was an excellent political expedient to make his ideas stick. Like all politicians, he was a master at exploiting patriotic feelings—at identifying his own cause with that of his country and identifying his enemies with national degradation. Poor Pinel had not only "tortured humanity," but had exposed *la patrie* to ridicule. Broussais' doctrine would regain France's world supremacy in medicine. The philosophical eclectics were vile "*Kantoplatoniens*," that is, spiritual bootlickers of the Prussians. Like all smart politicians Broussais (from his secure position as chief of the Val de Grâce) presented himself as a martyr defending the common man and his health and therefore persecuted by those in power. He knew the art of *amalgame*, of mixing up the accused with recognized public enemies, the tactic which had been so dear to the public prosecutors of the Revolution. His dispute with Laennec on phthisis was spiced by his exposing the latter as a member of the "*partimédicojésuitique.*" Pinel was a "disguised Brownian" (that is, a British medical agent). When one issue no longer worked, he knew how to shift to another, more popular one. Like most politicians, he constantly appealed to emotions instead of reason.

Broussais' case was by no means the only one in the history of medicine in which the fate of a scientific idea was profoundly influenced by the political convictions of its promotor. Benjamin Rush, a kind of American Broussais, stated repeatedly, and in our opinion rightly, that his opinions on yellow fever would have found much less opposition had he not been a political exponent of the then unpopular left.[76] Laennec would have found much less opposition had he not also been a royalist, pro-Jesuit pamphleteer, and Pasteur knew that his arguments against spontaneous generation would have en-countered less suspicion if he had not been well known as a pious Catholic. The rapid scientific acceptance of Broussais or Virchow must, on the other hand, be partly understood in terms of the popularity they acquired as exponents of political liberalism.

Not the least important element of Broussais' success was, of course, his personality. He was by no means lacking in attractive traits. He was generally described as a tall, impressive, vigorous, handsome man. His energy and industry were extraordinary. He was beyond any doubt a very powerful public speaker. He was apparently a sincere enthusiast; and only an enthusiast, not a skeptic, could have made a revolution. Thousands had known him in the battlefields, in the camps, and at the bedside as a helpful, warmhearted, devoted, and dignified friend. He saved his eruptions for the lecture room. In private life he was benevolent and gay. He had bubbling spirits but a sensitive heart.

Broussais' personality was also full of far less commendable traits, and it would be naive to assume that they did not serve him just as well as the morally more acceptable ones. Probably not since the time of Paracelsus had such fanatical, ruthless, megalomaniacal, and foul language been used in medical polemics. His adversaries (that is, for example, Laennec, Louis, and Andral) were "cockroaches, poor madmen, lacking good faith and represent-ing error, dissimulation, and vile speculation."[77] With great satisfaction, he noted how Paracelsus, Brown,[78] and Laennec[79] had died from their own faulty medical methods. An all-time low was certainly reached when he discussed the "increased spermatic secretion" of his phthisic (and by that time deceased) adversaries Bayle and Laennec.[80] Broussais was suffering from a permanent need of publicity, and all means seemed justified by this end. Others have already noted that such negative traits probably served him well.

With more knowledge of books and ideas, with convictions that were acquired more industriously and conscientiously, with distinction and taste, he would probably have moved the medical masses less. Great popularity is only acquired at the price of a certain vulgarity. Perhaps without these brutalities, the partial truth and common sense which formed the strength of his polemic would not have penetrated into the minds of the majority. He would not have created a revolution.[81]

This method conquered minds and created fanatics. In those periods of hesitation when nations and sciences look for a way out, it is not so important to hit straight; it is enough to hit hard, and one has the applause of the mob. Scared minds follow that master who differs most from their former masters.[82]

There was nothing noble in Broussais' unlimited aggressiveness. But this very trait seems to have endeared him to his terribly frustrated Restoration audiences. To put it bluntly, they liked him not only because they thought he was right or good, but also because he could be so infernally nasty. In science, of course, this type of success was bound not to last very long, and Broussais became a rather lonely man even in his own lifetime; but in view of the record, such victories seem perfectly possible even in science. It was perhaps only a fortunate accident that Broussais had more to offer than mere demagoguery, and actually did stimulate progress directly and indirectly.

Broussais was the result and the acme of several strongly developed medical trends of the time. He certainly did not invent localism and solidism, but as a localist and a solidist, he outdid Pinel, Bichat, and Laennec. Neither did he initiate the gastroenteritis trend, as is proven by the work of Prost, Petit, and Serres. It should never be forgotten that this trend was based on facts. In view of the frequency of typhoid fever at this period, it was unavoidable that changes in the intestinal tract would loom large in medical thought once autopsies became more frequent and more systematic, and the intestine better accessible through the newly invented intestinal scissors. In the 1820's, numerous non-Broussaisian doctors like Louis, Cruveilhier, Trousseau, Billard, Hutin, and Bretonneau were also intensely interested in this region.

The irritation-inflammation trend had been strong since 1800. Fourcroy, probably influenced by J. Brown, preached irritation.[83] Between 1800 and 1810, the decade of Broussais' *Phlegmasies*, fifteen Paris theses dealt with the subject. The most famous one of these was the 1807 thesis of Marandel on *Les irritations*, appearing one year before the *Phlegmasies* and known to propagate the ideas of Dupuytren. Between 1810 and 1820, ten such theses appeared, and between 1820 and 1830, eighteen; some of them were in-fluenced by Broussais, but others, like that of Prus in 1825, were decidedly anti-Broussaisian. The general shift to inflammatory interpretations is clearly visible when one compares the works of Rostan (1820) and Lallemand (1823) on "softening of the brain." One of the first to oppose exclusive inflammatory explanations, for example, of cancer, was Velpeau.[84]

While Broussais convinced many of the central role of inflammations of the gastrointestinal tract, others promoted different inflammations as the "basic disease." Probably the closest competitors of gastroenterits for the title of "basic disease" were the inflammations of the blood vessels. Schimuck and Sasse, Hunter and Travers had written on them at the end of the eighteenth century without finding much response. Around 1820, the notion of phlebitis (venous inflammation) suddenly became extremely popular among doctors. Again an observational basis was present. Phlebitis, iatrogenic (amputations, phlebotomies, etc.) as well as spontaneous (wounds, puerperal fever, etc.), was indeed found very often on autopsy. The phlebitis trend seems to have started with a paper read by F. Ribes before the Société Médicale d'Émula-tion in 1816. In 1819, Breschet, inspired by his friend Hodgson, followed suit. Dance (1826) and Cruveilhier (1834) developed the phlebitis notion in the following years, while Bouillaud propagated the ideas of endoarteritis and endocarditis. Particularly active experimentally in this field was A. N. Gendrin, a Hippocratist, who hoped to be able to preserve his humoralism in this way.[85]

In view of his limitations, Broussais was able to crystallize the trends of his time only for a while. Others would be able not only to indicate general directions, but to give valid, specific answers.

VII. CORVISART, BAYLE, LAENNEC During

the reign of Pinel and long before Broussais, Paris possessed in the person of Jean Nicolas Corvisart a clinician who represented a combination of physical diagnosis and pathological anatomy, the essence of the school's teaching, in a more accomplished way than either one of the two leaders. With him, as Knad Faber pointed out long ago, "observation" became "examination." Bayle reports true "miracles" which Corvisart performed in the field of diagnostics.[1] The fact that Napoleon selected him speaks for his superiority as a practitioner. Through him and his pupils, the Charité became the center of clinical medicine in Paris. Yet there was never a "Corvisart era" like the eras of Pinel and Broussais. The reason for this was probably that, becoming the personal physician of Napoleon in 1804, Corvisart was, like a Vesalius, Fernel, Brunner, and many other court physicians before him, taken away from teaching and research and transformed into a personal servant of his master. His skepticism and his specialism made him unsuitable for the role of the leader anyway. Still, his influence on an elite—on men like Leroux, Bayle, Laennec, and Lerminier—and on future generations was such that he deserves closer study. While J. Frank praised his teaching unreservedly,[2] Wardenburg was far less satisfied.[3]

Corvisart was born in 1755 (the same year as Hahnemann, Fourcroy, and Chaptal, and eleven years after Pinel), the son of a lawyer. He was strongly influenced by Desault, as well as by Desbois de Rochefort. When he started teaching, he taught surgery and anatomy but eventually specialized in internal medicine. He became *docteur régent* in 1782. When he refused to wear a wig, Mrs. Necker refused to make him a physician in her hospital. In 1788, he became a physician at the Charité as a successor to Desbois; in 1794, professor of clinical medicine in the new École de Santé; and in 1797, professor at the Collège de France. In 1804, he gave up these posts to become the physician of the Emperor. After the fall of Napoleon in 1815, he retired completely, not even speaking of medicine any more.[4] He died from a stroke in 1821.

Corvisart left only one book, *Maladies du coeur* (*Diseases of the Heart*), which were, according to him, the most frequent maladies next to those of the lung. He was aided in the composition of it by his pupils Horeau and F. V. Mérat (1780–1851; Mérat was also the main editor of the famous *Dictionnaire des sciences médicales*). Published in 1806, Corvisart's book was a masterful discussion of pericarditis, dilatation and hypertrophy of the heart (still called "aneurysm of the heart"), and diseases of the heart muscle, the

83

valves, and the aorta. It was full of excellent case histories and autopsy records. Corvisart was a pioneer of pathological anatomy; every case dying on his wards was autopsied. Likewise, the use of percussion allowed him to surpass all his predecessors. The book showed clear insight into the "moral" (psychological) factors of heart disease[5] and was particularly strong on differential diagnosis.[6]

The preface of this book, his aphorisms, and, above all, the commentary in his 1808 translation of Auenbrugger's *Inventum novum* of 1761 allow us to learn something about his thought and discoveries beyond his opinions on heart disease. His commentaries on his translation of Auenbrugger's work on percussion, at least four times as long as the original, are really a book in themselves. It is all to his honor that he emphasized the merits of the completely neglected and forgotten Auenbrugger instead of appropriating all the fame. His propagating percussion—by 1825 it was generally used in Paris[7] and had spread everywhere from there—was certainly his greatest single accomplishment. It opened the way for further development in the physical diagnosis of chest diseases. Percussion was very important to him because, with it, medicine could stop being "conjectural."

His approach is well characterized in the title of a book he planned but never wrote—a kind of super Morgagni: *De sedibus et causis morborum per signa diagnostica investigatis et per anatomen confirmatis (On the Seats and Causes of Diseases Investigated by Diagnostic Signs and Confirmed by Autopsy)*. Next to the signs of physical diagnosis came pathological anatomy; pathological anatomy itself had to be completed by pathological physiology.[8] Corvisart was the inventor of a heart function test. It is surprising to see how strongly he was influenced by the much younger Bichat in these areas. He took over from Bichat, for example, a pathology based on tissues, a physiology of heart action, and an inflammation theory.[9] But Corvisart was no vitalist. To him, man was a machine.

We already know of his aversion to "exclusive systems and speculative theories." He was an innovator, but in many ways he remained a traditionalist, that is, a humoralist, "reserved as to innovations" (Aphorism XVIII), and a Hippocratist. When Fourcroy wanted to have a laboratory in every clinic, Corvisart was opposed. In 1797, dedicating the book to Lepreux, he translated the Hippocratist Stoll—that is where he heard first of Auenbrugger—as a text for his teaching. (Post-Revolutionary students did not know enough Latin.) Yet he was too critical and skeptical to be an exclusive humoralist. Primary affections of the solid organs were seen too often.[10] He did not believe in critical days,[11] and he doubted the existence of the classic "crises."[12] Even the famous *vis medicatrix naturae* was unreliable; nature's errors were frequent.[13] His skepticism actually reached its height in thera-peutics. "Medicine is not the art of curing diseases; it is the art of treating them with the goal of cure, or of putting the diseased person at ease and calming him."[14] As to heart diseases, you can "sometimes prevent them, but never cure them." Most men are doomed because they are poorly constructed, often on account of heredity,[15] or because they are victims of a profession or of passions that the doctor cannot control.[16]

Like Desgenettes, Corvisart was and remained a great admirer of the philosopher of his youth, Voltaire. The "philosophy" he suggested for the physician was a strange mixture of eighteenth-century teachings—sensualist "education of the senses," skepticism, and anticlericalism (his testament proffers the unfulfilled wish: above all no prayers)—with the life-long personal melancholy of a divorced, childless, noble, embittered, and stoical man: "The Mesrour of Voltaire had lost the eye which sees the bad side of things. I am one-eyed like he was, but I lost the other eye."[17]

Gaspard Laurent Bayle (not to be confused with his nephew Antoine Laurent Bayle, the discoverer of general paresis) deserves attention as the pupil and successor of Corvisart at the Charité, as the friend and teacher of Laennec,[18] and as the oldest member of a loose grouping called the "patho-logic-anatomical" school (Laennec, Rostan, Chomel, Louis, Billard, Piorry, Dance, Calmeil, Ollivier, and colleagues). Actually he was an eminent practitioner and an original medical thinker and observer in his own right. Born in 1774 in Haute Provence, the son of a lawyer, he showed an early, intense interest in entomology. After studying theology and law, he entered politics at nineteen as a courageous counterrevolutionary, and he remained one all his life. This made it advisable for him to hide for three years as a medical student at Montpellier. At this time, he wrote a great deal of poetry, which he later burned. He was then drafted and worked in a hospital at Nice under Desgenettes. In 1798, he entered the École de Santé at Paris. He felt attracted to Corvisart on account of the latter's interest in pathological anatomy. Obtaining the post of *aide d'anatomie*, he became, together with Laennec, the collaborator of Dupuytren, then still in charge of anatomical studies there. At the same time, he became one of the founders of the no-torious Congrégation, a secret student organization directed by the Jesuit father P. Delpuits. Other medical members of this organization were Bichat's cousin Buisson, Fizeau, Savary, and Laennec.[19]

As an intern at the Charité, he was a rather independent collaborator of Corvisart, defending against his master's objections the value of counting pulse and respiration exactly. In 1802, he took his M.D. degree with a thesis entitled *Considerations sur la nosologie, la médecine d'observation, et la médecine pratique suivies de l'histoire d'une maladie gangréneuse non décrite jusqu'à ce jour* (*Thoughts on Nosology, the Medicine of Observation, and Practical Medicine, Followed by the History of a Gangrenous Disease Never Described Before*). The tachygraphy of his friend Laennec has preserved verbatim the discussion between Bayle and his examiners Petit-Radel, A. Leroy, Percy, and Pinel—in every respect a most revealing document[20]— in which Bayle shows the strange mixture of modesty and aggressiveness which was characteristic of him all his life. In 1805, he succeeded Corvisart as *médecin d'hôpital* at the Charité, and in 1816, he died from pulmonary consumption. Though never teaching officially, he strongly influenced Laennec, Chomel, Cayol, Prost, Mérat, Duplan, and his own brother-in-law, Moutard Martin. He was, like his friend Laennec, physically unimpressive, small, and thin. He was a physiological rarity, able to voluntarily influence the rate of his heartbeat.

He was probably the most theory-minded member of the "pathologic-anatomical" school. In his *Considerations* of 1802, he realized full well that "organic species have no relations with disease species. . . . These are actually only abstractions."[21] And yet, unlike Corvisart or Laennec, he believed in the necessity of these "scaffoldings for erecting the building of science." He wanted, like Pinel, to base nosography on lesions. His notion of phthisis was based on lesions, not symptoms. His sincere devotion to nosography was evident in the fact that he was able to catalog six species and forty varieties of phthisis.[22]

Besides nosography, medicine needed the purely factual observation, practiced by Hippocrates, Sydenham, and Stoll. The observer needed to know not only anatomy and physiology, but also pathological anatomy (of which Bayle clearly saw the limitations) and psychology. "Changes in intellectual and affective functions are sometimes cause, sometimes symptom, and sometimes consequence of diseases." Psychology was "an admirable and illuminating science, as long as one doesn't confuse its certainties with the hypotheses with which it is unfortunately overloaded."[23] Bayle differentiated between vital (we would say functional) and physical symptoms, vital and organic lesions, and vital and organic diseases.[24] He advocated complete observations instead of brief ones. He also gave blueprints for the writing of case histories.

The essential part of medicine was, of course, "practical medicine, the art of treating diseases." Like Corvisart, he knew that, at the current stage of knowledge, practical medicine would be only enlightened symptomatic medicine for a long time.[25] Like Corvisart, he emphasized the value of good diagnoses and prognoses for silencing the enemies and accusers of medicine.[26] Examination of Bayle's general ideas shows him influenced not only by Corvisart, but also by Pinel, with whom he was united by a predilection for nosography, as well as by extensive use of statistics.

Bayle published only one book during his short life—*Recherches sur la phthisie pulmonaire* (*Studies on Pulmonary Phthisis*) of 1810. Basing his ideas on 900 autopsies, he offered a new doctrine on what he called "the longest and the most dangerous of all chronic diseases." The essential characteristics of it were not the symptoms but the progressively degenerating lesions that led to ulceration and death. "In the beginning it is but a slight indisposition; at the end it floors the most vigorous individual. It devours, consumes, and reduces to a skeleton him whose belly, freshness, and health seemed unchangeable."[27] One shudders in realizing that these lines were prophetic, since they were written by a man suffering from the disease himself. But Bayle, who in 1810 gave the history of his own attack in 1802,[28] lived under the happy delusion that he had not suffered from true phthisis and that he was cured.

Bayle delineates six species of phthisis: (1) the tuberculous, (2) the granulous, (3) the melanotic (with anthracosis), (4) the ulcerative, (5) the calcifying, and (6) the cancerous. Today we would regard his ulcerative (lung abscess) phthisis and his cancerous phthisis as diseases *sui generis* and all the rest as states caused by the Koch bacillus. To the three classic stages of phthisis, he adds a fourth, initial, "occult" one.[29] The *tuberculous diathesis*, which is the most frequent cause of pulmonary phthisis, also produces changes in the larynx, intestines, abdomen and cervical glands, pericardium, pleura, and liver. Tuberculosis is a degenerative process. Its manifestations are related to scrofula but are not identical with it. It is noncontagious, but hereditary.[30] *It is a specific disease, not a simple inflammation.* Anybody can have a simple inflammation; only those predisposed can develop tuberculosis or cancer.[31] Fevers, pneumonia, pleurisy, and hemoptysis are not the causes but the symptoms or complications of the disease.

The differentiation of species is important to Bayle, since treatment differs according to species. He recommends "*calmants, delayants, revulsifs*" and furthermore—shadows of Bichat—drugs limiting organic sensibility.[32] His true attitude toward all these medicaments was revealed by the fact that, when he was attacked, he used none. Furthermore, he himself stated, "phthisis is almost always incurable and lethal"; "if a cure is obtained, the disease was neither phthisis nor cancer."[33] Two-thirds of Bayle's monograph consists of fifty-four excellent case histories with autopsy records. The case histories show that he used percussion as a routine procedure. They do not report his attempts at immediate auscultation, which Laennec continued.

History knows Bayle as a phthisiologist. The fact that his nephew published his two-volume works on cancer twenty-three years after Bayle's death has not changed this attitude. Actually, he paid as much attention to cancer as he did to phthisis; he wrote, in 1812, that he had studied the former for more than ten years, and he transmitted this interest to Laennec, Cayol, and Récamier. This is not so surprising, since cancer and tuberculosis appeared to him to be much more closely related than they appear to us today. To him both were degenerative diatheses producing heterologous neoplasms, so-called "accidental tissues." Bayle was actually an important figure in the history of oncology. His attempts, with the help of pathological anatomy, to differentiate benign and malignant lesions grouped in the hodgepodge classification of "scirrhes" are reflected in his memoirs on ulcers of the uterus (the year XI [1802–1803]—visibly influenced by Bichat); on fibrous formations in the wall of the uterus; and on "white induration" (fibrous, tuberculous, or cancerous). His 150-page article on cancer (with Cayol) in the third volume of the *Dictionnaire des sciences médicales* (Paris 1812) gives a masterful discussion of the diagnosis and treatment of cancer in fifteen different organs. He distrusted the causes usually given: sorrow or local irritation. He had seen too many "spontaneous" cancers. To him, cancer was the result of a diathesis, as it was to the ancients. This—and not transportation of a virus— explained recidivism and metastasis. "Cancer is never a local disease," he said.[34] It was not contagious. And was doubtful whether it was hereditary. He recommended early excision of mammary tumors, though he was conscious of the contradiction with his general theory.

Bayle was the only member of the pathologic-anatomical school to discuss the principles of therapeutics (*Bibliothèque médicale*, Vol. 10). We will take up this contribution in the chapter on therapeutics. One is rather surprised to see him, in this work, simultaneously demand a reform of therapeutics and literally take over the Galenic doctrine of indications.

The crowning glory of this line of Charité physicians was René-Théophile-Hyacinthe Laennec. Born February 17, 1781, at Quimper, he was a Breton like Broussais, Chateaubriand, and Lamennais and very much devoted to his home province and its archaic language.[35] When he was five years old, his mother died, probably from tuberculosis. His father, a poetry-writing lawyer, was unable to give him guidance or warmth. Fortunately Guillaume Laennec, a younger brother of his father and chief physician of the Hôtel Dieu at

Nantes,[36] took him into his house and treated him like one of his sons. This decided Théophile Laennec's future. Guillaume Laennec had had an excellent medical education in the citadel of Hippocratism, Montpellier, and in practical-minded Great Britain. Following in his uncle's footsteps, Théophile started the study of medicine. At fourteen, he became a military surgeon third class at Nantes. These surgical beginnings certainly contributed to his later preoccupation with pathological anatomy. He himself[37] and his teacher Bichat[38] both emphasized the fact that *pathological anatomy was imported into medicine by surgeons.*

At twenty, Laennec eventually succeeded in going to Paris to finish his medical studies. Four eminent men influenced him there: Corvisart, Bichat, Dupuytren, and G. L. Bayle. Though he disliked Corvisart personally, he always gratefully acknowledged him as his teacher, and Corvisart's stamp is unmistakable in Laennec's interest in pathological anatomy, percussion, the diseases of the chest, therapeutic skepticism, and medical traditionalism. Though Laennec accepted only part of Bichat's teaching, that is, pathological anatomy but not the latter's specific vitalism, he worshiped Bichat above all other men. For example, while proper names were generally not capitalized in Laennec's manuscripts that of Bichat always enjoyed this distinction! As little as he later acknowledged the influence of Dupuytren, there is scant doubt that he learned a great deal from him, especially in the field of pathological anatomy. G. L. Bayle, who became his friend, started him on auscultation, phthisis, and malignant tumors—and on royalist Jesuitism, an allegiance which was to bring Laennec honors as well as hatred and isolation.

That Laennec was more than an industrious student became obvious in 1802, when the *Journal de médicine, chirurgie et pharmacie* published his masterful article on several cases of peritonitis. This study of the little-known inflammation of a serous membrane was not surprising coming from a follower of Bichat. That same year the same journal published several of Laennec's minor anatomical discoveries. In 1803, he received the School's first prizes in medicine and surgery. This partly explains why the twenty-two-year-old lad mustered enough self-confidence to separate from his master Dupuytren, to give a course of his own on pathological anatomy, and to announce a textbook on the same subject. It never appeared, just as the text announced by his former teacher, who had now turned completely to surgery, never appeared.

Laennec too, though primarily interested in pathological anatomy, had to go into private practice for economic reasons in 1804. Thus it happened that one of the greatest clinicians of all times became a practitioner quite in spite of himself. He nevertheless became a much sought-after physician, taking care, for example, of Cardinal Fesch (Napoleon's uncle), Chateaubriand and his wife, Lamennais, and Mme de Staël.

Becoming a physician at the Hôpital Necker in 1816, he eventually had the necessary research facilities at his disposal again. In this very year, he invented the stethoscope and began writing his immortal treatise of 1819 on lung and heart diseases, *De l'auscultation médiate ou traité du diagnostic des maladies des poumons et du coeur*. We would like to report the invention of the stethoscope, the decisive step in his career, in his own words.[39]

> In 1816 I was consulted by a girl who showed general symptoms of heart disease but where laying on of the hand and percussion did not give results on account of her obesity. The age and the sex of the patient forbade me the direct application of the ear to the precordial region. I then remembered a well-known acoustic phenomenon [according to A. L. Bayle, he had observed it while watching children playing in the courtyard of the Louvre]: if one puts his ear at the end of a beam, he hears quite distinctly a needle scratching the other end. I felt that this quality of solid bodies could be exploited in this case. I took a blue book, formed a tight cylinder of it, put one end on the precordial region, and the other at my ear. And to my great surprise and satisfaction I heard the sounds of the heart much more clearly and more distinctly than I had ever done by applying my ear directly. I then presumed that this method could be useful not only in the study of the heart but . . . in examining respiration, voice and rattles, and perhaps even the fluctuation of liquids in the pleural and pericardial cavity.

He soon replaced paper by wood and gave his "cylinder" the name "stethoscope." It was typical of Laennec that, in his lectures at the Collège de France (No. 25), he called his invention an accident and stated, "In general, the really useful things are thus given to us, and not conquered by efforts."

The invention of auscultation completed his pathological studies. Muehry correctly stated, "Auscultation and percussion make possible a kind of *living* pathological anatomy or anatomical pathology."[40] In spite of the fact that Laennec was unpopular and under heavy attack by the Broussaisians, stethoscopy—its usefulness being recognized even by the "messiah" Broussais himself—spread rapidly. It was reported by foreign travelers in 1823 and 1825 that the stethoscope was on exhibit in all shops and was used by all students.[41] Unjustified priority claims also bespoke its popularity.

After completion of his great treatise in 1819, Laennec's health was so poor on account of pulmonary tuberculosis that he retired for several years to his Brittany estate, Kerlouarnec. In 1822, he returned to Paris and became in rapid succession professor of clinical medicine at the Charité, professor at the Collège de France, and physician of the crown princess, the enterprising Duchess de Berry.

It must be admitted that he owed these positions not to his genius but to his royalist-Jesuit ties. These same connections made him very unpopular with the majority of the professors and students, who, under the Restoration, were liberals. It remains puzzling why Récamier, Esquirol, and Cruveilhier, who entertained the same opinions as Laennec, did not face comparable unpopularity. Laennec was, of course, the victim of a systematic and ruthless Broussaisian campaign[42] which did not stop even at his death. The most widely read Paris medical journal wrote in its necrology: "His glory would have lacked nothing, if he had adopted the healthy physiological doctrines which are the honor of his century"; also, "his death was more irreparable for his party than for science."[43] In addition, he seems to have been a poor speaker.[44] He was very thin and stood only 5 feet 3 inches tall. The lively and confident boy had, in an unfriendly world, become an extremely reserved and cool individual, carefully hiding his sensitivity.

All this was bound to make him unpopular in France, and the man whom we admire today as the greatest French clinician of all times was, in his lifetime, unable to overcome the influence of Broussais and win general recognition. It is significant that his more eminent pupils were foreigners, who cared little for all these secondary things and recognized the man's substance better than his countrymen did. While none of his French pupils are remembered, we still speak of Hodgkin, S. G. Morton, James Clark, Fossati, and A. Retzius, to name a few of his foreign students. It was partly on account of his many foreign students that he spoke Latin in his clinical teaching.

The load Laennec carried was too heavy for his frail body. On April 1, 1826, he finished the second edition of his great book; on August 13, he died, quite composed, at Kerlouarnec, in the forty-sixth year of his short life. Two hours before his death, he took off his rings, since "soon somebody else would have to do it, and it might cause him chagrin." The inventor of auscultation and stethoscopy had been, at the same time, a gifted musician, woodworker, poet, philologist, political pamphleteer, and draftsman.

In view of the preceding, it is rather surprising that Laennec's doctoral dissertation of 1804, *Propositions on the Doctrine of Hippocrates concerning Medical Practice*, dealt not with pathological anatomy, but with ancient medicine. It revealed Laennec's great familiarity with and profound admiration for the latter. It was no accident that it was dedicated to his uncle Guillaume, who had insisted so strongly that he learn Greek. He saw quite clearly the difference between Hippocrates, interested primarily in the "common symptoms" of disease and prognosis, and his own generation, interested primarily in "proper symptoms" and diagnosis. It may sound paradoxical to us that, the future discoverer of so many "proper symptoms" considered a return to Hippocrates in his dissertation.[45] Yet he ended with a quotation from Klein: "I claim freedom in medicine. I belong neither to the ancients nor to the moderns. I follow both when they produce the truth. I believe in experience often repeated" (Laennec 1804, 38).

It is significant in this context that, from 1805 to 1814, Laennec reported annually on the "epidemic constitution." He was thus one of the last defenders of this concept in France. Pinel, Fodéré, Bichat, Broussais, Bouillaud, and Rayer had no use for it, and Corvisart had very little. Andral showed that it was not even a Hippocratic idea! Only some Hippocratists from Montpellier (Baumès, Double), Laennec and his reactionary friends Récamier, Cayol,[46] and Fizeau, and some provincial authors still used it. The latter no longer actually constructed Sydenhamian "epidemic constitutions," but simply reported on the diseases observed in their districts in a given period.

Laennec was extremely active in the field of pathological anatomy from the beginning to the end of his career. His manuscripts show that in the busy year of 1822, for example, he did no less than twenty-two autopsies in September and October. In 1810, Cuvier[47] enumerated Portal, Bichat, Dupuytren, Corvisart, Bayle, and Laennec as the leading French pathological anatomists of the period. Yet Laennec published very little in this domain: only several memoirs and several articles in the *Dictionnaire des sciences médicales*. The latter are all chapters from his unpublished course of 1803 or from his famous 1804 memoir on intestinal worms. We identified the *Dictionnaire* articles on *anatomie pathologique, ascaride, cartilage accidentel, crinon, cucurbitain, degénération, désorganisation, dytracheros, encephaloide, filaire, fibreux accidentel,* and *fibrocartilage* as Laennec's. Of course, his great *Traité* contained an enormous amount of pathological anatomy.

The most important of the *Dictionnaire* articles was undoubtedly the one on *anatomie pathologique* (1812, 2:46–61). He called pathological anatomy the "torch of medicine," even though it was applicable only to the "organic" and not the "nervous" (functional) diseases. He wanted to establish it as an independent discipline. To this purpose he gave a pathologic-anatomical classification which derived from that of Bichat but went beyond it. He had already offered this classification in his course of 1803 and in an article in the *Journal de médecine, chirurgie et pharmacie* (9:360–378) and successfully defended his priority concerning it against Dupuytren. He divided the organic diseases into four groups. The fourth, "changes of texture," was again subdivided into four groups. The last of these, the "accidental tissues" (the term was Bayle's), was formed by two groups: the "analogous tissues," that is, those which paralleled some normal tissue, and the "nonanalogous," which had no such parallel. This was a new concept, which was to be the object of debate among morphologists for decades to come,[48] since it was of great importance in cancer research and theory. The discussion reappeared among biochemists in the twentieth century. Laennec's "nonanalogous" tissues were the "tuberculous," the "cirrhous," and the two forms of cancer he had isolated—the "encephaloid" and the "melanotic." They all showed a tendency toward continuous change and influenced the general status of the patient.

Laennec's great accomplishment was his 1819 *"Treatise on Mediate Auscultation and on the Diseases of the Lung and Heart."* (We quote the following from the better arranged second edition of 1826.) In the preface[49] he called his goal: (1) to identify a pathological condition in the cadaver through physical change in the organs; (2) to recognize the same condition in the living, if possible, through physical signs independent of symptoms, that is, the accompanying variable disturbances of vital action; (3) to treat the disease with those remedies which experience has found to be most efficacious.

Even if he would not say so in his Latin dedication to the Paris Faculty, it was obvious that he disliked systems, especially the then dominant "etio-logical" system of Broussais. He also opposed Pinel's nosological endeavors.[50] In general he considered theories only "scaffoldings," aids to memory.[51] Another element of his "antitheorism" was his hostility to the microscope,[52] a feeling he shared with Bichat. Yet the tremendous differences in general approach between him and his successors, on the one hand, and Bichat, on the other hand, can easily be seen from a comparison of his program above with that of Bichat (see p. 57).

The first 130 pages of the *Treatise* were devoted to methods of examining the thorax—the traditional ones as well as Auenbrugger-Corvisart per-cussion and his own "mediate auscultation" with the stethoscope. Every-thing he described in the latter domain was, of course, new: the normal respiratory sound, the puerile one, bronchophony, pectoriloquy, egophony, the metallic tinkling, the cracked pot sound, the crepitous, mucous, cavernous rattle, the veiled puff, and so on. They are now familiar to every medical student. One is amazed by the fact that this enormous wealth of data was collected and sifted in such a short period of time by a single person. Laennec had his data checked by friends and colleagues. The one most often mentioned as "witness" was his friend Récamier. At the end of this first part, he examined the application of auscultation to the diagnosis of fractures, stones, liver abscesses, and ear affections.

The second part, lung diseases, began with an extensive discussion of bronchial affections, among them bronchiectasis, which he had discovered. He did not believe in the unhealthiness of stone dust. He knew that hilus glands could be black without being diseased. The examination of diseases of the lung tissue began with emphysema (he first described vesicular emphysema), edema, and pneumonia.

In the latter case, he gave tartarus stibiatus in high doses. He recommended the same drug in meningitis, polyarthritis, chorea, phlebitis, ophthalmia, and angina. He had taken over its use from Rasori without adopting the latter's theories, as he did in other cases as well.[53] He believed that he could offer statistical proof of a mortality-rate reduction in pneumonia cases from one in six to one in twenty-eight by use of this drug.[54] In the case of this antimony therapy, Broussais' criticisms seem justified. Laennec's enthusiasm for such a violent method is all the more surprising, since he was, in general, skeptically reserved and a great believer in the *vis medicatrix naturae*.

The book reached its acme in the 200 pages dealing with pulmonary tuberculosis—its macroscopic pathological anatomy and its physical signs. Little has been added since to what Laennec found in this respect! We may be allowed to quote at least a few lines from Laennec's description of this "nonanalogous" accidental tissue:[55]

> The tubercles develop in the form of small semitransparent granules, gray in color, though occasionally they are entirely transparent and almost colorless. Their size varies from that of millet seed to that of hemp seed; when in this state, they may be termed *miliary tubercles*. These granules increase in size and become yellowish and opaque, first in the center and then progressively throughout their substance. Those nearest together unite in the course of growth and then form more or less voluminous masses, pale yellow in color, opaque, and comparable, as regards density, with the most compact kinds of cheese; they are then called crude tubercles. . . .
>
> In whatever manner these crude tubercles are formed, they finish at the end of a longer or shorter time of very variable duration by becoming softened and liquified. This softening starts near the middle of each mass, which daily becomes softer and moister until the softening has reached the periphery and become complete. . . .
>
> When the tuberculous matter has completely softened, it breaks its way into the nearest bronchial tube. The resulting aperture being narrower than the cavity with which it communicates, both remain of necessity fistulous even after the complete evacuation of the tuberculous matter.

Taking Bayle's results as a point of departure, he went much further. Since he saw that Bayle's "species" were either stages of a single disease ("there is no more difference between miliary tubercles and granulations than between a ripe and a green fruit") or something completely different (for example, cancer),[56] there was, to him, only *one* tuberculous phthisis left. In tracing the manifestations of tuberculosis in all organs[57]—and none were exempt—he became the great representative of "unitarianism" in this disease. His point of view was much debated till Koch's discovery confirmed it. He continued Bayle's fight against Broussais' opinion that tuberculosis was only the final stage of an inflammation of the lung. He again asked the question—is tuberculosis curable? His answer was that sometimes nature could cure it, but that the doctor could not cure it yet.[58]

Among the many possible causes of tuberculosis the relatively most certain ones in his mind were "sad passions," which he thought also played a role in the genesis of cancer and other nonanalogous accidental tissues![59] His extreme psychosomatism made him interpret facts psychologically which we today would explain in a much more satisfactory way on the basis of contagion. He denied the contagiosity of tuberculosis, though he described his own infection while performing an autopsy.[60] He acknowledged hereditary predisposition. He described six stages in the evolution of phthisis, among them the latent as well as the acute one. He felt that these six mirrored reality better than the classic three stages. In scrofulous individuals, he asserted, tuberculosis begins in the glands.[61]

The "ossification" (calcification) of the lung, designated by Cullen as an effect of dust and by Bayle as a cause of tuberculous phthisis, was regarded by Laennec as a sequel of phthisis. He had seen (with Bayle) only a few cancers (encephaloids) of the lung. Against the fashion of the younger advocates of pathological anatomy (Rostan, Bouillaud) of regarding every asthma as cardiac affection, he maintained the existence of primary nervous spasmodic asthma.[62] He often treated with the magnet nervous disorders of the lung and the heart.[63] He first described the hemorrhagic form of pleurisy. He advocated surgical management of empyema. In a footnote to the autopsy record of a pleurisy case he created the notion of liver cirrhosis.[64] He also gave the first correct description of pneumothorax.

The third part, on the diseases of the heart, was not quite as original as the one on the lung. Here he followed his teacher Corvisart on most points, and deviated from the latter's views only occasionally. He had many controversies with the Broussais pupil Bouillaud, who saw "endocarditis" everywhere, just as his master had seen "enteritis" everywhere. There were, of course, Laennec's new auscultatory findings on the heart; the blowing murmur, the file sound, the rasp sound, the bellows sound, and similar indi-cations, which allowed previously impossible diagnosis of, for example, "ossification" of certain valves. The following comment on pulse-taking[65] illustrates Laennec's aristocratic temperament and perhaps explains some of his unpopularity: "This technique is better suited to those who are mediocre by nature and by education. Among physicians, as in other classes of society, these people always represent the majority."

Beside this publication, two manuscripts of Laennec's have survived: the notes for the 1803 private course in pathological anatomy (about 100 pages; the number of lectures is not ascertainable; half of this manuscript was pub-lished by Cornil in 1884) and the notes for the course "On Medicine" at the Collège de France, held in the years 1822–1824 and repeated in 1824–1826.[66] The latter manuscript comprises 1,600 pages and 161 lessons. The manu-scripts of 1803 and of lessons 1–35 of the Collège de France course are in the Library of the Medical Faculty at Paris. Lessons 36–161 are in the Library of the Medical Faculty at Nantes, which owns a number of interesting Laennec items.

The manuscript of 1803 did not offer anything of importance. The first lesson of the Collège de France course was published in the first issue of the *Archives générales de médecine* in January, 1823. Here Laennec declared himself a decided adversary of both the purely empirical and the so-called etiological trends in medicine. He traced the latter throughout history. It was always, he said, the refuge of those too lazy to think. It was characterized by its negation of disagreeable facts, contempt for detailed observation and for Hippocrates, megalomania, and exploitation of the enthusiasm of youth. Its prototype was Paracelsus. Neither Broussais nor anyone else had any doubts about whom Laennec was really referring to when he condemned "Paracelsus." Laennec called his own party that of "observation"; it avoided the uncertainties of the empiricists as well as the fanaticism of the etiologists, used observation and reasoning, and thus took the way of Hippocrates. This tradition was the one characteristic of his chair from Duret and Goupil to Corvisart and Hallé. Laennec was apparently convinced that he only continued the Hippocratic tradition. His friend Cayol, who had tried to do just that, knew better; all those devotees of pathological anatomy, Laennec as well as Pinel and Bayle, were, in spite of their admiration for it, actually its gravediggers.[67]

In his second lesson, Laennec stated that diseases were changes of either the solid or the liquid parts of the body or of the "vital principle." He doubted the existence of primary changes in the solid organs. In the following twenty-six lessons, under the heading "Pathological Changes of the Solids," he offered what was actually general pathological anatomy with the usual items: hypertrophy, inflammation, homologous accidental tissues, heterologous accidental tissues (now increased to eight, including cirrhosis), vermes, and so on.

Lessons 29 to 68 dealt with "General Diseases." Even local diseases—and Laennec doubted their existence—influenced the total body; and general diseases often produced local disease instead of being produced by it. The first general diseases discussed were, of course, fevers, which he divided into symptomatic and idiopathic (essential) ones. A local lesion could be acknowledged as causal only when it always appeared together with or before the fever, was sufficiently grave, and was not accompanied by another, worse lesion. The same lesion could not produce different symptoms in other patients.

In discussing fevers, Laennec gave his detailed position on the ancient notions of crisis, coction, and critical days (lessons 34 and 35). He adhered to all of them vigorously, though even the traditionalist Corvisart had already given up the critical days, coction had become meaningless to the solidists, and the notion of crisis had become problematic not only with Broussaisians, but, for example, with Andral.[68] His discussion of general diseases ended with the diatheses: the lymphatic, inflammatory, hemorrhagic, septic, tuberculous, cancerous, and so on.

Exposition of local diseases started with those of the brain and the spinal marrow (lessons 70 to 81). Then, as an interlude, followed nine lessons on "neuroses"—that is, on primarily mental diseases,[69] which were still discussed by the clinicians up to 1850.

In themselves, these lessons are of small interest. Laennec had little clinical experience in this field, and therefore followed Pinel more or less mechanically. But they are interesting for two reasons: Laennec, together with Dance and Georget and against Broussais and Rostan, maintained the notion of neurosis, founded by Cullen, propagated by Pinel, and still used quite extensively today. And for once, in these lessons, his reactionary ideology invaded his medical thought. He was the only French physician of the period to claim that mental disease, being neither an organic nor a functional disease, belonged not in the hands of the physician, but in those of "the philosopher and the moralist" (undoubtedly a pseudonym for the theologian). His interesting definition of mental disease—"it consists essentially in preferring one's own sentiment to the contrary sentiment of everybody else"—is but a variation of a definition created by his patient, the famous theologian F. R. de Lamenais. The remaining eighty-four lessons are competent discussions of poisons and the diseases of the eye, ear, nose, throat, thorax, and abdomen.

The Collège de France course is impressive in its diversity, but it does not add any absolutely new traits to the Laennec picture.[70] It nevertheless underlines one aspect of Laennec which *can* also be seen in his printed work, but which is, in general, overlooked in the context of his many new findings: his medical traditionalism, his "classicism," not to call it his hidebound conservatism. Of course, Laennec was above all the great innovator and inventor. But with his opinions on the primacy of generalizing humoral pathology, on "epidemic constitutions," on "bilious" diseases, on crises and critical days, and on the *vis medicatrix naturae*, he was also far more a traditionalist than any of his four famous teachers! This attitude of his might partly explain why so many preferred Broussais to him; Broussais was far less gifted and inventive but also far more radical in giving up the past. Today it has become almost impossible to develop the proper empathy for Laennec's faith in an eternal science of medicine, immutable and known in most of its aspects.

Laennec's traditionalism paralleled his political and religious convictions but was actually opposed to his true contribution to medicine. It was, after all, he who erected the foundations for a new localism and solidism, and he who invented the instrument which made localistic pathology dominant. The only possible conclusion is that Laennec was an *innovator in spite of himself*. His was not the only case in medical history where the dynamism of the period pushed a quite conservative individual into revolutionary scientific creations. Thomas Willis,[71] Theodor Schwann,[72] and I. P. Pawlow are other cases in point.

In view of Laennec's Janus-faced scientific physiognomy, it is quite logical that two trends developed out of his work and tradition. The one, represented by Louis and Andral, took up those aspects of Laennec which made him a most typical representative of, and the high point of, the Paris school: his interests in pathological anatomy, physical examination, statistics, specialization, and therapeutic skepticism. This work will be dealt with in the next chapter. The other group, mostly personal friends of his, and political reactionaries, tried to develop his traditionalism.

The most eminent member of this latter circle was undoubtedly Joseph-Claude-Anthelme Récamier.[73] Born in 1774, he was first a military surgeon, then one of the first students of the École de Santé; after 1806, he became a physician at the Hôtel Dieu, and after 1821, professor of clinical medicine;

in 1827, he inherited Laennec's professorship at the Collège de France. A faithful partisan of the Bourbons, he gave up both positions in 1830 rather than submit to the oath of the new government. He died in 1856.

The great accomplishments of this internist are found in the field of gynecology. Regarding cancer as a primarily local phenomenon forming later metastases, he reinvented the speculum to treat the cancerous uterine cervix, amputated the cervix, and eventually removed the whole organ (1829). In 1830, he invented the curette. He also constructed a pharyngotome and was, in general, an excellent surgeon. He tried to cure cancer by compression.

He was a very active therapist, applying cold baths in fevers and continually trying out new drugs. Andral compared him to Asclepiades. This strange but firm and not unattractive character was one of the most popular practitioners of his day and known for his generosity to the poor. He appears in Balzac's *Peau de chagrin*; Véron praises him as "*le médecin des agonisants.*"[74] He was a pioneer of auscultation and temperature studies. But his all-too-enthusiastic lectures, full of vitalism and animism, were indigestible to the younger generation.[75]

Together with his pupil Martinet, Antoine Laurent Bayle (the nephew of Gaspard Laurent Bayle—we will have more to say about him in our chapter on psychiatry), and Cayol, an honest reactionary mediocrity,[76] Récamier founded the *Revue médicale* in 1824 as the tribune of this group of Laennec's politicomedical friends. After 1834, it called itself the *Journal of the Progress of Hippocratic Medicine*; but there was no progress to report. The political constellation which had given the traditionalists power in the 1820's had vanished in 1830, and their ideas had lost their attractiveness.

VIII. THE ECLECTICS

When Broussaisism weakened visibly after 1830, the reactionary *Revue médicale* was jubilant—the era of anatomism was finished![1] But things did not work out so simply. Indeed, none of the old trends remained dominant any longer; but no new trends with dictatorial aspirations appeared either. A number of equally strong tendencies cooperated in synthesizing and developing in different ways the heritage of the first three "reigns." The fourth and last episode in the supremacy of Paris medicine was thus the period of so-called "eclecticism." This does not sound very heroic. But it was probably the richest and most brilliant period of them all.

Peisse described the mood in which eclecticism was conceived as follows: "The disgust with theories has generated a new kind of indifference, which does not consist of despising or abandoning research—it has never been worked at harder—but of simultaneously cultivating it in the most different ways and with the most disparate principles."[2] There is no doubt that medical eclecticism was closely connected, even personally, with the simultaneous philosophical eclecticism of Andral's friend Cousin—and that medical eclecticism tended to be combined with skepticism and political liberalism.

The first to publicly proclaim eclecticism in medicine was apparently Coutanceau, Broussais' colleague at the Val de Grâce, in 1823. Laennec's lecture notes of the same year surprisingly enough contain the same slogan. So does A. Desbois' Paris thesis of 1824, dedicated to Flaubert's father. Bouillaud used the term in 1828. It was definitely established through Jules Guérin's Academy speeches in May and June, 1830. It was, of course, not accepted by everybody. Récamier, Gendrin, Broussais, and Rochoux all fought it, though for very different reasons. Yet it won easily. Kratzmann,[3] in 1846, listed the following as eclectics: Andral, Magendie, Louis, Rostan, Piorry, Double, Coutanceau, Ribes, Saucerotte, Réveillé-Parise, Guérin, Petit, Trolliet, Cliet, Tacheron, and Odier. It seems to me that the most important figures in this period were Chomel, Louis, Andral, Rayer, Bouillaud, Piorry, Rostan, and Trousseau. I am therefore discussing them in what follows.

F. Chomel (1788–1856), the last member of an old medical dynasty, received his training at the Charité and had the signal honor of succeeding Laennec in 1827 as professor of clinical medicine there. He later transferred to the Hôtel Dieu. In 1852, he resigned rather than submit to a loyalty oath contrary to his Orleanist feelings. Today he appears only as an appendage of his friend Louis, whom he helped in his career. Actually, he was the leading Paris clinician[4] for many years and especially praised as a teacher by Stromeyer[5] ("careful diagnosis, mild therapy"), as well as by Ratier ("good, systematic, conscientious; little theory") and Sachaile ("completeness of examination").[6] He was less successful in his writings, probably because of his refusal to be dogmatic. Pathological anatomy was very important to him. A firm adherent of the numerical method, he was otherwise somewhat more traditionalist than Louis. He opposed clinical thermometry. He defended "essential fevers" against Broussais; he later changed his mind in 1834 in his book on typhoid fever, but he still regarded the intestinal lesion as secondary. He was rather open to contagionist arguments.[7] He attacked Bouillaud's rheumatic endocarditis idea through his disciple Requin. Schneider[8] has shown how late experiences with dyspeptics opened his eyes to psychosomatic phenomena. Actually, even in 1834, he gave nostalgia as one of the causes of typhoid fever. His best-known pupil was Grisolle.[9] Even less well remembered than Chomel is P. E. Fouquier (1776–1850), professor of clinical medicine for twenty years and physician of Louis-Philippe. And yet he drew more students than anybody else and was praised by Ratier and the terrible anonymous critic, "X."[10]

Today Chomel's greatest claim to fame is probably the fact that for many years he allowed his friend Pierre-Charles-Alexandre Louis (1787–1872) to collect thousands of case histories and autopsy records on his wards in the Charité in preparation for the latter's great works on phthisis and typhoid fever. This remarkable man had graduated at Paris in 1813 and practiced in Russia successfully for seven years, when the catastrophies of a diphtheria epidemic convinced him of the inadequacy of his training. He returned to Paris and, as Broussais could in no way satisfy this critical and superior mind, he became his own teacher, doing research on Chomel's wards for seven years. He thus became the ancestor of our full-time men. It is typical of the Paris Faculty that this true clinical scientist never became its member. He held only hospital positions, at the Pitié and at the Hôtel Dieu. He nevertheless influenced his contemporaries profoundly. It was really he who silenced Broussais. Holmes speaks of the "idolatry" of the American students for him. He calls him "modest in the presence of nature, fearless in the face of authority, unwearing in the pursuit of truth." Osler mentions no less than thirty-seven of his American pupils in his famous paper. Louis was a highly successful teacher, especially of diagnostics.[11]

Since he was particularly popular with students from the United States, it is no exaggeration to say that American medicine still bears his imprint. It was no accident that Osler organized a pilgrimage to his grave in 1905. But Louis also had very prominent students from Great Britain, Switzerland, Germany, and, of course, France, where in 1832 the Société Médicale d'Observation gathered around him. Though carrying on Laennec's work in some ways and fighting Broussais and Bouillaud, he was by no means a slavish imitator of the inventor of auscultation. He shared neither the traditionalism nor the antimicroscopic prejudices of the latter. He was condemned to live to a very advanced age, and to be the sad survivor of his young son, his dearest pupils like Valleix and Jackson, his closest friends like Chomel and Marshall Hall, and of his own importance.

Louis' great book on phthisis appeared in 1825. It contained 184 pages on pathological anatomy, twice that number on symptoms, and one-third on therapy. It enounced the not-so-important "law of Louis": after the age of fifteen, one cannot have a tubercle in any organ of the body without at the same time having tubercles in the lung. Qualitatively, he did not add many new facts to what Laennec and Bayle had found. And yet Louis' quantitative approach, his extraordinary, almost painful thoroughness, gave his statements a finality and certainty never attained before. In later editions, he incorporated the microscopic results of Lebert and N. Guillot.

In 1829, in his next book, *Recherches anatomiques, pathologiques et théra-peutiques sur la maladie connue sous les noms de fièvre typhoide, putride, adynamiques, ataxique, bilieuse, muqueuse, gastro entérite, entérite folliculeuse, dothiénentérie, etc.,* he tackled the other most important disease of his time, which he has taught us to call typhoid fever. The arrangement was the same as in the preceding book: pathological anatomy, symptoms, and therapy. Again he did not add many new discoveries to the findings of Prost (1804), Petit and Serres (1813), and Bretonneau (1820). But he succeeded in establish-ing typhoid fever as a specific disease on the basis of regular autopsy findings in Peyer's patches, the mesenteric glands, and the spleen. Like Petit and Serres, and later Andral, Bouillaud, and Chomel, he realized that a majority of victims were youthful newcomers to Paris and explained their affection by the absence of an immunity caused by prior attack. He was inclined to recognize the contagiousness of the disease, which he would not recognize in diphtheria.

Through his results, the question arose as to whether the British typhus and his typhoid fever were different diseases; the problem was put on the agenda by the Academy of Medicine in 1835. It was no accident that it was answered in the positive primarily by his own pupils, the Americans Gerhard and

Pennock (1836) and G. Shattuck (1839). In his discussions, he somewhat unjustly omitted Lombard of Geneva (1836), Staberoh (1838), and his contemporary Rochoux (1832). J. A. Rochoux (1787–1852) was a physician at Bicêtre and *agrégé*; had done early outstanding work on apoplexy (1812); had lived for a while in the West Indies; and had become well known as a protagonist of anticontagionism and neohumoralism in the 1820's.

Louis' *Archives générales* articles of 1828 (which appeared as a book in 1835) on the ineffectiveness of bleeding sounded, together with Marshall Hall's book of 1824, the death knell for a dangerous 1,000-year-old medical rite.

We have already reported Louis' medical philosophy, his *méthode numérique*. Others had used statistics before him: not only the hygienists Villermé and Parent-Duchatelet, but the clinicians Pinel, Esquirol, Rostan, Bayle, Laennec, Bouillaud, Rayer, and so on. But with Louis, the *analyse numérique*, the last incarnation of dear old sensualist analysis, became the basis of medicine. In 1832, with thirteen men—among them Barth, Bazin, Boudin, and six Geneva students, including Marc d'Espine and Bizot— he founded the Société Médicale d'Observation as the church of the new faith. The first volume of its memoirs (Paris 1837) contained a programmatic article by its president, "L'examen des malades et la recherche des faits généraux." The Society, which accepted only active members, was soon joined by Valleix, Grisolle, Rilliet, Nélaton, Walsh, Lebert, Woillez, Behier, and Vernois.

The numerical method was the object of many violent disputes, the most famous being the ones in the Academy of Sciences in 1835 and in the Academy of Medicine in 1837. At the latter occasion, Louis was supported by Capuron, Guénau de Mussy, Bouillaud, Chomel, Rochoux, Rayer, Andral, and Trousseau (who had fought him before and would do so again). He was attacked by Dubois d'Amiens, Piorry, Martin-Solon, Cruveilhier, and Double (who later joined him). Peisse[12] in his extensive analysis of the dispute, was equally opposed. The mathematical shortcomings of Louis' crude methods were criticized by Casimir Broussais and Jules Gavarret in 1840. The death of the method was announced many times. The Society itself declined after Louis' retirement in the 1850's and after he proved unable to use the method in new techniques like thermometry and blood-pressure measurements.[13] Claude Bernard criticized it quite aptly as the central pillar of medicine.[14] Yet it has never altogether ceased to exist and to render excellent service in certain situations.

The most many-sided and the most popular of all eclectics was undoubtedly Gabriel Andral. O. W. Holmes and Virchow placed him highest among the leaders of the Paris school. Wunderlich showed unusual esteem for him. Muehry, Isensee, and Otterburg devoted true panegyrics to him.[15] He called himself an "eclectic by necessity."[16] Astruc has shown that his eclecticism was far more fertile than the philosophical variety of Cousin.[17] To Andral, eclecticism had two functions: to reconcile the points of view of the warring factions (those of Broussais and Laennec) and to resist energetically any attempt at dogmatic dictatorship in medicine.

He was born in 1797, the son of Guillaume Andral, who had succeeded in being the personal physician of both Murat and Charles X. The younger Andral graduated in 1821. He obtained most of his training at the Charité under T. N. Lerminier (1770–1836), the former pupil of Corvisart and a Napoleonic physician. With Lerminier, between 1823 and 1827, he published the first edition of his extremely successful *Clinique médicale*. His friendship with Louis also dated from their common years at the Charité. He won the *agrégation* in 1824. In 1826, he founded the *Journal hébdomadaire* with Bouillaud and his close friend and collaborator A. C. Reynaud. (Death cut short the brilliant beginnings of Reynaud, M.D. 1829, *chef de clinique* 1832, famous for his temperature studies of 1830 and his memoir of 1831 on tuberculosis in monkeys; Reynaud was also a friend of Carswell, the British student who later became a famous pathologist.) In 1828, Andral became professor of hygiene. His rapid advancement was primarily due to his ability; yet the fact that he married the daughter of the influential politician P. P. Royer-Collard certainly did not impede it. His ascension continued under the Orléans. From 1830 to 1866, he taught medical pathology. He died in 1876. During the last decade of his life, he devoted himself primarily to the health of his ailing wife. When Pasteur suffered his stroke in 1868, it was Andral who was called and intervened successfully.

Andral once stated that he had studied medicine three times: when he learned pathological anatomy, when he learned the new methods of physical diagnosis, and when he started his study of hemopathology.[18] His prophecy that the latter would not remain his last transformation was only partially fulfilled when, in the early 1850's, he turned toward medical history. He did not achieve the same eminence there as in other fields, but the fact that, unlike Laennec, he discussed Hippocrates with respect, yet as a purely historical phenomenon, was significant.

His *Clinic*, especially its first two volumes on chest diseases, reflected his concern with physical diagnosis. It was primarily due to his influence that, in France, the birthplace of the stethoscope, *mediate* auscultation became predominant around 1840.[19] Though showing the greatest respect for Laennec, he frequently disagreed with him on details.

In discussing the dropsy of heart disease, he was aware of the fact that a different kind of dropsy appeared, for example, after scarlet fever. A voluminous heart muscle might function only weakly. With his "distressing skepticism,"[20] he could not close his eyes to the fact that form and function did not always correspond in pathology and that symptoms did exist without lesions and lesions without symptoms. This critical attitude separated him from Broussais, who always found a lesion when there were symptoms—and that lesion was always a gastroenteritis. Andral's recognition of the existence of symptom without lesion made him maintain the Bichat-Broussais notion of sympathy as a possible explanatory principle. He made it multiple instead of that one sympathy, caused by gastrointestinal inflammation, which Broussais always preached. He shared Broussais' denial of the existence of "essential fevers." His criticism of Broussais appeared mostly in Volumes 3 and 4 of his *Clinique*, which deal with diseases of the abdomen. Particularly famous was the fifth volume, which discussed diseases of the brain.

Andral's *Précis d'anatomie pathologique* of 1829 will be discussed later. This leading pathology text of the first half of the nineteenth century subdivided its subject matter according to functions. It contained a great deal of comparative material provided by, for example, Dupuy of the Alfort Veterinary School.

After an eclipse of almost forty years, humoralism had a comeback in the 1830's—in, of course, a new and scientific vein and mostly in the form of hemopathology. Lobstein felt that this happened primarily under the influence of the first cholera epidemic. As a matter of fact, the move had been prepared for by the experimental work of Prévost and Dumas, and that of Magendie and Gaspard in the 1820's (continued by Denis and Lecanu in 1830), as well as by the statements of Rochoux (1823) and Velpeau (1824). Bouillaud (1853) and Piorry (1840) came out in support of this trend. The 1840 memoir by Andral and Gavarret on *Recherches sur les modifications de proportion de quelques principes de sang* was decisive.[21] It was only logical that Andral, after his demonstrations of symptoms without lesions in the solid organs, should develop in this direction. His contribution was eagerly seized upon and copied, sometimes without discrimination and luck, as Rokitansky's adventure with the *"Krases"*[22] (specific changes in the blood, thought by him to be the basis of most disease) showed. Andral's book *Essai d'hématologie pathologique* (Paris 1843) examined the blood physically, chemically, and microscopically. The book acknowledged its indebtedness to Magendie. It contained this prophetic statement: "Thus where anatomy no longer finds changes, chemistry shows them to us, and I don't doubt that it will become more and more one of the foundations of pathogenesis, not only, as it does primarily today, in analyzing liquids changed by disease, but in studying changes in proportion or principal elements in the solid parts themselves." The blood changes examined corresponded primarily to the possibilities of the chemistry of the day and concerned the free and bound alkalis, fibrin, serum albumin content, red corpuscles in plethora, fevers, and inflammatory processes. Changes in albumins in the then not infrequent hunger edema were noted, along with changes in sedimentation in phthisis. The author wondered whether deviations in coagulation time could be corrected therapeutically.

Andral's collaborator in his blood studies, Jules Gavarret (1809–1890), known to us through his book on statistics (1840), was a product of the École Polytechnique in 1843. He then acquired an M.D. and, in 1844, became professor of physics at the Paris Faculty, a position he held most honorably for forty-two years. He was, together with Pugnet, Récamier, Bouillaud, Donné, Piorry, and especially Andral, one of the French pioneers of clinical thermometry in the 1830's. They built partly on the experimental studies of Despretz, Delay, and Dutrochet in the 1820's.

The evolution of Pierre François Olive Rayer (b. 1793) from pathological anatomy to the laboratory sciences was at least as direct as that of Andral. The fact that Rayer was the physician of the "financial aristocracy," and later of the imperial family, did not deter him from being one of the leading medical scientists of this time. A pupil of Duméril, he published a thesis entitled *Sommaire d'une histoire abregée de l'anatomie pathologique* in 1818 which contained a wealth of material and showed him opposed to the systems of Brown, Broussais, and the solidists (p. 96). His excellent two-volume book of 1826 on skin diseases was still written entirely from the anatomical point of view. In 1837, he made the momentous discovery that glanders was contagious and could infect man. His masterpiece was his two-volume treatise of 1839 on kidney diseases. Here he added chemistry and microscopy to clinical-anatomical methods. No less than 200 pages of this work were devoted to the chemistry and microscopy of urine. In the preface he made the significant statement, "Properly speaking, no local diseases exist; most of them ramify and become more or less general." The last chapter dealt with adrenal tumors. He had also described pituitary obesity in 1823 (AG 1823, 3:350).

Follin, Huel, Robin, and others founded the Société de Biologie in 1848 in the attempt to create a society for the cultivation of science in medicine.

Rayer was the one older clinician willing and able to preside over, defend, and promote the new Society. In the second volume of the *comptes rendus* of the Society, Rayer published, in 1850, Davaine's discovery of the anthrax bacillus. In 1858, Rayer served unselfishly as president of the Association Générale des Médecins de France.

Under Louis XVIII, Rayer had been barred from a university career because he had married a Protestant. Under Louis Philippe, he held hospital appointments at St. Antoine and the Charité. In 1862, an imperial decree finally made him professor of comparative pathology and dean of the Faculty. For political reasons, he encountered such opposition that he resigned from both positions in 1864. Nevertheless, he succeeded during his short tenure in creating a chair of histology for Robin and in establishing the beginnings of official instruction in the specialties. He died in 1867.

Rayer was a great clinician and scientist. He was unequaled as a discoverer and promotor of young medical scientists. Among others, he instructed and furthered Charcot, Robin, Claude Bernard, Brown-Séquard, Villemin, Davaine, Berthelot, Gubler, Tardieu, and Bouchard.[23] Littré dedicated his *Médecine et médecins* with the following words: "To the memory of Dr. Rayer. A friendship of forty years united us; when it began I was a humble student, he a famous physician. It lasted unaltered however different our ways were. I survive; but I have not forgotten."

Jean Bouillaud, born in 1796 near Angoulême, was brought into medicine by "*le meilleur des oncles*," a military surgeon of the same name.[24] He was a disciple of and later the physician of Dupuytren. He was profoundly influenced by Broussais. His first important contribution was a memoir, in the *Archives générales* of 1823, on the edema following blockage of venous circulation. In the next year, he published, with his "boss" R. H. Bertin, a treatise on heart diseases (re-edited and greatly enriched under his name alone in 1835), which became a classic in the field. He appeared there as a master of pathological anatomy and auscultation, sometimes greatly improving on Laennec's results. He created the notion of endocarditis and his "law" of the connection between it and polyarthritis. This relationship had been stated several times since Pitcairne (1788), but only Bouillaud made it stick.

In 1824, Bouillaud was barred from the *agrégation* (assistant professorship) for being a liberal. In 1830, he fought *permutation*. After the Revolution of 1830, he became, in 1831, professor of clinical medicine, a position he held till 1876. An earlier attempt to become professor of physiology had failed, apparently through falsification of the vote. From 1842 to 1846, he was a member of the lower house. Since he was a friend of L. Blanc and

Ledru-Rollin, it is not surprising that the Revolution of 1848 made him dean of the Faculty. Like his political friends, he did not last long. He was replaced by P. H. Bérard, who, with Trousseau, engineered his fall.

These political intrigues never affected his scientific creativity. His *Traité clinique et physiologique de l'encephalite* of 1825 on brain inflammation made him, with Rostan and Lallemand, one of the leading authorities on brain pathology. His experiments on cerebellum pathology are well known. In the same year, he took up Gall's idea of localization of aphasia in the frontal lobe. He remained its lonely defender till 1861, when Broca obtained its recognition. His *Traité des fièvres dites essentielles* of 1826 was his contribution to the typhoid-fever problem. His *Traité du choléra-morbus* of 1832 showed him an anticontagionist regarding cholera, a position he gave up later. His *Clinique médicale de l'hôpital de la Charité* of 1837 was rich in facts about clinical activities in this famous hospital but somewhat spoiled by his polemic zeal, directed mostly against Chomel and his pupils (Grisolle, Requin). A number of later books did not bring out any essentially new ideas.

In 1867, he presided over the first International Congress of Medicine in Paris. He died in 1881, assiduously attending to the end the meetings of the Academy of Medicine and illustrating, through his opposition to the rail-roads, Pasteur's work, and other innovations, the sinister effect of time, which makes old reactionaries out of so many young progressives.

In spite of his veneration of Broussais, it would be incorrect to label Bouillaud just a "disciple of Broussais." He rightly called himself an eclectic and, from the beginning, differed with his master on many points. He was never a monotheistic believer in gastroenteritis. It is true that he had three things in common with "the messiah": his aggressive megalomania, his overemphasis on inflammatory processes, and his murderous therapeutics. From Louis' demonstration that bloodletting in pneumonia was inefficient, he concluded that more and more frequent venesections were needed! He applied his *saignées coup sur coup* (bleedings in rapid succession) without mercy in endocarditis, polyarthritis, pneumonia, typhoid fever, and so on. It is amazing that so many of his patients survived, thus confirming him in his own prejudices.

Still, we should not allow these traits to obscure the very real merits of the man. His pupil Wunderlich rightly praised him, along with Louis, Andral, and Piorry, as one of the great teachers of diagnostics in Paris.[25] His research on cardiac edema, his studies of endocarditis and cardiac neu-roses, and his work on brain pathology were, for instance, great contributions. And it should not be forgotten that inflammations were more frequent then than now!

If his *médecine exacte* was not as exact as he thought it to be, even the attempt was laudable. He practiced the numerical method and his sympathy for Louis was such that he profusely apologized when criticizing him. He had none of the prejudices of the preceding generation. He preached the application of the microscope in pathological anatomy, used thermometry and chemical examinations of urine and blood, gave the first reliable measurements of the heart, and cultivated animal experimentation. He often praised Magendie, and he befriended Claude Bernard in the salon of Rayer. Among his pupils were men like Potain, Donné, Raciborski, Clemenceau *père*, Vulpian, and Laboulbène.

He must have been far more attractive personally than is reflected in his aggressive writings. He again was the students' physician. Dr. Bianchon, the outstanding doctor in Balzac's *Comédie humaine* and a thoroughly lovable figure, is modeled after him. Balzac knew him well. As young men, he and Bouillaud had been friends living in the same shabby pension in the Latin Quarter[26] described so masterfully in *Père Goriot*. It is said that, in his last agony, Balzac mumbled, "Go, fetch Bianchon."

A typical eclectic was Poitiers-born Pierre Adolphe Piorry (1794-1879). He regarded Morgagni, Sauvages, and Pinel, as well as Broussais, Rostan, Andral, Auenbrugger, and Laennec, as his scientific predecessors.[27] He took his M.D. at Paris in 1816, became an *agrégé* in 1826, and hospital physician in 1827 (he worked at the Pitié, Salpêtrière, Charité, and Hôtel Dieu). In 1840, he obtained the chair of internal pathology, and in 1850 one of clinical medicine. He was first strongly influenced by Broussais, later by Magendie. He was particularly close to Andral and Bally. He practiced the numerical method.

He is best known for inventing the plessimeter and mediate percussion in 1826 as a kind of corollary to Laennec's mediate auscultation. His *Traité de percussion médiate*, based on clinical observation and experiments on cadavers, received the Prix Monthyon in 1828. He discussed his technique, which he also applied to the abdomen (here Double preceded him), in later voluminous treatises like the *Traité de diagnostic et de séméiologie* of 1837. The instrument has now become obsolete, and percussion has lost its importance with the tremendous increase in diagnostic techniques, but what Piorry was able to accomplish with this simple technique remains most admirable. It once more illustrates the fact that the scarcity of diagnostic means forced the clinician to develop his powers of observation to heights that are no longer seen today.

Piorry was, of course, an accomplished pathological anatomist and a localist. This did not prevent him from becoming one of the promoters of the new hemopathology (see his treatise of 1833). He abandoned the vague notion of "sympathy" in its favor.[28] In this 1837 treatise, he seems to have inaugurated the erroneous, purely mechanical theory of icterus, which has survived into our time.[29] A justifiable skepticism toward then fashionable psychogenic explanations went together with valuable observations in this field.[30] He suffered so severely from migraine all his life that he suggested the condition be called "Piorry's disease." He was one of the rare defenders of the idea of specific inflammations. Piorry was also one of the pioneers of thermometry[31] and of chemical and microscopic examinations of blood and secretions.

He was greatly interested in therapeutics. His *Médecine du bon sens* (*Common-sense Medicine*) of 1864 defended the therapeutics of "little means," a "simple, hygienic, rational, inoffensive, humanitarian treatment." He fought "derivation" and exaggerated bleeding,[32] and he held only a limited belief in the *vis medicatrix naturae*.[33] As a hygienist, he fought overcrowding, which he thought caused typhoid fever (especially among newcomers) and many other diseases.[34] For the causation of certain epidemics, he went back to the ancient notion of the "epidemic constitution."[35] He was one of the very few to study the problem of hereditary diseases.[36]

Piorry was influential. He would certainly have been even more influential had he not been possessed by the idea of totally remodeling medical nomenclature and creating a new "organopathological" one, which nobody else used. Perhaps it was the poet in him—in 1854, he published a lengthy poem entitled *God, the Soul, and Nature*—which caused this regrettable addiction to neologisms in an otherwise quite sensible man.

Provence-born Léon Rostan (1790–1866) also synthesized some of the older antitheses. A disciple of Pinel, he gained a splendid reputation when substituting for his aged master in the Salpêtrière during the typhus epidemic of 1814. After 1814, he was a physician in this establishment, where he befriended Ferrus, Georget, and Chomel. He gave very successful private courses until he became professor of clinical medicine in 1833. Corlieu counted him among the twelve men who influenced the School most profoundly during the nineteenth century. (The others, were Cabanis, Bichat, Pinel, Broussais, Bouillaud, Laennec, Louis, Cruveilhier, Andral, Trousseau, and Pasteur).[37] Wunderlich mentioned how overcrowded his classes were.[38] Leonard von Muralt, a Zurich student, noted in 1831 (notebook in University of Zurich Medical History Institute): "The clinic of Mr. Rostan is the only one at Paris which is held at the sickbed and it is therefore more enlightening than the others. Although Mr. R. has too good an opinion of himself, his clinic is, with that of Mr. Chomel, one of the best. Just like Mr. Chomel likes to find his favorite disease, *dothiénentérie*, and Mr. Louis diseases of the lung and heart, thus Mr. Rostan sees brain disease everywhere."

It was through publishing on "*ramollissement du cerveau*" ("softening of the brain") in 1819 that Rostan became one of the leading medical scientists. His *Traité élémentaire de diagnostic* (1826) put forth his notion of "*organicism*" (the idea that every disease was basically the affection of an organ, never a general disease), to which he even devoted a book at the age of seventy-four. Though a pupil of Pinel, Rostan did not recognize the existence of essential fevers.[39] He wanted, instead of a medicine of symptoms, one exclusively of lesions. Every disturbance of function presupposed the disturbance of an organ. In this respect, he was close to Broussais. But he repudiated the dogmatic intestinal monotheism of the latter.[40] *All* organs could be the seat of the primary lesion. He assumed specific diseases,[41] and was an antivitalist. He was less interested in therapeutics, distrusted the *vis medicatrix naturae*, used specific remedies, and experimented with "animal magnetism."

Schneider has rightly emphasized[42] that Rostan can be fully understood only when his interest in hygiene (see his book of 1827—this interest was even more pronounced with him than with Piorry or Andral) is seen together with his clinical activities. Once a famous Don Juan, he died in 1866 after a long and painful decline—from "softening of the brain."

Today the best-remembered Paris clinician of this generation is undoubtedly its youngest member, Armand Trousseau of Tours (1801–1867). This lasting fame of his is primarily due to his great excellence as a writer— he was a professor of rhetoric when Bretonneau induced him to become a physician. Trousseau, the last "great man" of the clinical school, was certainly an eclectic, but the elements of his eclecticism differed from those of the other eclectics.

After several years of study under Bretonneau at Tours, Trousseau came to Paris, where he graduated in 1825. At Paris, he was closely connected with Récamier. He became an *agrégé* in 1826, *médecin des hôpitaux* in 1831. In 1836, he published, with Pidoux, a treatise on therapeutics, which made him famous. In 1839, he received the chair of therapeutics, which he exchanged in 1852 for one of clinical medicine at the Hôtel Dieu.[43].

The ideas which Trousseau propagated in Paris—on the nature of *dothiénentérie* and diphtheria, on contagion and specific diseases, on tracheotomy in diphtheria, and on cod-liver oil in the treatment of rickets—were actually those of his teacher Bretonneau, as he always underlined. Trousseau was interested most of all in therapeutics. While the other famous Bretonneau pupil at Paris, the surgeon Velpeau, was half an internist, Trousseau was half a surgeon. A strange mixture of overenthusiasm and skepticism, he emphasized expectative treatment[44] and the *vis medicatrix naturae* as well as active treatments. His ambivalence was also quite noticeable in a conversation with Delacroix on January 10, 1853, which the latter mentioned in his famous diary.

His special interests in pediatrics and in neurology, where, like Charcot, later, he leaned heavily on Duchenne de Boulogne, are quite noticeable. Both disciplines were still part and parcel of internal medicine. He emphasized psychogenic elements in, for example, hyperthyroidism, diarrhea, dyspepsia, angina pectoris, and asthma. The description of his own psychogenic attack of asthma is famous.[45] He was full of classic reminiscences: quotations from Hippocrates and Sydenham, the "epidemic constitution," the ill effects of dentition, and so on.[46] His last lecture, "On Percussion," was pathetic.[47] Though quite familiar with the work of, for example, Pasteur, Virchow, and Claude Bernard, that is, microscopy, chemistry, and experimental physiology, he refused to develop in this direction. He negated the future. He even abandoned the present, the legacy of his own generation. As a therapist, he was disappointed by the diagnostic trend of the Paris school, which he regarded as futile. His recommendation was an empty phrase: "Lift again the torch of the old medical traditions, which have been disregarded for a moment!" He left no school.

We can discuss here only the men who were the major links in the long chain of eclecticism. Many others were hardly less brilliant, but they were detoured. For example, C. F. Lallemand's (1790–1853) 1819 work on brain pathology was outstanding; but his jealous teacher Dupuytren found a surgical professorship for him at Montpellier in the same year, and he devoted himself thereafter to genitourinary diseases instead.

C. P. Ollivier d'Angers (1796–1845) published the first treatise on diseases of the spinal cord in 1824 but was sidetracked into legal medicine. Many, like J. B. H. Dance (1797–1832)—a victim of the first cholera epidemic—and the young urologist T. Ducamp (1793–1823), like F. G. L. Rouget (1795–1823) and A. Miquel (1796–1829), died so young that they could never realize the brilliant promise of their first steps. They suffered the same fate that had befallen C. J. Schwilgué (1774–1808), P. H. Nysten (1774–1817), and A. C. Savary (1781–1814) in the preceding generation.

IX. MEDICAL SOCIETIES AND JOURNALS

We have discussed in the preceding pages only a few generals of the large medical army of 1794–1848. Of necessity, we see the generals through the eyes of history. To the average contemporary bourgeois of the period, however, the fashionable "great practitioners," like Bourdois de la Mothe or Capuron, the "eloquent" professors like Fouquier or Marjolin, and the "elegant" writers like Richerand or Pariset were at least as important as Pinel and Piorry.

It is difficult to determine how large the medical army actually was. In 1792, according to Corlieu, Paris, with 610,000 inhabitants, had 139 physicians and 171 surgeons. Maygrier mentions in 1810 (700,000 inhabitants) 381 physicians and 379 surgeons. Of these physicians, 214 were products of the new École. In 1849 (1,035,000 inhabitants), 1,300 doctors and 160 officiers de santé were registered. The increase within fifty years, especially when compared to population figures, is quite impressive.

It is even more difficult to judge the income of our doctors. When Portal, a fashionable consultant, made forty-three thousand francs in 1788,[1] this might not have been less in actual purchasing power than the annual sixty thousand francs of Boyer or the one hundred thousand of Dubois in 1825.[2] The average practitioner could, at best, charge one-fourth of what the princes of the profession demanded. In 1822, Casper mentioned five to twenty francs as the price for a visit and ten francs to ten louis d'or (twenty-franc gold pieces) as the price for a consultation. Kuentzli charged three francs in 1846—and did not always obtain it. The impression is that even the lower sums were far more than what a large percentage of the population could afford. The "consultations" at the hospitals and the doctors of the bureaux de bienfaisance (welfare bureaus) or the dispensaires were available for the needy. In 1810, 162 medical men were attached to the bureaux de bienfaisance, 46 to the dispensaires.[3] In 1853, 250 doctors worked for the former, while the personnel of the latter had decreased.[4]

A great number of associations were organized by these physicians.[5] The French appear here no less "society-happy" than the much decried Germans or Americans. In the year VIII (1800), the Société de l'École de Médecine was formed. Members were the professors and some worthy associates. It disappeared when the Académie de Médecine was founded in 1820. In 1801, a Société d'Instruction Médicale was organized for students.

In 1796, the Société de Médecine de Paris originated. Sédillot was its guiding spirit for a long time, and Naquart, the friend of Balzac, its secretary. One-third of its members entered the Académie de Médecine. It was at times on bad terms with the Paris Faculty. In the same year, the young, under the leadership of Bichat, founded their own society, the Société Médicale d'Émulation. Among its first members were Alibert, Richerand, Larrey, Moreau, Ribes, Bretonneau, Burdin, Coutanceau, Duméril, Renauldin, Husson, and Dupuytren. The Société de Médecine Pratique, founded by Chaussier in 1802, the Société Médicopratique (1805), the Société Médico-philanthropique (1805), and the Athénée Médicale founded by Laennec in 1808 all flourished during our period. Guillotin tried in vain to maintain an Académie de Médecine in 1804. Dupuytren's Société d'Anatomie (1803) collapsed after a few years, but was revived with great success by Cruveilhier in 1826. In 1824, a Société de Chimie Médicale was established.

After 1830, a new wave of society-founding rose—the Société Médicale d'Observation (Louis, 1832) and the Société Médicopathologique (1834) came into being; and specialized societies (so far represented only by the Société Galvanique and the Société de Propagation de la Vaccine) like the Société Phrénologique (1831), the Société d'Accouchements (1836), the Société de Chirurgie (1843), the Société des Dermatophiles, and societies of Hippocratists, foreign physicians, and other groups appeared on the scene. The existence of sectional societies began with the founding of the Société Médicale du Temple (1832). The founding of the Société de Biologie (June 7, 1848) objectively ended the era of exclusive clinicism. Its founders were Rayer, Robin, C. Bernard, Huette, Follin, Brown-Séquard, Segond, Lebert, Davaine, Desir, Levois, and Montègre. In Paris medical circles, the birth of the Société Médicale des Hôpitaux (1849) was certainly regarded as a far more important event.

The Academy of Sciences had always had a few medical members, and membership in the Institut was regarded as the highest honor by French medical men. The Academy of Sciences, as a whole more science-minded than the trade-school-oriented Faculty of Medicine, occasionally honored people who were at odds with the Faculty, such as Fabre, Chervin, or Donné. A special medical Academy seemed desirable. It was created by royal decree on November 20, 1820, at the suggestion of Portal. His protégé E. Pariset became its first permanent secretary, followed in 1847 by F. Dubois d'Amiens. J. B. Bousquet (1794–1872) was for many years its *chef de bureau* and director of vaccination. It had first three, later eleven sections. For decades, the Paris Academy of Medicine was undoubtedly the leading medical assembly internationally, and its transactions were studied with the greatest interest everywhere. In the style of the liberal parliaments of the period, it was characterized by much factional dissension and many eloquent debates. Véron names as its outstanding orators in this heroic period Ricord, Bérard, Gerdy, Velpeau, Jules Guérin, Bouvier, and Dubois d'Amiens.[6]

The wealth of periodical publications was even greater than that of medical associations. Meding lists forty-nine journals appearing in Paris and eight in the provinces in around 1850.[7]

Some of the journals of our period were the continuation of pre-Revolutionary publications like the *Journal général de médecine, chirurgie et pharmacie*, founded in 1754 and lasting, under the editorship of Corvisart, Leroux, and Boyer, till 1822. The *Gazette de santé*, founded in 1773, was continued in 1830 by Jules Guérin as the *Gazette médicale de Paris*. Guérin enjoyed the collaboration of, among others, Littré, Malgaigne, L. Peisse, Michel Lévy, and Boudin. Stewart calls Guérin's the most popular medical journal.[8] A close competitor for this title was the *Lancette française ou gazette des hôpitaux* (1828) of the fierce A. F. H. Fabre (1797–1854). His collaborator A. Latour, who died a pauper, also founded the *Union médicale* with Aubert-Roche and Richelot. The *Revue médicale* of Cayol and his group (founded in 1820) and Raige-Delormé's *Archives générales de médecine* (founded in 1823) were also long-lived and influential. Specialized journals entered the field, beginning with the *Annales d'hygiène publique et médecine légale* (1829). Journals for surgery, pediatrics, medical psychology, therapeutics, magnetism, homeopathy, and military medicine were more or less long-lived. In addition, the academies and societies published their bulletins, memoirs, or annals.

The large medical dictionaries, unparalleled in any other country, were also excellent sources of information. Above all were the *Dictionnaire des sciences médicales* in sixty volumes (1812–1822), the *Dictionnaire de médecine* in thirty volumes (1832–1846), the *Dictionnaire de médecine et chirurgie pratique* in fifteen volumes (1829–1836), and the *Dictionnaire encyclopédique des sciences médicales*, directed by A. D. Dechambre (one hundred volumes, 1864–1881).

The relative numbers of periodical publications in Paris and in the provinces illustrates the predominance of Paris in French medical affairs, which had now become even greater than it had been under the *ancien régime*. Paris had eventually outdistanced Montpellier as a medical center, and several Montpellier chairs were now filled with Paris graduates! The extreme centralization characteristic of France in all areas of life should not blind us to the fact that many excellent men were active in the provinces. Especially in the field of surgery, Dupuytren's jealousy tended to exile other talents to safe distances.

Among the great provincial surgeons were Delpech of Montpellier, Flaubert of Rouen, A. Bonnet and Pravaz of Lyon, Goyraud of Aix, and Sédillot of Strasbourg. Excellent provincial internists were Barbier of Amiens and Gintrac of Bordeaux.

None of them equaled Pierre Fidèle Bretonneau of Tours (1778–1862), the lonely promoter of the ideas of specificity and contagion during our period.[9] He argued that inflammations differed not only according to tissue, but according to specific cause. Attempts at specific treatment and a clearer understanding of contagion and immunity resulted from these premises.

Bretonneau, offspring of an old Tours medical family, went to the École de Santé in Paris in 1798, where he became friends with his fellow students Duméril and Guersant the elder. Treated unjustly by Boyer, he returned to Chenonceaux near Tours in 1801 as a simple *officier de santé*. There he married a woman twenty-five years his senior, with whom he lived happily for thirty-five years. In 1815, his fame had become such that he was made director of the hospital at Tours.

There he observed an epidemic of typhoid fever (1816–1819) and one of diphtheria (1818–1821). He gave to the former disease, the particular nature of which he described, the name of "*dothiénentérie*." The second, which he first delineated clearly and fought with tracheotomy, he named "*diphtérie*." He recognized the contagious character of both diseases. In 1826, after much urging by his pupils, his book on diphtheria appeared. His books on "*dothiénentérie*" and specificity were not published until 1922! Still, his ideas became well known in Paris through the teaching and writings of his disciples, expecially Trousseau and Velpeau. Other of his pupils deserving mention are Baillarger, H. Gouraud, Moreau de Tours, and Georget.

Bretonneau's discoveries were based primarily on pathological anatomy; sixty autopsies form the background of his diphtheria study. But being original and independent in every respect, he did not submit to the prejudices of his generation, and used chemistry, the microscope, and animal experimentation. He was a much sought-after practitioner; for instance, Béranger, De Tocqueville, Lamennais, Mme Récamier, and Flaubert consulted him. Unfortunately, his memoirs seem lost.

He retired from the hospital in 1838. A remarriage at seventy-eight to a girl of eighteen, a niece of Moreau, made him prefer the Paris suburb of Passy to Tours. When at eighty-two he felt the beginnings of senility he forbade his wife to admit any more patients. Thus the most eminent provincial physician and one of the greatest minds of French medicine, who had not worked in Paris, at least died there in 1862 at the age of eighty-four—always an independent, in life and science alike.

X. THE DEAD END

With relatively simple methods—physical examination and macroscopic pathological anatomy—the Paris school added so many new insights to pathology within about forty years that this field acquired almost a new quality. Hemorrhagic and degenerative affections of the brain (Rochoux, Rostan, Lallemand, Serres), the inflammation of this organ and its envelopes (Parent-Duchatelet, Dance, Senn, Papavoine, Rilliet), spinal diseases like locomotor ataxia (Hutin, Monod), neuralgias (Jolly, Valleix), and tics (Itard, Toulmouche) were studied as never before. We have already seen how many of the acute and chronic diseases of the chest, lungs, and heart were discovered and especially how the vague "phthisis" became our "pulmonary tuberculosis." In the intestinal tract, typhoid fever and the peptic ulcer became known, and cirrhosis of the liver and epidemic jaundice were discussed. Great progress was achieved in the fields of kidney and urological disorders, skin and venereal ailments, infantile diseases (diphtheria!), and mental disorders (general paresis!). The knowledge of cancer, of poisons, and of malaria (Maillot) became far more specific.

Decades of unprecedented success—and yet, from the time of the mid-thirties, a justifiable feeling of uneasiness seized a few critical observers. A certain standstill, a certain sterility, a certain dead routine became more and more obvious. And the situation did not become any more reassuring through the fact that, simultaneously, France's previously medically underdeveloped German neighbors were now beginning to progress at a rate that could bring them to superiority within a few decades.

Buchez wrote in 1838: "We live today upon the works of our fathers—some more years, and we will have squandered our wealth, and our France will have fallen to the rank of industrial America."[1] The neohumoralism of these years was an attempt to overcome this crisis. But it continued. The content of the medical journals became, with the exception of some surgical contributions, more and more colorless. Jules Guérin notices in 1841 that "from passionate enthusiasm and faith, we have passed to indifference, inertia, individualism."[2] H. Royer-Collard came to similar conclusions. In 1841, Bichat, two years Napoleon's junior, would have been only seventy years old. Thus one normal life span could have covered the whole extraordinary, productive history of the School!

Wunderlich, a sympathetic foreign observer, also wrote in 1841: "The idea of physiological pathology originated in France, but the means and the proper understanding were lacking. Germany must develop them, must order and use its wealth, and a new epoch in medicine will open."[3] He stated retrospectively, in 1859, that the period 1815 to 1840 had been extremely brilliant in France; and that after 1840 outstanding publications, except those in psychiatry and neurology, had become rare, and French medicine had lived on its past glory.[4]

Hoefer in 1843 and Sédillot in 1846 felt that Germany was outdistancing France. A retrospective of the *Archives générales* for 1848 had no worthwhile acquisitions to report. Yet the admonitions of the few critics were laughed or sneered at; the reforms planned for 1848 never materialized.

In the 1850's, the signs of stagnation and decadence increased. The Anglo-Saxons ceased studying in Paris and began to go to Germany.[5] The Germans remained at home, while some French students went to Germany. The medical travel literature on Paris diminished. Wurtz, Pouchet, G. Tourdes, Bouchard,[6] Jaccoud (sent to Germany by Rayer in 1864), Lorain (1867), and Charcot (1867) became more and more alarmed. Said the latter in his first official classroom lecture: "For more than ten years this great intellectual movement has gone unnoticed in France. From time to time, some farseeing observer has tried to draw public attention to it. But we had to fight general indifference, and while everybody was active in Germany, we had other worries in France. Now the day has come when we understand that a great power has arisen beside us, and that from now on we must reckon with transrhenane science."[7] Again nothing was done, just as in politics. Only when, after the defeat of 1870, Pasteur[8] and Claude Bernard clearly blamed the disaster on a half-century of neglect of the sciences, the much-maligned Third Republic eventually instituted large-scale reforms and real improvements (real faculties of science, numerous laboratories, and the PCN—physics, chemistry, and natural sciences—examination for medical students, for example).

Laennec had clearly seen that the great problem ahead was to find the causes of disease.[9] Rilliet and Barthez had come to the same conclusion in the second edition of their *Traité des maladies des enfants* (Paris 1853). "For a great number of diseases, the local status daily becomes less and less important compared with the cause." But neither knew how to look for it. No wonder. According to the philosophy of the School, causes were unknowable. The only "legitimate" techniques—statistics, physical examination, and macroscopic pathological anatomy—did not yield the answer. It was to be found in pursuing those three activities which the majority of the founders of the School down to Trousseau had ostracized—experimental physiology, chemistry, and microscopy.[10] *French medicine had maneuvered itself into a dead end*, as all empiricisms had done so far in medical history.[11] Aversion to animal experimentation had even increased somewhat. In 1810, students had still witnessed experimental demonstrations.[12] Now even the physiology professor at the École, a certain Adelon, was opposed to animal experimentation.[13] We remember Trousseau's sermons against chemistry in medicine (see p. 11). As to microscopy, O. W. Holmes reports that, during his student days in Paris in the 1830's, he never even saw such an instrument, while J. Mueller, as a medical student in Bonn in 1820, received routine instruction in the use of the microscope.[14] It was no accident that French instruction in microscopy started at Strasbourg, the border university (Lereboullet 1839). In Paris, it had to wait until the mid-forties.

Now the "purely practical" approach of the French system, banishing research and its promoters from the schools and relying instead on "hospital staffs engaged in teaching" (Flexner), proved to be superbly impractical for progress. The defects of an establishment like the Napoleonic University, which was a university in name only and which did not have real faculties of science,[15] became glaringly visible. Since the structure of the schools faithfully reflected the prejudices of their founders, they were ideal instruments for the perpetuation of this situation. Those physicians, who somehow, somewhere, nevertheless did carry on research were punished by abominable working conditions. Fiaux described in 1877 [16] the miserable laboratories of Robin, Vulpian, and Béclard and the sufferings of Claude Bernard, Longet, and other researchers.

Pasteur wrote in his 1871 observations on French science, "Our laboratories are the graves of the scientists"; he reminded his readers of the fact that Dumas, Boussingault, and many others had had to pay for their own laboratories.[17] From Cabanis[18] to Trousseau,[19] the old lullaby that the physician was essentially an artist like the poet, sculptor, or musician had served as a screen for masking and excusing these unworthy conditions: thus the argument went, what did he need laboratories for?

French medicine paid for its practicalism, clinicism, and conservatism by losing its superiority to Germany. It would be incorrect to assume that the French did not know the progressive German work. Review journals and translations abounded. But the French were simply unable to assimilate foreign contributions. The provincialism of this generation was not a provincialism of ignorance, but a provincialism of conceit.

The most paradoxical and grotesque aspect of this situation was that France, which experienced a new understanding of the necessity of pure science and rapid advance in this direction after the peace of 1815, had very great scientists in precisely the three fields essential for medical progress, but the medical schools, that is, the almighty clinicians, ignored them. It would, by the way, have been surprising if France, which had just produced Lavoisier, Laplace, Lamarck, Jussieu, Cuvier, Gay-Lussac, and Arago, had not excelled in the "accessory" sciences too.[20]

Working in France during this period was the man who inaugurated modern experimental physiology, modern experimental pathology, and modern experimental pharmacology—François Magendie (1783–1855).[21] Magendie's stature was such that Lichtenthaeler, with good reason, sees him as the actual father of modern medicine (and the gravedigger of Hippo-cratism-Galenism).[22] Magendie's way was a long uphill climb. He "arrived" only at forty-seven, in the fateful year of 1830, when he became a professor at the Collège de France. He enjoyed the protection of Boyer, Berthollet, and Laplace. In general, he seems to have impressed scientists more than medical men, and foreigners (especially Germans and Americans) more than Frenchmen.[23] Wunderlich and Kratzmann wrote true panegyrics about him.[24]

French physicians (except Andral) took from him only the practical results of his drug experiments. He had a certain standing with them only because of his hospital position.[25] A typical example of the inability of the hospital physicians to assimilate experimental results was the fact that Ratier (like Billard) saw that his undernourished ward infants had the same corneal lesions as Magendie's undernourished dogs[26]—and then thought no more about it.

Yet Magendie was only one man in a brilliant galaxy of experimental physiologists, composed of his predecessors J. J. C. Legallois (1770–1814), Bichat, and Nysten, his rival P. Flourens (1794–1867), his pupil Claude Bernard (1813–1878), and men like E. R. A. Serres (1786–1868), J. L. Poiseuille (1799–1869), C. E. Brown-Séquard (1817–1894), and F. A. Longet (1811–1871). Experimental pathology had been explored before Magendie, for instance, by Portal in the 1780's. W. Edwards had experi-mented with light in 1824. Auzias-Turenne had inoculated monkeys with syphilis in 1845.[27]

The excellence of French biochemistry during this period is well known; the work of Fourcroy, Chevreuil, J. B. Dumas, and Vauquelin and his many pupils (for example, Bouchardat, Pelletier, Caventou, Robiquet, and Chevallier) comes easily to mind. A great many of these men were pharma-cists. A. Berman, drawing attention to the flourishing of hospital pharmacy during this period, has shown that the vacuum in biochemical research caused by the physician's absence of interest was partly filled through the excellent work of hospital pharmacists like A. Bouchardat (1806–1886), L. Mialhé (1807–1886), and J. J. Virey (1775–1846).[28] The chemist P. L. Dulong (1785–1838) and the physicist C. A. Despretz did important research on heat production in respiration. Through the work of Robiquet and Thillaye (1839), Boussingault (1836), Andral and Gavarret (1843), and Regnault and Reiset (1849), the foundation stones of modern metabolism and nutrition studies were laid.

That pharmacists could play such an important role was largely due to the excellence of the École de Pharmacie, founded in 1796 and taken over by the state in 1803. Berman has not only elucidated the medicoscientific role of the pharmacists of the period, in biochemistry, toxicology, and therapeutics, but has also described their close cooperation with medical men in the hygiene movement (for example, Chevallier, Labarraque, Parmentier,Gannal, Cadet de Gassicourt, Pelletier, and Bouchardat) and their aversion toward "theories." In 1818, Henry, Hallé, Leroux, and Richard published the *Pharmacopœa gallica*.

Another institution worthy of mention as a scientific medical center was the Veterinary School of Alfort, founded in 1766 by C. de Bourgelat (1712–1779), the friend of D'Alembert. Very valuable work, especially in the field of experimental pathology (inoculation of "putrid material"), was performed there before it was taken up in other places (Barthelémy and Dupuy 1816; Girard 1818; Renault 1833). Another expression of the high scientific status of these veterinarians was their presence in the Academy of Medicine and in the public health councils (for example, J. B. Huzard, 1755–1838). Eventually Alfort provided good working conditions for medical men who wanted to do experimental pathology; Vicq d'Azyr worked there, as Dupuytren (with Dupuy), Trousseau (with Dupuy and Leblanc), and Marey did later.

France possessed a whole phalanx of outstanding microscopists: R. J. Dutrochet (1776–1847), F. Raspail (1794–1878), A. Donné (1801–1878), F. Dujardin (1801–1860), Natalis Guillot (1804–1866), D. A. Lereboullet (1804–1865), J. J. Coste (1807–1873), and C. J. Davaine (1811–1882).[29] Milne-Edwards was greatly stimulated through the work of Dumas and Prévost in 1823 and felt it had rehabilitated microscopy.[30] The causes for microscopy's discredit were multiple; but it is my impression that it was handicapped far more through clinicians' prejudices (see p. 9) than through technical inadequacies,[31] the air of eighteenth-century dilettantism, or the prevalence of physiology.[32] Apparently the presence of excellent French microscopists was so little known or appreciated that, when the private teaching of microscopy eventually found a public, this teaching was primarily in the hands of two Austrians and one German immigrant: Mandl (first course in 1846), Gruby (first course in 1841; pupils included Magendie, Bernard, Flourens, and Milne-Edwards), and Lebert (first course in 1836; taught Verneuil, Follin, Robin, and Broca). Donné, starting private teaching of medical microscopy in the 1830's, was for a long time the only French representative of this discipline. Donné is still remembered for his early leukemia studies and the discovery of Trichomonas vaginalis.

The superb disdain in which French medicine held medical science was expressed quite simply and strongly by the fact that none of the following was ever a professor in a medical school: Bichat, Legallois, Magendie, Flourens, C. Bernard, Brown-Séquard, Longet, Poiseuille, Paul Bert, Marey, Chevreuil, Dutrochet, Raspail, Donné, Davaine, and Pasteur.

The School suffered from several structural deficiencies, which were not as fatal for its development as its "skeptical empiricism," yet were certainly not improving the situation. We have already mentioned the unjustifiable *permutation* system. Attacks by Bouillaud and by the famous surgeons Gerdy and Delpech in 1830–1831[33] remained just as unsuccessful as earlier and later attempts in this direction. Equally deleterious for the progress of medicine was the *cumul*, the habit of professors of simultaneously filling several chairs and jobs. In 1848 a society was even founded to combat this "institution."[34] In 1868, Pasteur asked in vain for its suppression. It is still flourishing to this day.

The value of the *concours* was quite debatable. It kept out people of the value of Bichat, Louis, and Maygrier. It lent itself to grave injustices—for instance, in the Broc case[35]—or to sinister machinations—as in the Bouillaud case.[36] Favoring mere eloquence, it was one more weapon against the sober scientist. It lasted all through our period, eventually being abolished in 1852. The last *concours* were those promoting Malgaigne (1850), Nélaton (1851), and Bouchut (1852).

A surprisingly frank speech by Sanson after an intern examination in 1825,[37] mentioning the intervention of "the man rich in titles, patients, and absolutism," indicates that here too things were far from being perfect. The continuous attacks on the free teachers (for example, the suppression of private amphitheaters) contributed to the increasing rigidity of the system. Eventually nepotism, another demoralizing and sterilizing influence, reached impressive proportions at the School. It was obvious and human that fathers would try to "place" their sons and sons-in-law, especially in a milieu like the surgical one, where craftsmen's traditions still survived. With the craftsmen, it was rather common that either the master's son followed his father or that the apprentice who married the master's daughter succeeded him. As long as only sons and sons-in-law of real talent were promoted, criticism was unjustified. Yet once the number of kinsmen became excessive, it was fairly certain that their quality would not always be above average. The following professors "placed" their sons during our period: Broussais, Boyer, Brogniart, Pinel, Royer-Collard, Falret, Voisin, Larrey, Guersent, Pelletan, Cruveilhier, and Cullerier (who also "placed" two sons-in-law). Nephews were Guéneau de Mussy (of Hallé), Hallé (of Lorry), and Cornac (of Portal). Sons-in-law were Andral (of Royer-Collard); Thouret (of Colombier, while Desgenettes was the brother-in-law of Thouret and O. Lesueur of Orfila); Adelon (of Sabatier, who had married the niece of Morand); Broca (of Lugol); Le Fort (of Malgaigne); and Blache (of Guersent). Vicq d'Azyr married the niece of Daubenton.

True records were achieved in the families of the surgeons Antoine Dubois and A. Boyer. Dubois "placed" his son Paul and his sons-in-law Béclard, Ferrus, Cadet de Gassicourt, and Richard. Three of Dubois' grandsons became professors too. The daughter of Professor Boyer married the future Professor P. Roux; Roux's daughter the future Professor Danyau; Danyau's daughter the future Professor Bucquoy; Bucquoy's daughter the future Professor Chauffard; Chauffard's daughter the future Professor Guillain; and Guillain's daughter the future Professor Garcin.

XI. THERAPEUTICS

No other aspect of the Paris School was attacked abroad as abundantly as its therapeutics.[1] Later, these criticisms were also taken up by some Frenchmen.[2] Eventually, certain French authors directed the same reproaches against the Germans which the latter had, in the period of their scientific impotence, addressed to their French neighbors.[3] The School was accused of a preponderant interest in diagnosis and pathology, of a too expectant, passive, and skeptical attitude toward therapy, of replacing drugs by a very strict diet, of neglecting general treatment in favor of local applications, and of not sufficiently individualizing treatment. Several foreign observers quoted the contemporary saying: "The British kill their patients; the French let them die."

It is undeniable that the School was more interested in pathological anatomy than in therapeutics (except anatomy-based surgery!). But it is equally undeniable that it was necessary to learn first what one was treating before considering how to treat it—all the more since critical analysis had recently revealed the ineffectiveness of most traditional methods of treatment. Rostan stated rightly that, in spite of the so-called neglect of therapeutics, mortality at the Hôtel Dieu was halved between 1789 and 1844. And he pointed out further that "the medicine of symptoms without knowledge of local diagnosis is absurd, perfectly impotent, and sometimes harmful and deadly."[4]

The criticisms concerning the absence of general treatment and of individualized therapeutics seem better founded. The localism of the Paris School did not favor general treatment. Likewise, its "ontology," its attempts to create definite disease units (typhoid fever, tuberculosis, diphtheria, etc.), its interest in the disease rather than in the diseased, and the "mass production" in the large hospitals were all factors detrimental to individualized treatment. They created, in contrast, a call for specific remedies and routine procedures.

There was, of course, never only one kind of therapeutic approach in the Paris School, and before coming to general conclusions, it seems desirable to review at least the main trends. The older generation around Pinel favored an "expectative" tendency, which was not entirely absent in pre-Revolutionary France (for example, Tronchin, Vitet, Voullonne, Desbois de Rochefort), though the majority of physicians practiced purging and bleeding as depicted in Molière's plays.[5]

Cabanis certainly strengthened empirical trends in therapeutics. He opposed the "vampirism"[6] represented by Bosquillon, professor of Greek at the Collège de France. But he himself suggested "copious bleedings"[7] and antimony[8] in fevers. His prescription of iron in chlorosis was carried on by Hallé and later by Blaud. Chaussier used only a few medicaments,[9] but he introduced the use of oxygen for the newborn. Portal generally waited five years before trying a new drug.

Most outspoken and most influential in this field was Pinel. He felt that therapeutics should undergo a general reform.[10] He showed a "feeling of extreme disgust"[11] toward polypharmacy. He gave examples of dangerous "heroic medication."[12] He quoted his pupil Bichat on contemporary materia medica—"a shapeless collection of formless ideas, childish observations, and deceptive means." He suggested, "Simplify materia medica to the utmost, reduce it to the use of a small number of indigenous plants of known effect and to simple chemical substances."[13] "Should one not deduce the true rules of treatment from the evolution and nature of symptoms, and modify them according to the accessory varieties of disease?"[14]

Pinel was undoubtedly a therapeutic skeptic; but, in theory, he could not completely decide between so-called rational and so-called empirical treatment. In practice, he solved his problem in an amazingly simple way, as perusal of his case histories shows—he did not treat at all. He was in favor of expectative medicine: "It would be a great project to discuss those diseases which get worse through thought—or methodless treatment or abuse of remedies, while one should have limited oneself to wise and measured expectation or, what is about the same, to the very cautious use of certain simple medicaments."[15] He firmly believed in the healing power of nature. "There are enough books in medicine praising medicaments. . . . It would be no less useful to make known the resources and the power of nature."[16]

Pinel opposed bleeding, purging, and specific remedies; he favored expectative surgery and opposed the use of cinchona even in malaria.[17] Even there, he preferred to let nature takes its course. In exchange, he energetically promoted psychotherapy (*traitement moral*), hygiene, and prevention, including inoculation and vaccination against smallpox.[18] Among Pinel's pupils, the one most interested in the field of therapeutics was Schwilgué, who published a treatise on materia medica in 1805. Well-known for his chemical analysis of urine, he praised chemistry "because it has eliminated many ineffective preparations and shown the defects of most pharmaceutical mixtures." He repeated the criticisms of materia medica leveled by Fourcroy, Pinel, and Bichat. He was the first to use the decimal system in pharmaceutics. His classification of medicaments was primarily a chemical one.

Pinel's most eminent pupil, Bichat, left in print only six pages on thera-peutics. They are found in the "General Considerations" of his *General Anatomy*. He criticized traditional therapeutics very strongly for having always followed the fashionable general medical theory. He tried to adapt therapeutics to his own general theories of "sensibility" and "contractility."

Bichat's interest and activities in therapeutics went far beyond this. His last unfinished course was one on materia medica. A student's notebook (that of L. N. Jusserandot) of 208 pages, which ends abruptly at the thirty-sixth lesson, is preserved in the Zurich Medical History Institute and gives us some information on the further evolution of Bichat's thought. He started his course with criticism: "The same drugs were successively used by humoralists and solidists. Theories changed, but the drugs remained the same. They were applied and acted in the same way, which proves that their action is independent of the opinion of doctors, and has to be studied only by observation." He saw the way out of this situation through a better knowl-edge of pathology. At that time, the same medicament was used for the same symptom and the same organ, even though the organ could be affected by different diseases demanding different remedies. On the other hand, different curative actions could have the same physiological effect.

He said, "The subdivisions of materia medica have often changed. They are bound to be insufficient . . . especially with drugs which act on the whole system. One ought to know the action of a medicament. Classification should be based on this knowledge, and not on whether the drug belongs to the animal, plant, or mineral kingdom, which is unimportant." He emphasized, "One ought to study the effect of a drug. If one does not know it, it is better to say nothing than to invent hypotheses."

Bichat now used a classification different from the one in the *General Anatomy*. He differentiated medicaments acting on the fluids from those ("the greatest number") acting on the solids. He studied general and local action, the latter having many varieties. In his Hôtel Dieu ward, he began to examine the effects of single drugs and medications: laudanum, ipecachuana, helleborus, ice, milk, and so on. But he was interrupted abruptly. We will never know what position eventually would have been Bichat's: the em-piricism of Laennec, the experimental pharmacology of Magendie, or the "rational therapy" of Broussais, based on insufficient physiological-patho-logical knowledge.

In 1804, Alibert published *Elements of Therapeutics*, a mixture of the "healing force of nature," "influencing the vital properties" à la Bichat, and lots of old and new rubbish. It was soon superseded by the very sensible therapy books of another Bichat admirer—J. B. Barbier d'Amiens (1776–1855), very popular with both students and practitioners. Barbier was one of the most radical defenders of the notion of the lesion: "The medicine of lesions is today the only one which my conscience allows me to practice. . . . I have experienced in adopting it a feeling of security, calm, and happiness I had not previously known."[19] But he realized that it was still quite early and would be quite difficult to write a pharmacology of lesions.[20]

It is certainly due to the Pinel tradition that Double attacked "British drug mania"[21] and L. Dufour polypharmacy,[22] that Guersent showed "great caution and wise distrust" in using medicaments[23] (his colleague Jadelot was more active), and that Fouquier's approach was expectative.[24]

This skepticism, directed particularly against the use of drugs, revived older and more comprehensive notions of therapeutics. Therapeutics had, up until this time, been more and more identified with materia medica. Now drugs again became, as with Hippocrates and Galen, only one weapon in the therapeutic armamentarium. This was reflected in the therapy definitions of the period. To Schwilgué, therapeutics had two large branches: hygiene and materia medica. For Barbier d'Amiens, there were three: hygiene, materia medica, and physical methods. G. L. Bayle even counted four such subdivisions, adding surgery to the above.[25] L. B. Guersent called thera- peutics a combination of physical and chemical agents (water, electricity); surgery; hygiene (subdivided into diet and "moral" treatment); and finally drugs.[26] Trousseau and Pidoux mentioned, for example, the necessity of adding rich food, gymnastics, and baths to iron medication;[27] they also de- bated between coffee, diuretics, and heat, and between opium, digitalis, and cold as medical agents.

The notion of hygiene had several meanings in the French medical litera- ture of the period. It sometimes indicated public hygiene, which we will discuss later; it was sometimes an equivalent for preventive measures; or, as in the above context, it usually stood for treatment by means other than drugs: diet, heat, cold, water, electricity, or psychotherapy. Therapeutic skepticism brought with it a new and intensive interest in prevention and the revival of long-neglected methods, such as open-air treatment, gymnastics, baths, magneto- and electrotherapy, and "moral" (psychological) treatment.[28]

The world of Pinelian pathology and therapeutics was shattered by the Broussaisian revolution of 1816. Fascinated by the streams of French blood that the medical Napoleon shed, historians have overlooked the fact that, in one respect, he remained faithful to his erstwhile master: he did not give any drugs. His bleeding orgies were continued by Bouillaud, who drained up to 3,000 cubic centimeters within six days, and Cruveilhier, who bled even in hematemesis.

While Pinel's attitude can be characterized as expectative skepticism and mild rationalism, and that of Broussais as extreme rationalism and activism, Corvisart and his school showed a very characteristic mixture of skepticism, empiricism, and episodes of activism. We have already described Corvisart's extreme skepticism. Laennec told his class how Corvisart had often said, "One does not disturb this condition." He nevertheless used much Kina (cinchona) and occasionally cauterized phthisis.[29]

G. L. Bayle's famous *General Idea of Therapeutics* ended with the skeptical sentence, "Therapeutics is thus by no means in all cases the art of curing diseases, but the art of treating them conveniently."[30] Of his seventeen "principles" of therapeutics,[31] several expressed disapproval of the use of medicaments (II, III, IV, XI). In exchange, five of them emphasized the healing power of nature (I, VI, VII, VIII, XII). Phthisis, the disease he studied most, was, in Bayle's view, "almost always incurable and deadly."[32] Still, on paper, he suggested a number of remedies, following the old saying of Celsus (3: Chapter X): "It is better to try a remedy of doubtful success than to wait for certain death." Yet in his own case (p. 478) the great skeptic did not use anything but fresh air and good food.

He was clearly an empiricist. "In considering all diseases, one would see that in most cases we do not know the rational, curative indication. . . . In several, one treats successfully with the specific or with the empiric method, which is about the same." "Pathology, cultivated in our days with such ardor, will keep away a lot of hypothetical indications and the hope of curing all diseases."[33] He clearly saw the "fashion" element in therapeutics: "Variations or nuances in the way of following the same indications depend on the century in which one lives, the country where one practices, or, let us dare to confess it, in large part on fashion. There is nothing which is not submitted to its whims, be it a most serious or a most frivolous matter."[34] His pupil Prost was a skeptic too.

We know from Laennec's *Treatise* that he was a skeptic. He eliminated bleeding, cantharides, blisters, the emollients, twenty-six other drugs, and gases as useless in the treatment of phthisis. All he used was the "artificial sea climate."[35] Of his 171 pages on phthisis, only sixteen deal with treatment. Many more examples of skepticism could be given from his course notes. "I gave Kina, blisters, and an emetic," he said. "After a while she recovered. I was honored as curing her." This skepticism goes, of course, with the belief in the *vis medicatrix naturae*. "I cured with all these methods. This disease is rarely incurable. Nature often pays all the expenses." "The curing of tuberculous phthisis is not above the forces of nature. But we must confess that the art does not yet possess a sure instrument to reach this goal." "Nature cures fevers better than art."[36]

We already know Laennec as an empiricist. It was in this sense that he adopted Rasori's antimony treatment, the magnet (the latter was also used by Pinel, Trousseau, Chomel, and Récamier), iodine, Kina, and citrus fruits. He kept statistics on his treatments: "The best method of evaluating a method of treatment is to judge it by its results."[37]

Skepticism was also quite pronounced among the eclectics, whose therapeutics more and more lacked a clear outline. Sachaile reports of Chomel, "His confidence in medicaments is by no means exaggerated,"[38] though Chomel still occasionally did prescribe viper, frog, and tortoise, substances which had disappeared from the Codex of 1818.[39] Wunderlich recommended him, Andral, Gendrin, and Magendie as teachers of therapeutics.[40] Louis' skepticism and radical empiricism are well known. His attack against bleeding in 1828 actually started the end of this 1,000-year-old method. It was hotly debated in the Academy in 1836. And Louis had only dared to ask for less bleeding! The only one to abolish bleeding entirely was Magendie. But his interns secretly continued it, feeling that they were not entitled to deprive the sick of this panacea![41] While Broussais bled his patients and Laennec gave tartarus stibiatus for typhoid fever, Louis gave fluids, ice on the head, and a few tonics. Bretonneau and Rostan proceeded in similar fashion.

Andral was little inclined to bleed the sick. He reversed the classic saying, "Better something doubtful than nothing," to read, "Better nothing than something doubtful." Yet he used a goodly number of drugs, especially purgatives and emetics. Piorry rightly characterized man's predilection for drugs as superstition: "Man is a passionate lover of superstitions. . . . He is quite willing to admit what he does not understand and to deny the evidence. Drugs please him. Hygiene, which is opposed to his habits, he finds repulsive." We already know Piorry as a protagonist of "common-sense therapeutics."

In 1836, Trousseau and Pidoux vigorously attacked the "habits of skepticism, in which the minds [of our colleagues] languish." But fortunately they too were expectative in tonsillitis, pneumonia, and erysipelas! They did not bleed in apoplexy or pneumonia. In the latter case, they gave antimony, though Trousseau loudly proclaimed his belief in the healing power of nature. He rightly thought the latter had been proven indirectly by the homeopaths. He proudly called himself an empiricist.[42] He is known as a protagonist of tracheotomy and paracentesis, typical local treatments, which he learned from his teacher Bretonneau. In the latter, it is interesting to observe the shift from 1818, when he treated diphtheria with general medication (mercurials), to 1827, when he applied local remedies—HCl, silver nitrate, and tracheotomy.

Under these circumstances, it must be said that Ratier faced a difficult task when, in 1827, he tried to give a summary of Paris therapeutics of the period.[43] He solved the problem rather well by saying:

> The physiological doctrine, more or less modified, is adopted almost everywhere, openly or in a modification easy to trace. Thus one shows great reserve in the use of tonics, stimulants, and other perturbing remedies. . . . Observation and reasoning have led the practitioners back to expectant medicine. One has some confidence in the preserving efforts of nature, and polypharmacy has often given way to the wisely combined use of hygienic agents. But one does not despise the resources of materia medica, and one tries through repeated experiments in hospitals and private practices to discover the properties of new substances and to verify those which the ancients have attributed to the medicaments which they have transmitted to us.

It seems undeniable that, in spite of occasional outbursts of activism, the most prominent and lasting trait in Paris therapeutics, the common denominator, was *therapeutic skepticism*. This was not identical with therapeutic nihilism, as developed in Vienna in the 1840's.[44] Radical remarks like Piedagnel's "the best treatment is the absence of treatment" or Andral's "all treatments fail, all treatments succeed"[45] are rare in Paris literature. They are more often found in the American pupils of the Paris school, for example, in Bartlett.[46] O. W. Holmes was the author of this famous saying: "I firmly believe that if the whole materia medica, as now used, could be sunk to the bottom of the sea, it would be all the better for mankind—and all the worse for the fishes."[47]

Skepticism does not advocate the abolition of all drugs, but its critical attitude certainly brings about the elimination of numerous drugs and procedures which have been proven to be ineffective or detrimental. It is grounded in belief in the healing power of nature, and it tends toward empiricism. But it is in the nature of medicine's periodic skeptical reform movements in therapeutics that they cannot last; they come to a dead end. This fate also befell Paris skepticism. Nevertheless, this fact should not blind us to its merits. Abolishing deleterious therapeutic procedures requires a lot of courage and intelligence and is almost as important as inventing new remedies.[48] It was in this direction that Paris medicine influenced European medicine. Yet it went one step farther.

The Parisian skeptics would perhaps also have ended in nihilism if a number of chemical discoveries and their applications in medicine had not evoked new interest and confidence in drug treatment. In this context, a new era of therapeutics, dominated by the newly created experimental pharmacology, began; in this movement, the old opposition between "rational" and "empirical" treatment disappeared.

Foremost among these chemical discoveries were those of the alkaloids, due mostly to the work of the Parisian pharmacist J. Pelletier and his collaborators. Morphine had been discovered by Sertuerner in 1804. In 1817 (with Magendie), Pelletier discovered emetine; in 1818 (with Caventou), strychnine; in 1819 (with Caventou), brucine and veratrine; in 1820 (with Caventou), colchicine and quinine. Robiquet found caffeine in 1821 and codeine in 1832.[49] The halogens too were discovered during these years. Now, for the first time in history, the clinician and the physiologist had at their disposal a number of chemically pure substances of known composition, which allowed true quantitative experiments. This had been impossible with the old extracts and raw substances, which varied tremendously as to concentration of the effective principle.

Paradoxically enough, the introduction of these new drugs into the clinic, the resulting renaissance of drug treatment, and the creation of a new science, experimental pharmacology, are all due to the most skeptical of Paris skeptics,[50] François Magendie! His *Formulary for the Preparation and Application of Several New Medicaments*, appearing in 1821, saw one edition after another. Though others followed Magendie rapidly, (Barbier, second edition of his *Treatise on Materia Medica*; Julia Fontenelle, AG 1824, 4:152), his *Formulary* remained the basic document of the new trend.

In his preface, Magendie stated that his work had been made possible by the preparation of chemically pure substances and by his having overcome the age-old prejudice that drugs and poisons acted differently in man and animal. He started his discussion with strychnine, of which he was, not incidentally, the codiscoverer. As far back as 1809, he had demonstrated the influence of nux vomica on the spinal cord. Here, as in all other cases, he proceeded in the following order: preparation of the substance from raw materials, physical and chemical properties, effect on the animal, effect on the healthy and diseased human, indications, and application (prescriptions for pills, tinctures, and the different salts of the substance). In this way, he also discussed brucine, morphine, narcotine, narceine, meconine, and codeine;

likewise, emetine, veratrine, and the alkaloids of the Peruvian bark: quinine and cinchonine.

It was he who, together with Double, Villermé, and Chomel, introduced the latter into everyday practice against strong resistance. His doses were less excessive than those of Louis, Andral, Bally, Trousseau, and Maillot.[51] He also resisted the temptation to use it as a panacea.[52] In 1817, Magendie did not hesitate to prescribe Prussic acid as a cough medicine, though he warned against overdoses.

Iodine, discovered by Courtois in 1811, had been introduced by Coindet as antigoiter drug. Here Magendie fell for the panacea trend,[53] recommending iodine as antisyphilitic, antiscrofulous, antituberculous, anticancerous, and antiepileptic. He also found other properties of the substance: "In using it in amenorrhea in an unmarried young lady whom I had no right to suspect, an abortion occurred after three weeks." Magendie regarded bromine (Balard 1826) as an equivalent of iodine. Chlorine (Scheele 1774) was used for disinfection, fetid wounds, and in pulmonary disease.

He examined solanine, delphinine, gentianine, and lupulin through animal experiments but found no clinical use for them. He found that oil of croton was a drastic; given intravenously to animals, it killed. Intravenous urea was a diuretic (Segalas). Intravenous medication had been used long before Magendie[54]—Percy and Laurent had given opium intravenously for tetanus in 1797—yet Magendie's intravenous treatment of rabies drew particular attention to the method.[55]

With François, he regarded thridax (lettuce juice) as a sedative which reduced pulse and temperature. Gold salts, used in syphilis and scrofula, were found very toxic by Orfila in animal experiments. While Magendie regarded grenadine and fern as good anthelmintics, he was skeptical as to others' miraculous results with phosphates; but he foresaw a great future for their therapeutic use after Couerbe found phosphates in the brain.

Sodium and potassium carbonate were given for hyperacidity on Darcet's recommendation. The digitaline of the Geneva apothecary Auguste Leroy needed closer scrutiny. It was due to French skepticism that France was the one European country in which digitalis was not misused extensively as a panacea during our period.[56] For fever, Magendie frequently used salicine, not an alkaloid. For dyspepsia, he gave lactic acid.

These were the new remedies which, in Paris, now were added to or replaced the old traditional plant and mineral products. Magendie's pharmacological research was continued by Claude Bernard.

For a while, two traditional Chinese remedies—acupuncture and moxa—

became very fashionable. The latter, a form of cauterization, was, according to Casper, recommended by Roux, Larrey, and Percy for Pott's disease, rickets, tuberculosis, and cancer. In the 1820's acupuncture was widely used, especially through the energetic propaganda of Jules Cloquet, whose attention had been called to this technique by his friend Bretonneau. Other promoters were Berlioz *père*, Béclard, Haim de Tours, Pelletan the younger, Morand, Sarlandière, Dantec, and Fabré Palaprat.[57]

In spite of earlier academic condemnations, the question of "animal magnetism" never came to a rest. "Magnetic" treatments obtained results, and several surgeons (e.g., Georget, Jules Cloquet, Oudet) operated successfully on hypnotized patients. In 1825, the Academy of Medicine formed a commission, but its report of 1831 was never published. A second commission was formed in 1831, and it came to negative conclusions in 1837.[58]

Psychotherapy was by no means used only in this disguised fashion. Voullonne had asked for large-scale "moral treatment" as early as 1776.[59] It was typical that an ordinary Paris medical thesis of 1821 (F. Berthier: *Considérations physiologiques et médicales sur le plaisir*) quoted Hippocrates, Chaussier, Richerand, Cabanis, Corvisart, and Pinel on such treatments and reported their success with malaria, scurvy, "mesenteric atrophy," and wounds.[60]

XII. SURGERY

The great contribution which surgery made to the evolution of Paris medicine has already been examined. It remains to be seen what its own specific characteristics were during this period and what it accomplished as a branch of therapeutics. Unlike eighteenth-century Paris internal medicine, its surgery and its Academy had been world famous.[1] Even they had eventually shown signs of decline, but it was obvious that surgery neither needed nor experienced a revolution comparable to the one transforming medicine. It could afford to continue a tradition, to be more conservative. No man in internal medicine would have written the famous sentence with which Baron A. Boyer (1757–1833), the Charité surgeon, friend of Cabanis, and pupil of Desault, started his classic treatise on surgical diseases in 1814: "Surgery has made the greatest progress in our time and seems to have reached, or almost reached, the highest degree of perfection, which it seems able to attain" (1:1).

P. J. Desault (1744–1795) himself, the last great surgeon of the old school and the first great surgeon of the new, must be called conservative. His most radical innovation was the introduction of clinical teaching. His much vaunted work in topographical anatomy was nothing completely new. It was brilliantly expanded by Roux, Béclard, and Velpeau. Paris surgeons of this period dissected with unique intensity. Lisfranc, for example, used about 1,000 cadavers per year in his operation course.[2] Lisfranc is still remembered for the partial amputation of the foot, an operation originally devised by Villermé.

Most of Desault's problems were traditional ones, for example, amputation. He resorted to it as rarely as possible. Here the parallel with the skeptic, expectant attitude of Pinel or Corvisart in internal medicine is obvious. The treatment of fractures, another forte of Desault, and lithotomy, and ligation of arterial aneurysm were old surgical themes too. Desault avoided trepanations as well as amputations, reduced the number of drugs, and treated aneurysms through compression rather than operation. Both his pupil Bichat[3] and C. Daremberg[4] emphasize his conservatism. His competitor Sabatier was even more conservative.

His expectant attitude would have been even more prevalent if France had not been engaged in war without interruption during the first twenty years of the school. This situation strengthened surgery and the influence of military surgeons within surgery. Military surgery had, in any case, been highly developed in France since Henri IV. Circumstances forced military surgeons to give up the innumerable wound ointments used in private practice and to replace them with water (for example, Percy, 1785). University surgeons recommended water in wound treatment much later (Bérard Jeune and Josse, 1835). The same primitive battle environment suggested to French military surgeons a drastic and beneficial reduction in the number of instruments and dressings used. Ammon was surprised in 1823 by the contrast with Germany in this respect.[5] Army surgeons were also reserved in the question of *débridement*. It was typical that A. L. Willaume (1722–1863), Percy's favorite, published a thesis on expectation in surgery in 1805.

But there was one condition in which military surgeons had to act immediately: wounds necessitating amputation. They obtained hemostasis through ligation, and most of the time sutured the wound immediately, counting on healing *per primam intentionem*.

This widespread belief among the military in *per primam* healing probably facilitated Roux's introduction of the technique into civilian practice after his famous trip to England in 1814. Dupuytren, Dubois, Richerand, and Maunoir approved of it, while Pelletan, Boyer, and Larrey remained opposed.[6]

Of the French military surgeons, the two greatest were P. F. Percy (1754–1825), a disciple of A. Louis and a man of superior intelligence, and the valiant J. D. Larrey (1766–1842). Their most valuable contribution was the invention of mobile ambulances. Larrey participated in twenty-five campaigns, sixty battles, and four hundred skirmishes. At Borodino, he supposedly did 200 amputations within twenty-four hours. He excelled in peacetime too, for instance, in rhinoplasty. A particular kind of "military" surgical experience was provided by the street fighting of the period, for example, that of July, 1830, about which Dupuytren, Roux, Jobert de Lamballe, Larrey, and others later published their experiences.[7]

In spite of these military influences, French surgery remained relatively conservative, even with Baron G. Dupuytren (1777–1835), the dictator of French surgery from 1815 to 1835. This becomes quite evident when he is compared with the simultaneous "Napoleon" of internal medicine, F. V. Broussais. The latter's regrettable influence on Dupuytren was responsible for his extensive use of leeches,[8] cataplasms, and starvation diets among the wounded. Dupuytren's treatments for hernia, hydrocele, cataract, fistulas, bladder stones, and aneurysms were developments of traditional themes. Air embolism during operations had been observed before him, by Beauchêne in 1818, and was cleared up by others.[9] The description of contracture which bears his name was not an achievement of the first order. But he also, as we will see, made some important new contributions. Paris surgery, in spite of its traditionalist limitations, was creative too.

Dupuytren did not publish much, but he was beyond any doubt the greatest French surgeon of his time. The testimony of Rochas, Wunderlich,[10] and von Walther[11] is sufficient guarantee for this evaluation. Dupuytren symbolized the great progress in teaching and practice which surgery experienced after 1815, after the return of peace. Dupuytren was a profound scientist, as honest Pagenstecher correctly observed in 1820.[12] Before turning to surgery, he had excelled as an anatomist, a pathological anatomist, an experimental physiologist, a biochemist, and a hygienist.

While questions of personal character are usually of minor importance in a figure of this stature, it seems nevertheless necessary to examine briefly whether and to what extent Dupuytren deserved Percy's bitter characterization: "the first of surgeons, the last of men."

The insults of jealous competitors like Richerand, Dubois, and Lisfranc, all themselves lacking candor, are irrelevant; but even the facts reported by his own panegyrist Delhoume or by an impartial traveler like Otto[13] are rather damning. On the other hand, J. S. Frank, impressed himself, reported Dupuytren's tremendous effect on patients, to whom he said coldly, "I will cure you."[14] The fairest judgment is perhaps the Paris saying reported by Pagenstecher—"a fine surgeon, but hard like a horse"— or that of Casper: "a genius, but of unprecedented unkindness and coldness."[15] And there must have been, in spite of all that rudeness, something humane in him; Véron,[16] Poumiès,[17] Balzac,[18] and Sainte-Beuve, once his *externe*, experienced it and reported it with much enthusiasm. Nor was his idea of educating the surgeon through animal surgery that of an insensitive man. His ex-disciple Lisfranc, who had once publicly called him "the highway robber from the Hôtel Dieu," described, in a memorable conversation with Malgaigne on October 30, 1839,[19] how the penniless boy had turned into a ruthless man through suffering on his long way up: prosector (at eighteen!) in 1795, assistant surgeon of the Hôtel Dieu by 1802, professor by 1812, and chief surgeon of the Hôtel Dieu by 1815. Pelletan, whom he squeezed out so brutally on this occasion, must after all have been a rather worthless individual.[20] Unlike his favorite disciple Sanson, who died so poor that funds had to be collected for his burial, Dupuytren left four million francs when he died in 1835. This is not too surprising, if one remembers that Boyer obtained, for one single operation on Marshal Suchet at Valencia, four thousand francs from the patient and forty thousand from Napoleon.[21]

The greatest accomplishments of the Paris School in the field of surgery were, beyond any doubt, the generalization of clinical instruction; the reunification of medicine and surgery in the *écoles de santé* in 1794; and the conservation of this unity in spite of reactionary attacks after 1815. How beneficial and necessary this reform was is evident from the fact that Maygrier's *Annuaire* of 1810 still lists no less than eight categories of surgeons! Lassus, one of the first professors of the Paris École de Santé, symbolized this new situation by calling his surgery text of 1794 *Médecine opératoire*, and R. B. Sabatier (1732–1811), J. Lisfranc (1790–1847), A. Velpeau (1795–1867), and J. F. Malgaigne (1806–1865) later did the same with theirs. Nowhere have internal medicine and surgery ever been so closely united as in France in the first part of the nineteenth century. It is significant that internists like Récamier, Billard, and Ollivier contributed to surgery and that surgeons like Velpeau (a favorite of American students), Dupuytren, Menière, Lallemand, Lisfranc, and Jobert made valuable contributions to internal medicine.

Surgery became the very active discipline that we know today only during the second half of the nineteenth century. Before that, it was primarily the art of treating wounds. Sigerist has shown that, in addition to the discoveries of anesthesia and asepsis, the new localist pathology of the solid organs, as developed by the Paris School,[22] was decisive in this change. This activation of surgery on the basis of localistic pathology even before the introduction of anesthesia and asepsis was quite pronounced in the Paris surgery of our period. Surgeons had been quite influential in the elaboration of the localistic point of view in medicine; now the localistic theories served as a powerful stimulus for an activation of surgery, a development opposed by traditionalists.[23] This was the second great surgical innovation brought about by the Paris School.

On the first page of his *Nouveaux éléments de médecine opératoire* (1832), Velpeau enumerates those operations invented since Sabatier, that is, since the birth of the new school. His catalogue corresponds in all essential points to one composed at about the same time by Monfalcon[24] and the one by Pariset.[25] Laennec[26] and Peisse[27] had noted before, with some bitterness, that progress in surgery was much less disputed than that in medicine. Velpeau mentions the plastic operations (rhino-, chilo-, blepharo-, oto-, and bronchoplasty, and staphylorrhaphy); torsion of arteries; lithotrity; hysterectomy and ovariectomy; extirpation of the anus; and resectioning of bones and joints.

From today's vantage point, Velpeau's list still seems correct. We would perhaps prefer to start our discussion with resections. Priority in this field belongs to Charles White of Manchester (1768). Yet the simple country surgeon who inaugurated this technique in France in 1782, Moreau (even his first name is unknown) of Bar-sur-Ornain, was certainly not familiar with White's work. After an accidental meeting between Percy and Moreau in 1792, the technique spread rapidly. The mandibular resection, undertaken by Dupuytren in 1812, is regarded as his finest innovation. In the field of operations for aneurysm, he and Roux were only epigoni of the British.

Most consequential were, of course, those new operations which foreshadowed abdominal surgery, like Lisfranc's extirpation of a cancerous rectum (1830), the creation of an artificial preternatural anus by Amussat (1839), and the gastrotomy of Sédillot (1846). In 1828, Dupuytren invented the enterotome for treating spontaneous preternatural anus. Jobert de Lamballe (1824) and Lembert (1826) greatly improved the technique of intestinal suture.

Bérard operated a meningioma in 1833.[28] Roux performed a thyroid operation in 1836, but did not follow it up. In the field of surgery of the uterus —Dechambre's Dictionary still felt in 1876 (16:434) that it would disappear again—Lisfranc had made cervix amputation a routine procedure after 1825. He was, by the way, accused of manipulating his results in this field. The same accusation was leveled against Larrey, Dupuytren, and J. Guérin.[29] Récamier removed the whole uterus in 1825.[30] P. C. Huguier (1804–1873) became almost a specialist in uterine surgery.

Paris obstetrics were, by the way, so mediocre during this period that a discussion seems superfluous. Debate on puerperal fever produced no results, since anticontagionist theories (for example, those of Cruveilhier) dominated this field too.

Béclard introduced the bilateral method into bladder surgery in 1813, and Sanson the rectovesical in 1817. Far more significant after 1820 was the invention of a *bloodless* method of removing the stone by Civiale, Leroy d'Etiolles, Amussat, and Heurteloup; this discovery signaled the emergence of urology as a specialty (see below).

Velpeau was particularly impressed by the autoplasties, a field in which Roux (staphylorrhaphy of 1816) was leading. We tend today to admire the subcutaneous sections of tendons and muscles by Delpech (Achilles tendon, 1816) and Dupuytren (sternocleidomastoid) even more. These were the beginnings of the new orthopedics about which we will report more in what follows. It is significant that, in this branch, gymnastics were cultivated even more vigorously than operative procedures (see Pravaz, Lachaise, Delpech, and Amoros). Fracture treatments were improved.[31] Neither preparatory nor postoperative treatments were unknown, though the latter were supposedly bad.[32]

The influence of surgery on internal medicine was reflected in the adoption of tracheotomy in diphtheria by Bretonneau and his school and in the operation of empyema by Récamier and Fleury. The treatment of hydrocele by iodine injections (Velpeau 1835) was another expression of the bloodless tendencies of the Paris School.

These tendencies increased very strongly after twenty years of activism. Even Lisfranc, once the most aggressive surgeon of the school, preached the utmost moderation in his *Précis de médecine opératoire* (*Compendium of Operative Medicine*) of 1843. Velpeau and Magendie attacked frequent amputations in 1848.[33] The reason was obvious: without antisepsis and anesthesia, the new active surgery proved to be murderous. Shock and infection transformed technically successful operations into saddening defeats. Phlebitis raised its ugly head everywhere. (See, for example, the studies of Dance in 1826, Maréchal recte Schmidt in 1828, and of Sédillot in 1832; it was no accident that Sédillot was one of Pasteur's first partisans.) Malgaigne's 1841 mortality statistics on major operations in Paris hospitals are frightening (see AG 1842, 3:13). Of twenty-one patients undergoing uterus extirpations in 1832, twenty-one died during or immediately after the operation.[34] Even discoveries in surgical pathology, like that of appendicitis (Louyer-Villermay 1826; Mélier 1827; Menière 1828), were practically worthless under these circumstances.

The two great necessary innovations, asepsis and anesthesia, were neither found nor even systematically looked for in Paris. Jules Cloquet (1790–1883), the brilliant anatomist, hernia surgeon, instrument inventor and a close friend of the Flauberts, Bretonneau, and Larrey's son, attracted much attention with his breast amputation under hypnosis in 1829 and became professor in 1834. But that was all that ever came of it.

Wound treatment with Eau de Javel (Cullerier), skin prophylaxis with silver nitrate (Chassaignac), bandaging with absorbent cotton (Mayor, A. Guérin), and subcutaneous operations were gropings toward antisepsis or asepsis, but they were badly lacking in clarity and direction. The same Chassaignac (1804–1879) who introduced drainage made things even worse by inventing his *écraseur*, a horrible contraption which used sharp chains to squeeze off organs, on the theory that only knife wounds would become infected. The result of this form of "surgery" was even more serious infection. In order to discover anesthesia or asepsis, an interest in chemistry and microscopy was necessary. Paris surgeons lacked it just as much as their internist colleagues did. Only Malgaigne, a professor in 1850, began to experiment, and only his students Broca and Follin used the microscope.

French surgery during the first half of the nineteenth century was brilliant and famous. Surgeons from all over the world were its disciples. But while it accomplished much, French surgery did not create a new epoch as its sister, internal medicine, did. This was not surprising. Surgery could decisively stimulate the thought of men like Pinel, Bichat, Broussais, or Laennec. But being a therapeutic technique, surgery could not create a new medical theory. Even as a technique, it was not free from contradictions—on the one hand, it was skeptic-expectant like the rest of therapeutics and even more conserva-tive, and on the other, it showed, due to war conditions and the new localism, outbursts of activism, which were present in internal medicine as well. Surgery did not produce an innovator like Magendie. Nevertheless, Roux was probably right[35] in claiming that the years 1800 to 1830 were the most brilliant period in French surgery.

XIII.

XIII. HYGIENE Though it has been overlooked by most historians of medicine and hygiene, France was, during the first half of the nineteenth century the international leader in hygiene, that is, in individual and communal prevention,[1] as well as in clinical medicine. While the great rise of hygiene during the eighteenth-century Enlightenment[2] lost considerable momentum in Great Britain and Germany during the first decade of the succeeding century, the opposite movement was noticeable in France. The impressive French literary output in this field during our period, which I surveyed for the first time in 1948, and the admiration of such competent observers as the Germans Kopp, Virchow, and Casper, the British Alison and David Johnston, and the Americans Dunglison and Stephen Smith[3] for French hygienic institutions emphasize this point. It was from France that O. W. Holmes brought home ideas like the following: "The bills of mortality are more adversely affected by drainage than by this or that method of practice."[4]

The French movement had its roots in the Enlightenment and its *idéologue* continuators, who were the legislators of 1800. Cabanis again had a great formative influence. It was no accident that hygiene was taught in the revolutionary *écoles centrales*. The large number of military or ex-military medical men active as hygienists points toward another, later source of this movement: the long Napoleonic wars, during which experience taught intelligent participants the value of and need for prevention. The Industrial Revolution, furthered in France through Napoleonic policies, made public health objectively more necessary than ever before and produced, subjectively, a strong socialist trend in the Restoration intelligentsia. Many doctors were followers of Saint-Simon. The cholera epidemic of 1832 certainly served as a stimulus and produced a large literature, but it cannot be regarded as a major causative factor, since the movement was by then well under way. The medicine of the period was bound to further hygiene not only through its general excellence, but, as Baas has pointed out, because distrust of and disappointment in therapeutics produced a heightened interest in prevention.[5] Claude Bernard felt that hygiene was the only form of therapeutics to be logically derived from the so-called medicine of observation.[6] It seems significant that such a confirmed clinician as Louis preached a "crusade" against tuberculosis and "progress through association" (Preface 1835).

A chair of hygiene existed in the new École de Santé from the beginning. Its first occupant was Jean Noel Hallé (1754–1822), known as the scion of a

149

family of painters, a former member of the Société Royale, and a courageous defender of Lavoisier. He also became a professor at the Collège de France and a member of the Academy of Sciences. He started his numerous detailed hygienic observations in 1785 with a memoir on the poisonous gases emanating from latrines. In 1802, he published an interesting study on the high incidence of anemia among coal miners. His course was apparently somewhat amorphous, judging from the outline of it published in 1806, which reappeared in the *Dictionnaire des sciences médicales* in 1818. He was one of the early promoters of vaccination.[7]

The teaching period of Hallé's successors Bertin and Andral was too short to leave any traces. The liberal Baron R. N. D. Desgenettes (1762–1837), who held the chair from 1830 to 1837, enjoyed great popularity. Desgenettes, in his youth a friend of the Girondists, became famous as the chief physician of Napoleon's Egyptian army, and later as inspector general of all military medicine under Napoleon. His writings, among them his famous memoirs, deal mainly with military medicine. Together with N. Dally (1792–1862), he became the great promoter of gymnastics. He was succeeded by Hippolyte Royer-Collard (1802–1850), a somewhat erratic man who did interesting studies on cells, nutrition and body size, and alcoholism, but who, in spite of great brilliance,[8] never achieved much and died early from locomotor ataxia. Hygiene was taught at the Athénée by the *idéologue* Jacques-Louis Moreau de la Sarthe (1771–1826), librarian and professor of the history of medicine at the Faculty.[9] The outline of his course (1797) introduced the new "physiological" classification of the subject matter, later imitated by others.

Perhaps the greatest of the hygienists of this generation was François Emanuel Fodéré (1764–1835), an admirable personality and professor of legal medicine at Strasbourg from 1814 to 1835. Fodéré earned early fame through his book on goiter (1790), his *Treatise on Legal Medicine and Public Health* (1798), and a number of epidemiological, psychiatric, and statistical studies. Particularly important for our field were his *Lessons on Epidemics and Public Hygiene* (1822) and his *Historical and Moral Essay on the Poverty of Nations* (1825).

Of the numerous general treatises on hygiene published during our period, we have just mentioned a few—those of Hallé, Moreau, and Fodéré. The most widely read for many years was the *Elementary Course* of the clinician L. Rostan (1822). The treatises of the Broussaisian C. Londe (1827), of the hospital pharmacist J. J. Virey (1775–1846) in 1828, and of Philippe Buchez (1796–1865) and Ulysse Trélat in 1825 were also important. Buchez, who successively was a Carbonaro, Saint-Simonian, leftist Catholic philosopher, and historian, influenced a number of men who worked in the field of hygiene (L. Cérise, L. Simon, J. P. Tessier, etc.). The meritorious chemist and hy-gienist J. B. A. Chevalier (1793–1879) published his *Public Hygiene* in 1836. For the 1840's we should at least name Motard's *Treatise* of 1842 and Michel Lévy's famous book of 1843. The much higher quality of the treatises in the 1840's, as compared with those of the 1820's, shows the cumulative and progressive nature of the movement. It might also be partly explained by the fact that certain shortcomings, described by A. Bouchardat[10] in the following quotation, were more and more avoided: "If at the beginning of this century we tried to incorporate everything into hygiene, we must today leave out a great number of either superfluous or nonprovable details. . . . Before the new era into which hygiene has entered now, all authors tried to enlarge its frame. We tried to take an inventory of all human knowl-edge in its relation to hygiene. The program was endless, formed by an assemblage of shreds borrowed from all sciences, especially physics, the teaching of which was for a long time mixed with that of hygiene."

Nothing would be further from the truth than the assumption that the French hygiene of our period was primarily a literary or academic subject. It had a great number of practical realizations and institutional innovations to its credit. They began with the laws for the health protection of children and expectant mothers, and for antimalarial drainage in 1795. In 1802, the famous *Conseil de Salubrité*, composed of Cadet de Gassicourt,[11] Thouret, Parmentier, Deyeux, and Huzard, was created for Paris. It dealt with, among other things, the following problems: prevention of epidemics, disposal of dead animals, and control of burials, sewerage, prisons, factories, and hos-pitals.[12] Other health councils were created in Marseille in 1825; in Lille and Nantes in 1828; in Troyes in 1830; and in Rouen, Bordeaux, Toulouse, and Versailles in 1831. Paris was famous for its public bathtubs, which increased from 200 in 1789 and 500 in 1816 to over 4,000 in 1839. In 1822, the Hôpital St. Louis dispensed 128,000 baths.[13] in 1810, labor legislation was inaugurated. In 1822, 120 voluntary health-insurance societies existed. The founding of the Academy of Medicine in 1820 had, to a large extent, public-health goals. In 1822, Labarraque introduced Eau de Javel as an important disinfectant. A. Pastoret opened the first *crèche* in 1825, and F. Marbeau began day nurseries in 1844. In 1833, medical inspection of schools was started, and in 1834, the manufacturer Koechlin initiated better housing for his labor force. In 1841, a law against child labor was created, and in 1843 one for safety with steam engines. In 1848, a national Hygiene Council was instituted. Théophile Roussel (1816–1903), a physician and legislator still remembered for his 1879 law for the protection of infants and famous for his research on pellagra and occupational phosphorus poisoning, began his legis-lative activities in 1849. Rameaux was able to point in 1839 to great progress in child hygiene; vaccination; public baths; prison, military, and naval hygiene; sanitary police; and the fight against alcoholism.

An event of great importance was the founding of the incomparable *Annales d'hygiene publique et médecine légale* in 1829. Listed as editors were: Adelon, Andral, Barruel, D'Arcet, Devergie, Esquirol, Kéraudren, Leuret, Marc, Orfila, Parent-Duchatelet, and Villermé. Of the two latter men, more will be said later on. Esquirol's presence in this list reflected his deep interest in hygiene. The great psychiatrist died in December, 1840, of the aftereffects of exposure sustained when going to preside over the Comité de Salubrité. The introduction to the journal's first issue was written by C. C. Marc (1771–1841), a disciple of J. P. Frank and later personal physician of King Louis Philippe.

A great number of problems were tackled during these decades. We can only list them here with the names of a few who made outstanding contribu-tions (for bibliographic details, see my 1947 paper in the *Bulletin of the History of Medicine*).

Vaccination: Husson, Fiard, Bousquet, C. E. Gaultier de Claubry, Marc.

Big-city problems: (sewerage, housing, water, etc.): Bourgeois, Bujeon, D'Arcet, Lachaise, Monfalcon and Polinière, Parent-Duchatelet, Peclet, Piorry, Sainte-Marie.

Rural hygiene: Beaunier, Bon, Bottex, Chambeyron, Chevallier, Demangeon, Hodel, Jolly, Loubeyre.

Hygiene in Algeria: Herrman, Perier, Fix, Boudin.

Dangerous trades, industrial poisons, and factory hygiene: Benoiston de Châteauneuf, Cadet de Gassicourt, Chevallier, Chevreuil, Combes, Follet, Gosse, Grisolle, Guépin, Lombard, Mélier, Pigeotte, Roussel, Saucerotte, Sédillot, Tanquerel de Planche, Villermé. It seems signi-ficant that twelve memoirs were submitted for the Academy's prize medal in this field in 1837.

Naval and military hygiene: Kéraudren, Boudin, Forget, Bégin.

Prisons: A. L. Gosse, Colombot, Villermé, Raspail.

Gymnastics: Desgenettes, Amoros, Friedlaender, Londe, Lachaise, Delpech, Pravaz, Foissac, Dally.

Child hygiene: There were more than twenty theses on the subject be-tween 1815 and 1848.

Water: Grimaud de Caux, Scoutetten.

Life preservation: Marc.

Of particular importance were the first-rate statistical studies which formed the backbone of hygienic science at this developmental stage. L. F.

Benoiston de Châteauneuf (1776–1856), an ex-army doctor, published his first memoir in this field in 1820. F. Melier (1789–1866), one of the rare contagionists, became inspector general of sanitary services in 1850, founded the international sanitary congresses, and left valuable statistical studies on tobacco factories, grain prices, swamps, and other topics.

The two most important figures of the hygiene movement after 1820, A. J. B. Parent-Duchatelet (1790–1836) and Louis René Villermé (1782–1863), were also statisticians. Parent-Duchatelet, too timid for teaching or practice, was directed toward hygiene by Hallé. Between 1820 and his early death, he examined, mostly for the Academy or the Conseil de Salubrité, some twenty problems, most of them somehow connected with sewerage (the *cloaques* of Paris, the Bievre river, the disposal of dead horses, and the sanitation of dissection rooms, old-people's homes, tobacco factories, etc.).

His friends, among whom were Leuret, Louis, Andral and Chomel, published a collection of his memoirs after his death under the title *Hygiène publique*. The memoirs were preceded by an excellent biographical essay. His best-known study, also published posthumously, was *Prostitution in Paris*. His work was impressive in its practicability, its striving for exactness, its absolute lack of oratory, and its unwillingness to take anything for granted.

Louis René Villermé (1782–1863) had been a military surgeon on European battlefields for ten years when he published his Dupuytren-inspired thesis on "false membranes" in 1814 and then an account of the technique for partial amputation of the foot, later named after Lisfranc, in 1815. He had done experiments on pseudarthrosis and membranes of fistulas for Breschet and had experimented with quinine and potassium cyanide, when, disappointed with medical practice, he turned to hygiene and statistics in 1818. Through his forty years of friendship with Quetelet,[14] he became one of the central figures of modern statistics. In 1823, he was elected to the Academy of Medicine, and in 1832, to the Academy of Moral Sciences, for which he undertook research trips in 1835, 1836, 1837, 1840, and 1846 to all the manufacturing centers of France and neighboring countries. He submitted the results in 1840 in his *Tableau de l'état physique et moral des ouvriers employés dans les manufactures de soie, de coton et de laine* (*The Physical and Mental Condition of French Textile Workers*), one of the most depressing and most useful medical books ever published. An 1841 law against child labor was the immediate consequence. His research on factory conditions was only one element of a very extensive contribution, which, among other things, also dealt with mortality and social conditions, mortality and age, and the statistics of cholera and other epidemics, of accidents, and of crime. Due to almost incredible industry, Villermé was a prominent contributor not only to the *Dictionnaire des sciences médicales* and the *Annales d'hygiène publique*, but to half a dozen other periodicals. He was a member of the Conseil de Salubrité from 1831 till 1836. Thanks to him, epidemiology lived on, despite neglect by both leading schools of the 1820's, the "nosologists" and "physiologists." As P. Astruc has stated, he combined direct observation, statistics, and reform proposals in his work. He was a rare man whose moral value equaled his high intellectual stature.

In recent years, two 1848 aphorisms of R. Virchow have been quoted again and again: "The physicians are the natural attorneys of the poor, and social problems should largely be solved by them"; and "medicine is a social science, and politics is nothing but medicine on a large scale."[15] But it has not been recognized that Virchow took over the philosophy underlying these statements from French doctors writing forty years and more before him.

Throughout our hygiene literature, the doctor and the hygienist are often called upon to direct society. Just a few examples:

It is important for the happiness of all that man be placed under the sacred power of the physician. That he be brought up, nourished, clothed after his counsel and that the systems according to which he should be governed, educated, punished, etc., be designed by him as well as the causes which can change or modify him. Who is better qualified to play this role than the physician who has made a profound study of his physical and moral nature? (Thouvenel 1806)[16]

Hygiene has another future in the moral order. It derives from the investigation of habits, of professions, of social positions of all kinds, ideas and advice which influence the strength and wealth of states. (Marc 1829)[17]

Public hygiene studies man in society, and as a species. Religion, government, mores, institutions, human relations, and the relations of nations are all in its domain. It touches all facets of our social existence; it does more. It tries, as Cabanis wanted it, to perfect human nature. (Rameaux 1839)[18]

The basic justification for these somewhat exaggerated notions lay, of course, in the generally adopted thesis of Cabanis on the relationship between the physical and the mental, or "moral." If one knew physiology, he also knew sociology and psychology! The social sciences before Comte were so immature that they accepted this verdict, implicit in Saint-Simon's opinion that humanity followed the same laws as physical man. Actually, this idea went back to Descartes, who said, "The spirit depends so much on temperament and disposition of the bodily organs that, if there is a way to make man wiser and cleverer, it must be looked for in medicine." But while physiology during our period was supposedly the basis of the science of man, and medicine-hygiene omnipotent, biology actually inherited such basic methods as statistics and such basic concepts as evolution from social thinkers like Condorcet.

Another fundamental problem tackled by the men of our hygiene move-ment was that of the causation of crowd diseases. Since Hippocrates, climatic causes had been the most frequently assumed. Then, during the late eighteenth century, some had rebelled against climatism in general (Volney, Helvetius) and against climatism in medicine in particular (Chassanis). J. P. Frank had written about "the people's misery: the mother of disease." But Cabanis and Hallé still adhered to the classic tradition, though the former occasionally mentioned social environment as a disease cause.[19]

Things changed entirely in France in the first decades of the nineteenth century. For a while, the majority of hygienists entertained a social theory of disease till the results of bacteriology overshadowed every other argument. Fodéré began his 1825 *Essay on the Poverty of Nations* as follows: "A bad distribution of all the parts of the social system has always been one of the main causes of physical and mental disease in man." Virey pointed out in 1828 that, with the same climate, diseases had changed in Rome over and over again throughout history. Villermé stated in 1829,[20] "Far too often, charac-teristics by which nations or their life expectancies differ are attributed to differences in climate." Similar opinions can be found in Buchez and Trélat (1825), Esquirol (1838), Rameaux (1839), and many others.

Gerardin and Gaymard concluded their 1832 report on cholera in Poland as follows: "Your commissaries think that the best preventive against cholera is the improvement of the social condition of the population." Aubert-Roche ended his 1840 book on plague in Egypt with the words, "Only civilization has destroyed the plague in Europe; only it will destroy plague in the Orient." This was also the essence of Prus's 1846 Academy report on plague. The idea of social causation of disease was commonplace in France long before Virchow and his British predecessors appeared on the scene.

This was, by the way, no purely theoretical question. If climate is respon-sible for disease, reforms are impossible. You cannot reform the climate, but you can reform social conditions! It was logical that, in this milieu, the term "social medicine" was coined in 1848 by Michel Lévy and Jules Guérin.

Another corollary of these opinions was the following: "If disease has social causes, if the state of freedom is the best social state, health should also be best under freedom." This idea was vigorously defended in a speech of

September 24, 1797, by Chaussier; in an early memoir by Alibert,[21] who derived the cachectic and pituitous temperaments, as well as several skin diseases, from tyranny; in a thesis of 1814 by Lemare, the old accomplice of the conjurer general Malet; and by Virey, who wrote in 1828: "Liberty fertilizes life just as much as slavery extinguishes its energy and fire. All other things being equal, nations under bad laws waste away and suffer the most diseases."[22]

But does civilization not undermine health and increase disease? Rousseau had thought so, and Hallé and Tourtelle still followed him. Some continued in this vein, like Virey, who thought civilization was a neurosis, and Brièrre de Boismont, who thought it increased disease. But Cabanis had already fought Théry's thesis of the increase of catarrhs through degeneration, and when Frédéric Bérard gave his opening lecture as hygiene professor at Montpellier in 1826 "On the Progressive Improvement of General Health through Civilization," his was the majority opinion. He used Villermé's statistics as support. He concluded: "Civilization makes public health gain more than it makes it lose in certain fields." Marc[23] claimed that modern science produced modern industry, with its health hazards, but also produced modern medicine to prevent and cure these afflictions. Villermé showed how civilization reduced epidemics and increased life expectancy.[24] The same attitude toward the influence of civilization on disease was entertained by, for example, Rostan, Fodéré, Esquirol, Rameaux, and M. Lévy. This was not surprising, since beside statistics, two important emotional arguments acted upon these people: their belief in progress, and their will to reform. Reforms would be senseless if civilization automatically furthered disease.

French hygiene was successful in spite of the fact that the majority of its leaders entertained quite erroneous opinions on one of its central problems —contagion. Like the majority of the clinicians—we have encountered the opinions of Broussais, Laennec, Bayle, and Bouillaud in this respect—they were anticontagionists. Actually, it is, for a while, of secondary importance whether somebody improves housing, water supplies, and sewerage in order to eliminate "miasmata" or in order to fight "contagia"; as long as he im-proves conditions, the health situation will improve. Of course, in the long run, incorrect theories can be a great deterrent to progress; for example, they explain why Pasteur and his disciples encountered such enormous difficulties in their own country during the first decades of their activity.

Contagionism was, by 1820, considered an old, "medieval" theory. It was often defended by feudal bureaucrats having a vested interest in quarantines. Approached with the same critical spirit which had dispatched humoral pathology and heaps of worthless medicaments, it was found wanting. It was very difficult indeed, as I have explained in detail in my 1948 Garrison lecture on anticontagionism, to prove contagiosity before pathogenic microorganisms and their carriers were known. The existence of spontaneous generation was still above any doubt in the minds of Cabanis and his successors.[25] It was experience which seemed to devaluate the contagion theory in the eyes of the physicians: Chervin's battle cry was *"non verbis sed factis,"* and Rochoux pointed in this respect to war experiences with yellow fever and typhus and to the first cholera epidemic.[26]

In addition, contagionism was the theory which justified bureaucratic quarantines, so much hated by the commercial middle class and her medical sons. The "filth-miasma" theory of disease fitted much better into a social theory of epidemics. Anticontagionism was also a fight for freedom! It was no accident that its best-known protagonists, Magendie, Chervin, and Aubert-Roche, were also well-known radicals.

The complete sincerity of the anticontagionists was evident in the long series of experiments they undertook on themselves, beginning with Des-genettes' famous plague inoculation in 1798, and continued by Fay, Scipio Pinel, Guyon, Alibert, Biett, Chervin, Lavallée, Clot-Bey, and others.

The 1802 book on contagion by Cattet and Gardet, who were disciples of Pinel, Hallé, and Bichat, shows that the phenomenon was not very well understood during the first decades of the century, but that the virulent anticontagionism which later dominated the scene was not yet noticeable in Paris. European anticontagionism crystallized only after 1820, in debates around three diseases: yellow fever, cholera, and plague. On all three, the Paris Academy of Medicine, the great national and international medical authority of the period, took an anticontagionist stand.

Yellow fever was primarily an American disease at the end of the eighteenth century. The great majority of North American physicians had, after 1793, following B. Rush, embraced anticontagionism. The pre-Revolutionary French physicians in Santo Domingo, like Devèze, and the French medical officers who had observed the catastrophic epidemic[27] during Napoleon's 1802 expedition (Bally, Gilbert, François, Valentin, and Duchambon) were also anticontagionists. Pugnet was the only contagionist among them. Alexander von Humboldt, the great authority on America in Paris during the first decades of the nineteenth century, was an anticontagionist.[28] Blin and Assalini returned anticontagionists from the Cadiz epidemic of 1805.

A yellow fever epidemic in 1821 in Barcelona stirred up unprecedented discussions and emotions in France. The causes of this excitement were, as

Hoffmann has shown recently, in the last instance of a political nature. A French invasion of Spain was in the air, but the medical aspects were debated very thoroughly too. The Restoration government dispatched a commission to Barcelona, headed by the permanent secretary of the Academy of Medicine, Etienne Pariset (1770–1847), more an elegant writer than a scientist or an independent thinker, and composed of Bally, François, Audouard, and Mazet. The latter died from yellow fever. The commission delivered the contagionist report it was supposed to bring back, and quarantine laws were strengthened. But Lassis and Rochoux came out with anticontagionist counterreports. And in 1822, Nicolas Chervin, a great authority on yellow fever and the leading French anticontagionist, returned from America and took things in hand. Under his continuous prodding, the Academy of Medicine accepted the anticontagionist Coutanceau report in 1828 in spite of Pariset's findings and governmental pressure. The 1828 report's actual author was Villermé, and its main defenders were Desgenettes and Louyer-Villermay. In the same year, the Academy of Sciences gave Chervin its *grand prix* on the basis of a report by Dupuytren.

Chervin, who is completely forgotten today and was officially powerless during his lifetime, nevertheless dominated the epidemiological thought of his contemporaries, as can easily be seen from the admiring obituaries by Dubois d'Amiens and Peisse.[29] Even twenty years after Chervin's death, the contagionist Charcot thought his opinions on yellow fever to be the final word.[30] After being a hero of the resistance of 1813, Chervin had studied yellow fever for eight years in North and Central America and had brought back enormous documentation on the subject. In 1828, the government sent him, with Louis and Trousseau, to study the yellow fever at Gibraltar. In 1832, he became a member of the Academy of Medicine. He was the personal friend of men like Réveillé-Parise, Londe, Rochoux, and Civiale. He impressed people through his integrity, factual precision, industry, and intelligence. This soldier of science died poor, courageously defending to the last a lost position.

The great cholera pandemic of 1831, which eventually reached Paris in 1832 and took 18,402 victims within 189 days, transformed the question of anticontagionism from an academic one into an immediately practical one. Quarantines and cordons failed completely. The French commissions sent to Russia (Gerardin, Gaymard, Jules Cloquet), Poland (Dalma, Sandras, Boudard, Dubled, Alibert, Londe, Foy), and Germany (Scoutetten) in 1831 all brought back anticontagionist reports. After a trip to England in 1831, the great Magendie stated that cholera was due to horrible social conditions and was a noncontagious "filth" disease, just like the four other quarantine diseases: leprosy, typhus, yellow fever, and plague. He concluded that quarantines were, therefore, useless.

It is not surprising, then, that the staffs of the Hôtel Dieu and of other hospitals, as well as the Academy of Medicine, came out during the epidemic with anticontagionist instructions. As a matter of fact, anticontagionism was so generally accepted that it is impossible to list the anticontagionists, while it is very simple to enumerate the few prominent contagionists. They were the surgeons Velpeau and Delpech, the psychiatrists Foville, Pariset, and Parchappe, and a colonial officer, Moreau de Jonnés. In the next epidemic (1848–1849), the situation was the same. It changed only slowly in the 1850's—so slowly that, during a cholera epidemic in 1884, the Academy of Medicine still received thirty-six anticontagionist reports from the provinces together with 119 contagionist ones!

The last great triumph of anticontagionism was the anticontagionist report by C. Prus (1793–1850) on the plague, adopted by the Academy in 1846. The problem came before the Academy on account of the very strict Marseille quarantines, which were reconsidered. Marseille had much traffic with that old plague spot, Egypt, and had bad memories of the plague of 1721. Desgenettes and Assalini had concluded during Napoleon's expedition that the Egyptian plague was not contagious. A. B. Clot (1793–1868) and L. R. Aubert-Roche (1809–1874), who organized Egyptian medicine between 1825 and 1868, defended the same opinion with much vigor. The anticontagionist Aubert-Roche had excellent practical results when organizing the health services of the Suez Canal Company. Thus the decision of the Academy was not surprising.

We cannot follow anticontagionism into all its ramifications and applications here. What we have reported seems sufficient to show that the somewhat vague notion of the contagious "virus," still freely used by Fourcroy, Alibert, Nysten, and Moreau,[31] had been nearly drowned in the wave of anticontagionism, which had been enormously strengthened by the Broussaisian attack on specificity. The defenders of contagion and specificity, like the provincial Bretonneau, were outsiders, not to speak of those who entertained the "absurd," "medieval" idea of living microscopic parasites (animalcula, "insects") as the cause of epidemic diseases. The chemist Raspail,[32] the homeopath Hahnemann, and the country doctor Jean Hameau belonged to the latter group. Raspail, backed by Velpeau (AG 1831, 25:215), prophetically claimed, "All living beings are in turn parasites and pasture ground." But it was only very occasionally that the idea of animalcula slipped into respectable writings like those of Requin (1843) or A. Guérin (1847). And it must be admitted that numerous inoculation experiments, except those of Rayer on glanders, had remained unsuccessful. Villemin did not succeed until 1862.

The emphasis on anticontagionism and the disregard for contagion as a cause of disease inevitably brought about a regression to older, classic causal explanations. Things had to be explained somehow. We have already mentioned the sporadic reappearance of the "epidemic constitution" with Piorry and Trousseau. Far more substantial and lasting was the regression to heredity as an explanation of disease. Details may be found in H. Semadeni's excellent discussion of 1960; in the contemporary books of Lereboullet (1834), Piorry (1840), and Béclere (1845); and in the great treatise of P. Lucas (1847). This work found numerous continuators in the 1850's.

The anticontagionism of our hygiene movement is probably one of the main reasons why it has been so completely forgotten. After the sun of bacteriology had risen so high, the hygienists' anticontagionism looked a little embarrassing, and the whole movement receded into the shadows of insignificance. It was easier to forget it than its clinical sister. The latter was identified with technical acquisitions (stethoscopy), and with institutions (hospitals) which were of central importance for a long time to come. Unlike hygiene, the clinic was remembered through its spectacular "heroes"—Pinel, Corvisart, Broussais, Laennec, and the many others.

Belonging, like its clinical counterpart, to the prelaboratory era, the Paris hygiene movement of our period looked rather clumsy and stupid to the young enthusiasts of the bacteriological era. But for those whose lives it had saved through better water, sewerage, housing, food, and working conditions, through vaccination and child care, it had been good enough.

XIV. SPECIALTIES

Nowhere was the general tendency toward the development of medical and surgical specialties at the beginning of the nineteenth century more noticeable than in Paris. Paris became the cradle of most of them. The others originated in Vienna. All medical travel books of the period commented on this situation. For example, Wunderlich wrote: "The specialties in France are a curious phenomenon, which is found in Germany only occasionally and to a very limited degree. In former times, only dentists, oculists, and hernia surgeons existed, and they were despised. Now a specialty is the necessary condition for everybody who wants to become rich and famous rapidly. Each organ has its priest, and for some, special clinics exist."[1]

The quantity of Paris specialists should not be overestimated. In 1845, they formed not yet 12 per cent of the total number of physicians. Yet even these relatively low numbers clearly indicate the trend. Sachaile's book gave the following figures. Among the 1,499 medical men he listed were:

dentists (*officiers de santé dentistes*)	53
obstetrician-gynecologists	37
psychiatrists	23
orthopedists	17
ophthalmologists	15
urologists	13
venereologists	8
dermatologists	7
pediatricians	7
otologists	4

Contemporaries explained the existence of specialism by the existence of special hospitals (Gardner) and of the central bureau of admissions, which fed the special hospitals (Casper). Kratzmann[2] thought it the result of intense competition. The special instruments, later often regarded as the source of specialism, did not exist yet, or were too rudimentary (like Desruelles' endoscope) to explain the development of specialties.

The best explanation for the advance of specialism in Paris (according to Guardia, Strasbourg preceded it)[3] seems to have been the wave of localism and solidism which accompanied the formation of the new school. Only when diseases were no longer general humoral events, but located in different organs, could they be studied and treated separately. It was no accident that Bichat, the patron saint of the school, poked fun at "universalists" (though he was one!) and regarded specialization as one of the "great laws of animal economy."[4] The Paris picture of that time confirms George Rosen's thesis: "The development of medical specialization derives not so much from an extensive accumulation of specialized factual knowledge, but rather from a conception of disease which permits an intensive application to certain circumscribed problem areas."[5]

The evolution of specialism was by no means a smooth one. Although the general climate for the practice of specialism was a little more favorable in Paris than elsewhere, resistance in the ranks of the profession was still very strong. For example, Roux opposed special infirmaries in 1815, and Bricheteau opposed pediatrics as a special discipline in 1829. Raige-Delorme introduced the *Dictionnaire* of 1832 with a rebuttal of specialism. Trousseau was, of course, against it. In 1840 and 1843, a majority in the Academies arose against it (AG 1840, 3:7, 373; AG 1843, 5:3), as did the committee of hospital physicians in 1848. Only Peisse[6] fought these "prejudices." The power of the opposition was reflected in the fact that official courses in dermatology, venereology, psychiatry, urology, pediatrics, and ophthalmology were instituted as late as 1862,[7] and even then against the will of the Faculty. Chairs in these disciplines came into being only about twenty years later.

1. Pathological Anatomy

Insofar as it underlay most of what Paris clinicians did and taught, pathological anatomy has already been discussed and was, of course, not considered a specialty. In a way, almost every Paris clinician was a pathological anatomist.[8] But the very eagerness with which this discipline was cultivated was bound to transform it into a specialty. Formally, this transformation took place with Cruveilhier, who obtained a special chair in 1836. But to begin with him seems inaccurate since, on the one hand, even he remained a clinician, and on the other hand, Bichat, Laennec, Bayle, Dupuytren, Louis, Andral, and Rayer had already cultivated pathological anatomy as an independent discipline, whatever the formal arrangement was. To omit them here would be a grave injustice. Compared to them, the pre-Revolutionary pathologists—Senac, Lieutaud, Vicq d'Azyr, and Portal—were of minor stature or (like M. Baillie) were exclusively experts in special pathological anatomy. As to Lieutaud, Cabanis' judgment[9]—"a man of common sense and even some spirits, but his books are below mediocrity"—seems not unjustified.

Of Bichat's work in this field, we possess only P. A. Béclard's 1801 lecture notes, later published in 1825.[10] Even in this crude form, Bichat's mastery of the subject emerged. It took many years for his opening statement that marasmus, jaundice, and dropsy were only symptoms and that pathological anatomy had to find the disease behind them to become common opinion. His course first discussed changes in the liquids and inflammation, which was to him primarily a capillary phenomenon. He then dealt with pathological changes in the tissues or bodily systems canonized in his *General Anatomy*. He began with the serous tissue. His "miliary eruption" of serous membranes was certainly tuberculous. His notion of peritonitis was not even found years later in Portal. Under the lesions of mucous tissue, he described "croup" in the confused form customary before Bretonneau. The diseases of connective tissue were followed by those of the lung. Phthisis was, to him, either hereditary or tuberculous. Tubercles were formations *sui generis* or represented the last stage of chronic pneumonia.

The contagiosity of phthisis was, in Bichat's view, "a ridiculous prejudice."[11] It is not quite possible to decide whether the "steatomata" of the liver in his "gland diseases" are carcinomata, and whether the "granulations" are cirrhosis. Spasms caused by mental anguish could, he held, produce jaundice.[12] Inflammation of the testicle could end in cancer. In the diseases of the skin, he recognized the contagious nature of the itch but denied the animalcular cause. He mentioned skin eruptions following the consumption of sea food.[13] Chapters on diseases of the muscles of organic life and animal life and of the arterial, venous, and the nervous systems followed. Insanity was a brain disease (p. 368). Chapters on diseases of the absorbent, the fibrous, the synovial, the cartilaginous, medullary, osseous, pilous, and epidermic systems closed the course. Even in its rudimentary form and in this even more rudimentary summary, Bichat's greatness and the indebtedness of Laennec, Broussais, and Dupuytren to him are obvious. Mérat[14] also credits him with the subdivision of neoplasms into the analogous and nonanalogous, an achievement usually attributed to Laennec. Béclard's lecture notes do not mention this division.

Laennec was the first to give a classification of lesions that was not anatomical, physiological, or nosological, but really autonomous.[15] His classification was, therefore, in spite of its shortcomings, the first sketch of a general pathological anatomy. He taught it in his course in 1803, and he published it again in the *Dictionnaire des sciences médicales* of 1812. It ran as follows: (1) changes of nutrition (hypertrophy, atrophy); (2) changes of form and position (for example, hernias); (3) changes of texture; and (4) living foreign bodies.

Most original and most important was his third group, which was sub-divided into changes of texture by solution of continuity (wounds), by extravasation, by inflammation, and by the development of accidental tissues. The last were subdivided into those analogous to normal tissues (ossification, etc.) and those for which no normal analogies existed (tubercle, cancer). This classification, especially through the analogous-nonanalogous dichotomy, profoundly influenced all later work.

Laennec's special contributions to pathological anatomy have, like those of others, already been dealt with. His course of 1822 shows him fighting the overemphasis on inflammation by Broussais and on "transformation" of tissues by Dupuytren and Cruveilhier. His very exacting criteria for the recognition of the causal nature of a lesion[16] and G. L. Bayle's 1812 article on pathological anatomy in the second volume of the *Dictionnaire des sciences médicales* show the clear insight of the leaders of the pathologic-anatomical school into the limitations of pathological anatomy and expose the cheap demagoguery of Broussais' and Bouillaud's attacks in this respect. As early as 1803, Laennec recommended routine examination of all three cavities at every autopsy; Petit and Serres repeated this rule in 1813. In Germany, this was not yet customary in the 1850's!

Like Laennec, Dupuytren was and, to a certain extent, remained—all deaths in his ward were autopsied[17]—a pathological anatomist. As such, he was Laennec's equal in the eyes of his contemporaries. Today it is very diffi-cult to decide whether this was justified, since all we have to go on is the Paris thesis of his student Marandel on irritation (1810) and some lecture notes of his disciple Cruveilhier (1810), published in Delhoume's biography of the latter. Marandel divided pathology into irritations, atonies, organic transformations, foreign bodies, malformations, displacements, fevers, and disturbances of cerebral function. He subdivided irritations into the nutritive (Bouillaud also used this notion, expressly referring to Dupuytren), the secretory, the hemorrhagic, and the inflammatory.

Cruveilhier's lecture notes on Dupuytren's course of 1810[18] show a very similar classification—irritation, atony, perversions, malformations, and changes through external mechanical influence—which mixed functional and anatomical notions in the same disadvantageous way. Dupuytren was also an experimental physiologist—and in this respect more faithful than Laennec to their teacher, Bichat; in his 1803 thesis, he designated pathological *physiology* as his goal! This orientation continued in Cruveilhier's essay of 1816, which was not surprising since he used his teacher's notes in its com-position.[19]

Jean Cruveilhier (1791–1874) was the descendant of a Limoges medical family, and had therefore been forced into becoming a doctor in spite of his theological leanings. He studied under Dupuytren and later became his intern. This and his membership in the Congrégation brought him the professorship of anatomy at Paris in 1825. He immediately reorganized the Société d'Anatomie, with great success, and began publishing his marvelous atlas of pathological anatomy. He performed the necessary autopsies in his clinical service at the Salpêtrière. At the same time, he was the doctor of the upper crust of Paris society.

In 1836, Dupuytren willed the money for creating a chair of pathological anatomy, which Cabanis had insisted upon in 1799;[20] Caen had possessed one since 1756, and Strasbourg, thanks to Cuvier, had had one since 1819. The state financed the chair itself; the money was used for the Musée Dupuytren. The chair was given to Dupuytren's favorite, Cruveilhier, who held it till 1866. He published his five-volume treatise on general pathological anatomy between 1849 and 1861.

Cruveilhier's essay of 1816 gave more or less the old Dupuytren classification: (1) mechanical lesions; (2) transformations, productions, degenerations; (3) irritations; and (4) fevers and neuroses. He did not use this classification either in his atlas or in his treatise, in which he practically returned to Laennec.[21]

Cruveilhier's true importance lies in his detailed studies on, for example, progressive muscular atrophy (1853), gastric ulcer (1839), disseminated sclerosis (1835), colon diverticula (1849), and so on. Neither his postulation of a generalized "cancer juice" (1827) nor his joining the phlebitis trend ("phlebitis dominates all pathology") in the 1820's was very successful.

The 1829 treatise on pathological anatomy by J. G. Lobstein (1777–1835), nephew of the great J. F. Lobstein, a Strasbourg obstetrician who had been professor of pathological anatomy there since 1819, cannot be regarded as progress in spite of its interesting details. The general classification was that of Laennec; special pathology was discussed according to tissues, as everybody had discussed it since Bichat. There was a somewhat Germanic attempt to "lead facts back to ideas and higher views of nature," in this case a mixture of speculative neuro- and humoral pathology.

Yet the *Précis d'anatomie pathologique* by Gabriel Andral, published in the same year (1829), impressed Mériadec Laennec so much that he did not carry through his project of publishing his uncle's manuscript on that subject. The first of Andral's three volumes was devoted to general pathological anatomy. It was here that Andral gave up the notion of inflammation, which was, to him, hopelessly confused and vague, and tried to lead pathological anatomy back from the Broussaisian monotheism of irritation, which he regarded as an offspring of sensualism. An extraordinary amount of space was devoted to arguments against Broussais, which are no longer of major interest to modern readers.

Andral divided all pathology into lesions of capillary circulation, of nutrition, of secretion, of the blood, and of innervation. The largest classes were the lesions of nutrition and those of secretion. The former had twelve subdivisions, going from the monstrosities (the experimental work of Geoffrey Saint-Hilaire is extensively discussed), through hypertrophies, atrophies, ulcerations, and indurations, to serous, fibrous, and osseous transformations. The latter category included pus as well as tubercles, false membranes, and cancers. In the lesions of the blood, leukemias as well as anthrax infections were described without being understood.[22] The remaining two volumes gave a magnificent picture of the above lesions in the different organs (stomach, lung, heart, etc.). Andral's work was the culminating point of the classic macroscopic pathological anatomy of the school. The next decisive step, microscopic pathological anatomy, was introduced into France by the ubiquitous, German-born Hermann Lebert (1813–1878), the teacher of Robin, Broca, Follin, and Verneuil, through his *Physiologie pathologique* (Paris 1845).

2. Psychiatry

Psychiatry[23] too was, in its all-pervading way, not a specialty in a theoretical sense. But, institutionally, it did develop into one in Paris during our period—through transformation of the beggar prisons, where mental patients had usually been kept[24] since 1656, into mental hospitals; through progressive laws; through the establishment of psychiatric teaching; and through the growth of psychiatry as a science. All this made Paris the leader in psychiatry during the first half of the nineteenth century.

All these developments were connected with the internist Philippe Pinel (1745–1826), whose life has been recounted in Chapter V. It is not surprising that he was an internist; till the middle of the century, all textbooks of internal medicine contained chapters on psychiatry. Pinel's famous unchaining of the insane in September, 1793, when he became a physician at Bicêtre,[25] and again two years later at the Salpêtrière, when he transferred there, was symbolic of the transformation of the prison into a hospital. But it was more than a purely philantropic act. It was part of Pinel's plan to use the institution as the main therapeutic instrument, one of his great contributions. He achieved this goal by forming different and separately housed categories of inmates and by replacing bleeding, purging, dumping, and other such prac' tices with "moral treatment," a firm but benevolent attitude, and work therapy.[26] That was the form his Hippocratism took in psychiatry.

Unlike Daquin,[27] Pinel was not only a philanthropist; he also created new foundations for psychiatry as a science. He not only liberated the insane from their chains, he also liberated psychiatry from the chains of systems and hypotheses. In his *Medico-philosophical Treatise on Mental Alienation* of 1801, he put the emphasis on clinical observation and statistical control. He used the simplest possible classification, the classic quartet: mania, melan' choly, dementia, and idiocy. To him, most causes of insanity were of a psycho' logical order; the basic disturbance was emotional, not intellectual. His most important new concept was the *manie sans délire* or *folie raisonnante*, a form of insanity in which the intellectual functions appeared intact. He has been dubbed an "eclectic," which, under the circumstances, was the best attitude he could adopt.

Unlike his medical instruction, his teaching in psychiatry was informal,[28] and he had many fewer psychiatric than medical pupils. Still, he was the father of the "school of the Salpêtrière"; men such as G. Ferrus and Jean Dominique Esquirol were among his psychiatric students, who came from as far away as Geneva.[29]

Jean Dominique Esquirol (1772–1840) was no longer an internist like his master. He was a full-time psychiatrist, living with his patients in the institutions.[30] His pupils were so numerous that, for more than half a century, the majority of French psychiatrists were products of his school. In many ways he resembled his teacher Pinel. His character represented the same mixture of greatness and modesty. He too was originally destined for the priesthood. He too had studied in Toulouse and Montpellier. Coming to Paris in 1799, he had attached himself to Pinel. In 1811, he became a psychiatrist at the Salpêtrière, and in 1826, at Charenton. He simultaneously ran a private institution, first on the Rue Buffon, and later at Ivry. From 1817 to 1826, he gave the first formal courses in psychiatry in Paris. He showed the same tendencies as Pinel, in that he too was an eclectic. But he was a better statistician, a better observer, and a more penetrating analyst. Alcoholism and onanism, which were neuroses to Pinel, were mere symptoms with him. He clearly saw the pathogenic nature of social change.[31]

For thirty years, the changes in our mores have produced more mental diseases than our political troubles. We have exchanged our old habits, our ancient opinions, for speculative ideas and dangerous innovations. Religion enters the most solemn acts of our lives only as a custom . . . and cold egotism has dried up all sources of feeling. The affections of the home —respect, love, authority, and mutual dependance—do not exist any more. Everybody lives for himself. Nobody forms those wise combinations which united present to future generations any more. The bonds of marriage are but toys the rich man uses as a speculation or a decoration for his vanity; the poor man neglects them out of hatred of the priests, out of indifference or dissolution. . . .

One of his main interests was in hallucinations, also later studied by his pupil Brièrre de Boismont, the man who eventually buried the legend of the menstrual origin of insanity.[32] Esquirol propagated Pinel's *folie raisonnante* under the label *monomanie affective*. With the total lack of prejudice so characteristic of him, he gave up the old idea of the abdominal origin of mental disease and took over Gall's theory of the cerebral localization of insanity. The French model law of 1838 was based on his surveys and suggestions, and many institutions were built according to his plans.

His pupils included E. J. Georget (1795–1828), L. F. Calmeil (1798–1895), and particularly J. P. Falret (1794–1870) and J. Baillarger (1809–1890). Both of the latter taught at the Salpêtrière. Falret founded an organization for the protection of discharged patients and practiced "mutual instruction" of the sick.[33] In 1854, Baillarger delineated the "double-formed" mental disease: manic-depressive psychosis. He was instrumental in founding the *Annales médico-psychologiques* in 1843, and the Societé Médico-Psychologique in 1847.

Yet the greatest single discovery in psychiatry during our period, the discovery of general paresis, was not made by a pupil of Esquirol, but by Antoine Laurent Bayle (1799–1858), the nephew of G. L. Bayle, the protégé of Laennec and A. Royer-Collard's intern at Charenton.[34] In his 1822 doctoral thesis, that is, at twenty-three, he described a chronic meningitis ("arach- nitis") accompanied by paresis and characteristic progressive psychosis, going from monomania through mania to dementia. Bayle's discovery was a work of genius. All attempts to rob him of his priority have failed. It is extremely regrettable that, in 1825, due to the death of Royer-Collard and his replacement by Esquirol, Bayle lost his job at Charenton and that "politics" blocked his further career, directing it far away from practical psychiatry. He became primarily a librarian and an editor.

Bayle's discovery was the end of ancient psychiatry. Here for the first time an objectively provable picture of a mental disease was given, and it became obvious that the manias and melancholias of the past were only symptoms, not diseases. Of course, his discovery strengthened somaticist tendencies in psychiatry tremendously. The last influential French contribution to psychiatry, the degeneration hypothesis of progressive, hereditary mental disease, elaborated by Esquirol's pupil J. Moreau de Tours (1840–1884) and by B. Morel (1809–1873), was pseudosomaticist.

French pioneer work in the education of the feeble-minded (J. E. Belhomme 1824; Ferrus 1828; F. Voisin 1834; E. Séguin 1839) should be at least mentioned.

Psychosomatics are today regarded primarily as a part of psychiatry. We have preferred mentioning them mostly in discussing internal medicine. But this might be as good a place as any to add a few observations on Parisian psychosomatics after 1800.

Cabanis was an active practitioner of psychosomatic medicine as well as its general theoretician, as Schneider has rightly emphasized. (Cabanis said, for example, "Shame on the physician who has not learned to read the heart of man just as well as to recognize fever, who while treating a sick body, is unable to recognize the signs of a disordered mind!"[35]) He went into numerous somatic details like the occurrence of phosphorus or electrical phenomena in the brain. [36] Madness and epilepsy were, he said, based on changes of the nervous system.[37] He described a case with delusions and an abscess in the *corpus callosum* and considered castration in mania.[38] On the other hand, he emphasized the power of the "moral state" on the body, discussed the relations between delirium and dream,[39] highly recommended psychotherapy,[40] and, choosing Swammerdam as an example, described the coexistence of delusions and rational thought,[41] that is, the later *folie raisonnante* of Pinel.

That Pinel's disciple Alibert wrote a whole study on the *Power of Consolation on Suffering Man* is not surprising. Corvisart offered psychosomatic passages not only in his cardiology, but also in his Auenbrugger translation on nostalgia,[42] in case histories on the *jalousie des enfants*[43] (this was apparently where Laennec acquired the notion of this disease entity), and in his discussion of the problems of heredity.[44] His pupil Bayle offered two cases of psychosomatic death.[45] Even Véron (M.D., Paris 1823) had a whole chapter on psychosomatics in his memoirs of 1853. Lachaise ("Sachaile"), orthopedist and disciple of Esquirol, offered, in his *Topographie médicale de Paris* (1822), very pertinent remarks on the physical and mental problems of big-city children and the necessity of psychological medicine in large urban agglomerations.[46] On the other hand, the long survival of classic somaticist notions in certain quarters is obvious from the fact that Louyer-Villermay, as late as 1832, published a last edition of his *Traité des maladies nerveuses ou vapeurs.*

We cannot leave psychiatry without saying a few words concerning the impact of F. J. Gall (1758–1828) on his contemporaries.[47] Phrenology, the doctrine of bumps, which was the brain "physiology" of this first-rate brain anatomist, was certainly at least as influential in the first half of the nineteenth century as psychoanalysis was in the first half of the twentieth. Coming to Paris from Vienna in 1807, Gall soon was an extremely successful practitioner and private teacher. It was in Paris (1810–1819) that he published his magnum opus, *The Anatomy and Physiology of the Central Nervous System,* that he was naturalized, and that he eventually died. He is buried at the Père Lachaise. His collection can still be found at the Musée de l'Homme.

Gall impressed such eminent physicians and scientists as Corvisart, Broussais, Bouillaud, Saint-Hilaire, Adelon, Morel, Georget, Calmeil, Lallemand, Desmoulins, and Broca, whose "speech center" was actually Gall's discovery. He fitted very well into the pattern of Paris medicine in those days. Like the Parisians, he was a localist, solidist, and organicist. He did a kind of physical examination. That he was also a comparative anatomist, a liberal, and came from Vienna, the city of Stoll and Auenbrugger, could only recommend him further. It is thus not surprising that his influence was, in spite of decided adversaries, very widespread and that it still lives on in the French vernacular ("*On a la bosse du travail, de l'amour,*" etc., that is, "One has the bump of work, of love," etc.). When the Société de Phrenologie was founded in 1831, its president was Andral, and Amussat, Broussais, Bérard, Bouillaud, Falret, Rostan, Ferrus, Voisin, Jules Cloquet, Foissac, H. Royer-Collard, Parent-Duchatelet, Lélut, and Foville were among its members. Among Gall's partisans were the admiral Dumont d'Urville and the Duke of Montebello, the sculptor David d'Angers and the painter Gérard. His imprint is discernible in the writings of Balzac, George Sand, De Vigny, Baudelaire, Flaubert, Sainte-Beuve, and Comte. It was eventually a French physiologist, P. M. Flourens, who was most effective in reducing Gall's influence.

3. Pediatrics and Geriatrics

Two creations of the Revolution put Paris into the forefront of rising pediatrics: the Hôpital des Enfants Trouvés (Foundlings Hospital) on the

Rue d'Enfer and the Hôpital des Enfants Malades (Hospital for Sick Children) on the Rue de Sèvres.[48] The former was opened in an expropriated monastery in 1795. The mortality rate in the first year of its existence was rather frightening: 2,425 of 2,637 newborns and infants died. By 1837, the figure was 1,458 out of 5,467. The medical director of the institution was J. Baron (1782–1849), also physician to the royal children under the Restoration. It was here that Véron was an intern in 1820 and that Heyfelder[49] and Billard collected the materials for their treatises in the 1820's. They all describe the strange "sclerema" and ophthalmias as very prevalent there. Digestive disorders, pneumonia, typhoid fever, and the usual children's exanthemata (no isolation of any kind!) were commonplace, as were scrofula and tuberculosis.

The Hôpital des Enfants Malades was opened in 1802. It was the first children's hospital in the world. So far, children had simply been kept together with grownups in the hospitals. Its 300 beds soon increased to 600. Its first directors were J. F. N. Jadelot (M.D. 1791) and L. B. Guersent (1777–1848), who together with the latter's pupils (Senn, Rilliet, etc.) did much to clear up the meningitis problem.[50] His son P. L. Guersent (1800–1869) was a surgeon at the hospital, beginning in 1832 and specializing in child surgery.

Numerous other outstanding clinicians like Trousseau, F. L. Valleix (1807–1854; died from diphtheria contracted from a child patient), and L. B. Blache, the son-in-law of L. B. Guersent, worked at this hospital.

Both institutions were frequently described by travelers as clean and "modern" (that is, they used thermometry, percussion, and auscultation). Their chiefs apparently diagnosed gastroenteritis too often but abused neither purging nor venesection.

Obstetricians, especially those working at the Maternité, were equally interested in diseases of the new born (see the publications of Baudelocque, Capuron, Dugès, and Lebreton).

C. M. Billard of Angers (1800–1832), who, like Bichat, died young left a *Traité des maladies des enfants nouveau-nés et à la mamelle* (printed in 1828 in Balzac's ill-fated shop) which was infinitely superior to anything published so far in the field of infants' diseases.[51] Old superstitions, like "dentition diseases" among infants, were discarded. Clinical observation was refined to the utmost. The new methods of auscultation and percussion were, of course, particularly helpful in pediatrics. Statistics and, above all, pathological anatomy played a preponderant role. Billard's book was superseded in 1843 by the masterful *Traité clinique et pratique des maladies d'enfants* by F. Rilliet of Geneva (1814–1861) and E. Barthez (1811–1891); it dominated the field till the end of the century. These pupils of Louis felt the limitations of pathological anatomy in pediatrics very keenly, but not having the later results of laboratory science at their disposal, had to rely on rather artificial concepts like the "diatheses," which were also resorted to by Chomel, Piorry, Roche, and Grisolle.

Geriatrics[52] is no invention of the twentieth century. It is as old as medicine. In its evolution into a medical and scientific specialty, the large assemblies of elderly patients at Bicêtre and the Salpêtrière could and did play a great role,[53] once the Revolution had transformed these places into medical institutions. All early protagonists of geriatrics in France worked in both hospitals, or at least in the Salpêtrière. Between the beginning of the century and the characteristic article by Pinel (AG 1823, 2:1), at least a dozen books on the subject were published in France.[54] We have already mentioned Bichat's contribution to gerontology. Pinel's pupils Landré-Beauvais and Rostan worked on arthritis, cardiac asthma, and degenerative brain disease in the aged. Hourman and Dechambre studied pneumonia in elderly patients (1835). Early outstanding treatises were those of 1840, written by C. R. Prus (1793–1850), of 1854 (M. Durand Fardel), and of 1867 (J. M. Charcot). Furthermore, a host of articles and theses survive from this period. Esquirol, Chevallier, Villermé, and Parent-Duchatelet published a note "On the Conditions Necessary for Hospitals for People of over Sixty" in 1833 in the *Annales d'hygiène publique.*

4. Dermatology and Venereology

Dermatology and venereology had, of course, been cultivated before, especially in the eighteenth century. In France, we are reminded of Astruc and Lorry. But dermatology and venereology became specialties only after 1800.[55]

Besides the general upswing in medicine, the founding of specialized hospitals was instrumental in this evolution. The changes of the Revolution furthermore provided, for the first time, qualified medical personnel for the cultivation of these disciplines. These diseases had, so far, been handled mostly by low-grade surgeons. The unification of medicine and surgery made dermatology part of a highly developed internal medicine, and venereology became the domain of medically trained surgeons. The internists-dermatologists unavoidably handled a great deal of syphilis, so dermatology and venereology eventually coalesced into an internal specialty.

Not only moralizing prejudices impeded progress in this field. According to J. Cross, humoralistic ideas prevented the treatment of skin diseases as late as 1815! Both of these prejudices declined during our period.

In both disciplines, a sensualist orientation furthered teaching and research tremendously. Wax modeling reached its peak. No longer were pathological conditions described in books without illustrations. Excellent atlases (Alibert, Devergie the elder) appeared. In venereology, new techniques like the use of the speculum and mass inoculation furthered research and specialization.

In 1801, the 200-year-old Hôpital St. Louis became a hospital and polyclinic specializing in skin diseases. It was the merit of J. L. Alibert (1768–1837) to have immediately seen and developed the potentialities of this institution as an instrument of teaching and research. Through him, it became a world center of dermatology. This pupil of Pinel, whose main dermatological books appeared in 1806 and 1833, might have had many weaknesses as a medical theoretician, but his role as an activator and teacher is undisputed (for a list of his pupils, see his *Monographie des dermatoses* of 1832, p. ix). With rare perseverance, he held out for the animalcular origin of scabies till it was eventually proven for good by his student Renucci in 1834.

It was a great disappointment to him that his favorite pupil, Swiss-born L. T. Biett (1781–1840), replaced his classification of skin diseases with that of R. Willan, derived from the one by J. J. Plenck. P. L. Cazenave (1795–1877) continued Biett's teaching at the St. Louis, and in his famous *abrégé*. Unfortunately, the great discoveries of Hungarian-born David Gruby (1810–1898) concerning the fungi which caused dermatoses were regarded by this traditionalist antimicroscopist as mere optical illusions. Of the men working at the St. Louis, J. L. Lugol (1786–1851) is probably the best remembered on account of the iodine solution bearing his name; but the poor opinion Trousseau had of him was probably justified. A great number of dermatological syndromes were first described during this period at the St. Louis—lupus erythematosus and pemphigus foliaceus by Cazenave, pityriasis rosea by Gibert, and mycosis fungoides by Alibert.

Outstanding work in dermatology was also done by the younger Devergie, who was the director of the morgue, and by Rayer.

Venereology acquired a special hospital in the 1780's on the Rue St. Jacques (and, in 1836, another one on the Rue Lourcine). Cross probably rightly described conditions in this institution in 1815 as below general Paris standards. Neither Cullerier nor the younger Cullerier, his nephew, were great luminaries (only the son of the nephew was outstanding). P. Weidmann has shown how, in connection with Broussaisism, venereology at this hospital and at the Val de Grâce was invaded in the 1820's by some "antispecific" nonsense, equally disastrous in diagnosis and in treatment. Its main protagonists were Cullerier the younger, Desruelles, Richond, and Devergie the elder.

Things changed for the better only when, in 1831, witty Philippe Ricord, born in Baltimore in 1800 as the child of French refugees, took over at the hospital. He had been trained by Dupuytren, and after his dismissal by the latter, by Lisfranc. He was equally great and beloved as a teacher, practitioner, and scientist. His magnetism was extraordinary. His *Traité* of 1838 incorporated the results of thousands of inoculations. It is no empty phrase to say that it opened a new era in venereology. It definitely established the specificity of syphilis. It definitely differentiated syphilis from gonorrhea. It showed the existence of a hard and a soft chancre. It established the classic three stages of spyhilis—and here, of course, Ricord leaned heavily on the work of dermatologists like Alibert, Biett, and Cazenave to describe the skin changes of the second stage.

Ricord also promoted iodine treatment of tertiary syphilis and greatly improved prophylaxis. He fortunately did not support the idea of "syphiliza-tion" (preventive inoculation with syphilis) propagated by Percy and Auzias Turenne. Casper stated in 1820 that there only seemed to be more syphilis in Paris than in other big cities because it was talked about more freely there; actually, there was less. But even in this relatively unprejudiced city, Ricord, a genius but a specialist in a "filthy" disease, had to wait twenty years till he was admitted, in 1850, to the sacred precincts of the Academy of Medicine.

5. Orthopedics

The word "orthopedics" was coined in Paris by Andry in 1741; gymnastics were promoted by Jean Vervier in 1776; and Venel of Orbes invented useful new apparatus in his home for crippled children. Yet it took his inventions forty years to reach Paris via England and Germany. The decisive stimulus for the development of orthopedics as a specialty in Paris came out of the work of Jacques-Mathieu Delpech of Montpellier (1777–1832), whose magnum opus, *De l'orthomorphie*, appeared in 1828.[56] Delpech brought two great innovations to orthopedics. He added gymnastics, specifically swimming, to the treatment of cripples by apparatus and practiced subcutaneous tenotomy. His reporting was scrupulously truthful, unlike that of some of his contemporaries. Two years after the appearance of Delpech's book, the

Paris Academy of Medicine published an orthopedic prize question for the Monthyon prize. In 1837, Jules Guérin and Bouvier won the prize.

In the 1820's, Paris saw the rise of several private orthopedic institutes directed by medical graduates (for example, Maisonabe and Jalade Lafond), who also extended treatment by apparatus to include gymnastics. A special journal was published by Maisonabe, Bellanger, and Dupau (1825–1830).

In the thirties, subcutaneous tenotomy, practiced by Delpech at Mont-pellier as early as 1818, was introduced in Paris by V. Duval (1835), Bouvier (1836), and Jules Guérin (1837). Duval (1796–1876) continued the institution founded by his father-in-law, Lafond, in the Bois de Boulogne and was orthopedist of the bureau of admissions. Bouvier (1799–1877) had an institute at Chaillot and a division in the children's hospital, and was a *professor agrégé*. We have already encountered the Belgian Jules Guérin (1801–1886), a protègè of Chaussier, as the director of the *Gazette de santé* and a pro-tagonist of eclecticism. In the thirties, he became an orthopedist, with an institute at Passy and a division at the children's hospital. He exaggerated tenotomy beyond all reason. Bouvier protested in 1839. An 1843 publication by Guérin which was teeming with untrue data on recoveries was attacked in the Academy by Malgaigne, Roux, Baudelocque, and Velpeau and was eventually condemned.

Orthopedics had, so far, been a "specialty" of poorly trained surgeons, bandagers, and instrument makers. The unification of medicine and surgery in the new school made it possible to transform orthopedics into a ture medicosurgical specialty. The seven or eight private institutions existing in Paris in the 1820's either came into medical hands or at least hired graduate physicians. As long as the "specialty" had been the domain of instrument makers, emphasis was, of course, on corsets and medical beds. This changed. now. Especially active in this fight against misuse of apparatus were the many-sided Esquirol pupils Lachaise ("Sachaile") (b. 1797) and C. G. Pravaz (1791–1853), who worked with Guérin before he went to Lyon and who became an authority on the congenital dislocation of the hip.

6. Urology

Paris had long been famous for its bladder surgery, but, even in the hands of the best, stone-cutting was a very risky operation. It is therefore not surprising that a bloodless procedure—lithotrity—was intensely searched for and eventually found in the 1820's. As A. Gadient has shown in his study on the beginnings of urology as a specialty (Zurich 1963), it was around the *virtuosi* of the new instrument, the lithotrite, that urology—the word is Leroy's—crystallized as a new specialty. Due to this invention, Paris remained the world's leading urological center for a long time.

The suggestion of an instrument that could destroy stones in the bladder came from the Bavarian Gruithuisen (1813), who ended up as an astronomy professor. In 1818, Civiale submitted an impracticable instrument; in 1824, Amussat followed with three of them, and Leroy d'Etiolles with one. Improving this latter instrument, Civiale performed the first successful lithotrity on January 13, 1824. Many hundreds followed. Not only kings submitted to Civiale, even the surgeon A. Dubois did so, though he was the most famous surgeon in this field and had earlier yelled at his ex-pupil Leroy d'Etiolles, "You are crazy, you are crazy, you are crazy," (Huard 1963). In 1829, Civiale, who was a poor teacher, but a magnificent operator, received a small service at the Hôpital Necker. His two competitors, Amussat and Leroy, operated with equal success and were joined in 1831 by Heurteloup the younger, who created an even better instrument. The four had endless priority disputes. They were bitterly attacked as "specialists" by the "encyclopedists" Velpeau and Blandin in the Academy of Medicine in 1835 and 1847. But they held their own, became members of the Academy, and also improved treatment of strictures and tumors. T. Ducamp (1792–1823), a very promising urologist, died young. P. S. Ségalas (1792–1875) found the diuretic effect of urea and invented a kind of urethroscope. Jobert de Lamballe began operating on the vesicovaginal fistula successfully in 1834.

J. Civiale (1792–1867) and C. L. Heurteloup (1793–1864) were exclusively urologists. J. J. Leroy d'Etiolles (1789–1860) had a somewhat larger field of action; he was an indefatigable gadgeteer, a passion also besetting Heurteloup. Both constructed firearms, among other things. J. Z. Amussat (1796–1856), though never a member of a faculty or a hospital staff, was a first-rate and enormously popular scientist, teacher, and surgeon. He received Academy prizes not only for his urological work, but also for his work on artery torsion, air embolism, and the preternatural anus.

All of these men enjoyed financial success (Civiale left seven million francs), but they all remained outsiders; and after their deaths none received the respectful attention of the medical press which was the lot of their "encyclopedist" adversaries. It is true that they had helped more people and killed less. But, alas, they had not arrived through the proper channels.

7. Otology

Otology acquired its status at Paris primarily thanks to one institution and one man.[57] The institution was the Institut des Sourds-Muets (deaf-mutes), which was founded by the Abbé de l'Epée (1712–1789) around 1750 and existed precariously till adopted by the state after the Revolution. The man was J. M. G. Itard (1775–1838), who quite accidentally came into contact with the Institute in 1800, saw the enormous task there, and stayed for over thirty years. He published his *Traité*, the result of twenty years of experience, in 1821. His point of departure was the diagnosis and treatment of the various kinds of deafness. He tried to identify the lesions causing these different conditions. He did not particularly favor surgical treatment, but used catheterization of the Eustachian tube a great deal.

A master of this technique was the Lyon surgeon J. A. Saissy (1756–1822), who cultivated otology quite successfully at the end of his career. Equally able in this field was N. Deleau (1797–1862), physician of the orphan asylum, who introduced the "air douche" via the Eustachian tube and auscultation of the middle ear. Unfortunately, his reports of successful treatments lack reliability.

Itard's successor was not Deleau but, through Orfila's good services, Prosper Menière (1799–1862), another acquaintance of Balzac, whose name is still remembered through the syndrome he discovered. J. P. Bonnafon (1805–1891) introduced otoscopy (1840) and hearing tests with tuning forks. Mantel has pointed out the interesting phenomenon that the young specialty otology borrowed certain instruments, for example, Deleau's *"soufflet"* ("bellows") and catheter and Bonnafon's *"bougies,"* from another specialty, urology.

It is surprising that, during our period, ophthalmology was extremely weak in the country of Anel and Daviel.[58] Casper was puzzled by these deficiencies in a period when French surgery as a whole was outstanding. But perhaps the explanation lies in this direction: the "encyclopedists" were simply too strong. Wunderlich called ophthalmology in Paris "as poor as obstetrics." It was the German immigrant Julius Sichel (1802–1868), a pupil of Schoenlein trained in ophthalmology in Vienna, who opened the first ophthalmological clinic in 1832 and became the leading Paris ophthalmologist.

8. Legal Medicine

Legal medicine[59] had, of course, existed in Paris before. But its scientific progress during our period was incomparably greater and so were its institutional advances. A chair for legal medicine had existed at the École since 1794, and as insignificant as most of its occupants (Lassus, Mahon, Leclerc, P. Sue, A. Royer-Collard, Adelon) were, they could not avoid teaching the discoveries others had made. Beginning in 1803, an obligatory examination forced the students to acquire this knowledge. The introduction of a modern code also furthered medicolegal evolution.

Real clinical teaching of the subject centered around the morgue, especially after 1830, when Alphonse Devergie (1798–1879) became its director. Devergie was either too young or too old for the chair of legal medicine at the École, that is, always too capable and outspoken. He was also very instrumental in developing the second great center of medicolegal progress, the *Annales d'hygiène publique et de médecine légale*, founded in 1829, which played as great a role in legal medicine as it played in hygiene.

G. Bass, author of an excellent monograph on legal medicine as a specialty in Paris between 1800 and 1850 (Zurich 1964), describes scientific progress under three headings:

1. *Pathological anatomy.* Here Chaussier (technique of dissection and report) and Devergie (postmortal changes, docimasia, asphyxia, wounds) are especially worthy of mention. Béclard introduced the use of ossification centers.

2. *Toxicology.* Orfila was the great master in the application of methods to convict the culprit as well as to liberate the innocent. His dramatic talents gave some trials, like the famous affair of Mme Lafarge, an enormous amount of publicity. The actions of an official like Orfila did, at times, have political overtones.

3. *Legal psychiatry.* Pinel, Esquirol, and their school, aided by Marc, began, against furious resistance led by E. Regnault, a battle to limit the barbarous and unscientific practice of executing insane murderers.

XV. POLITICAL AND MEDICAL REFORM

The participation of doctors in politics reached such proportions during our period that it deserves some special attention. Physicians played a role in all three assemblies of the Revolution.[1] There were seventeen in the Constituante; the best-known among these were Guillotin, Gallot, and Blin, all moderate partisans of the Revolution. The same held true of Tenon, Gastellier, and Broussonet, who were among the twenty-seven medical members of the Legislative Assembly. The majority of the forty-nine doctors who belonged to the Convention voted for the death of the king. Prominent medical Jacobins were Marat, Levasseur, Fourcroy, and Guyton de Morveau, all scientifically eminent as well. If the name of Dr. Guillemardet has survived, he does not owe it to his activities as *conventional*, *Thermidorian*, ambassador to Spain, *préfet*, or inmate of an insane asylum, but to the portrait which Goya painted of him.

Some of the Girondist martyrs of the Convention, like Salles or Le Hardy, were physicians. The moderate Vitet had to emigrate; later, it was the turn of the ex-Jacobins to engage in involuntary travel. Some leading medical men were close to moderate politicians: Pinel to Condorcet, Hallé to Lavoisier, and Cabanis to Mirabeau. Cabanis was also a member of the Revolutionary Tribunal for a while, and later of the Five Hundred and the Senate. One of the most ferocious Revolutionary judges was the lithotomist J. Souberbielle, a nephew of Brother Côme, and still a fervent admirer of Robespierre when dying in 1846 at the age of ninety-two. The epidemiologist N. Chambon de Montaux served as moderate mayor of Paris in 1792, J. Gilibert, the well-known author of *Medical Anarchy*, was a counterrevolutionary mayor of Lyon in the same year. Several physicians, like F. Doppet and J. Dessaix, became generals of the Revolutionary army. Some young men who acquired later medical fame, like G. L. Bayle, Legallois, and Esquirol, engaged in counter-revolutionary activities.

As Emperor, Napoleon more or less abolished politics. He liked to use scientists as administrative instruments—for example, Chaptal, Laplace, Fourcroy, Cuvier, Lacepède, Monge, Lagrange, and Berthollet. Among these, several had been trained as physicians. Dr. Jean Montain of Lyon participated in a political conspiracy in 1809 and had to flee the country.

Politically, the Restoration was as lively as the Empire had been dull.[2] The returning Bourbons were greeted by the Faculty with the same servility that was exhibited by most of Napoleon's former marshals and ministers.

But the majority of the medical profession intensely disliked a setup which owed its existence to occupying armies and in which the doctor was again regarded by the upper crust as a mere domestic.

None of the great liberal orators of the Restoration were physicians, but most of them were patients of Broussais or Gall, men of a similar political complexion. A great deal of the political battle was fought underground. The Jesuit Congrégation was secret, as were the Amis du Peuple (1818) and the Carbonari (1820). In both of the two latter organizations, two young medical men, P. Buchez (1796–1865) and Ulysse Trélat (1795–1879), played important roles; they escaped execution by a hair's breadth. Trélat later became a leading psychiatrist. Buchez more or less left medicine, and produced, in the next decade, a forty-volume history of the French Revolution and a number of historicophilosophical treatises. He was one of the early promoters of the social-science trend in history, of leftist Catholicism, and of production cooperatives as a solution to the evils of industrialism.

For the time being, disappointed by the failure of nine armed uprisings and the duplicity of liberal parliamentarians, Buchez joined, with his friend Bazard, the heirs and followers of the socialist (and capitalist) utopian Comte Henri de Saint-Simon (1760–1825), who attracted a great number of medical men. Saint-Simon himself had had several close medical friends: Bailly, Burdin, Prunelle, and Peclet. The Saint-Simonians included Buchez, Rigaud, Peisse, L. Simon, and Séguin; the editors of the Lancette française; Ange Guépin of Nantes; Ribes of Montpellier, Borrel, and Astric in Southern France; and a number of physicians like Perron and Toché, who went with Father Enfantin to Egypt to build the Suez Canal.

Student riots occurred throughout the whole Restoration period. In 1821, the Paris Law School was closed. In 1822, after a noisy manifestation probably produced by agents provocateurs, it was the turn of the Medical School. It was the stormy year of Saumur and the four sergeants (events in which Pinel's nephew, Casimir Pinel, was involved, and because of which Dally and Comet had to flee to Belgium). When the School reopened in 1823, eleven of the old professors (for a list, see p. 40) were retired and replaced by friends of the Congrégation. Among the new agrégés were a certain number known for their royalist affiliations: Gaultier de Claubry, Kergaradec, Parent-Duchatelet, and Pavet de Courtille. In 1822, the École Normale Supérieure was closed too, which brought unemployment to its director, the later clinician Guéneau de Mussy.

In these years, Bricheteau, Rostan and Ferrus suffered in their advancement for political reasons, and Rayer, because he had married a Protestant. Being a

Protestant cost A. P. Candolle of Geneva his chair at Montpellier. Prunelle lost his chair there for political reasons in 1819, and Lallemand lost his in 1823. Reactionary persecutions were directed particularly against military doctors, prominent ones like Larrey, Percy, and Desgenettes, as well as many less prominent ones. Opposition activities under the Restoration were reported among people later well known in medicine—like Raspail, Chervin, and Malgaigne—as well as among doctors known only politically, like A. Thierry, the friend of Armand Carrel, or F. M. Leroux of Rennes. The famous revolutionary A. Blanqui (1805–1881) studied medicine but devoted his life to political action.

The role of doctors in politics became even more noticeable during the period following the Revolution of July, 1830, that is, during the reign of Louis Philippe d'Orléans. Numerous doctors and medical students participated in the street fighting of 1830 and later received the medal of July fighters; among them were Littré, Bixio, Beunaiche La Corbière, and Faivre. Lami, the editor of *La clinique*, and the medical students Labarbe and Léon Morin were killed during the fighting. Quite a number of physicians were elected to the lower house, among them Prunelle, Goupil, Dariste, Virey, and Flourens. The latter soon became the lifetime secretary of the Academy of Sciences as well. He ended with the coveted position of *pair de France*—membership in the upper house. His son and colleague was less fortunate in politics as a general of the Commune; he was lynched by Versailles soldiers in 1871.

Under the reign of Louis Philippe, Bouillaud, Malgaigne, Dezeimeris, Richond, and Bérard of Montpellier also became deputies. Even more doctors were elected mayors of their communities in 1830—Desgenettes, Prunelle, Dariste, and Gendron, to name a few. An expression of the liberal or radical mood of the times was the large number of physicians—Eugène Legallois, Brièrre de Boismont, Scipio Pinel, Malgaigne, Sédillot, and others—who rushed to Warsaw in 1831 to help the Polish insurgents. The events of 1830 carried Andral, Chomel, and Rostan to the top. But the monarchy, which preached "Enrich yourself," was not to everybody's taste, and conspiracies continued. Aubert-Roche, involved in one, had to flee in 1834.

The unpopularity of this monarchy became obvious in February, 1848.[3] The Revolution of 1848 saw maximum political participation by physicians. Buchez, the first to enter the Tuileries, was the president of the first assembly of the Second Republic, and Trélat, Bixio, and Récourt were its ministers. Thierry was director of public assistance, and Gervais and Ducoux police commissioners; Sanson, Londe, Aubert-Roche, and E. Kuess held other public positions; and Trousseau, Lelut, Roussel, Maissiat, and Gerdy, among many others, were members of the lower house.

But the Revolution ended in utter confusion and eventually in the *coup d'état* of Napoleon III in 1851. The martyr of that event was the deputy Dr. A. Baudin, who was shot when trying to stop the seditious troops. Dr. A. Deville and others became refugees. Medical participation in French politics went on after that. Ange Guépin, Trélat, and Raspail reappeared in 1870; Paul Bert, G. Clemenceau, and "Petit Père" Combes were still to come. But it would never be the same. Too many hopes had been disappointed too often. As Villermé wrote in one of his last letters to Quetelet (September 13, 1862), "I am sad, especially since 1848–1852."[4] Lost illusions.

As the foregoing shows, physicians were found in all political camps. P. Menière gives, in his *Journal*, a witty description of his own rather typical tergiversations (p. 409). Nevertheless, there seems to have existed a certain predilection for radical democracy among them. The more radical an assembly was, the more physicians it contained (Constituante, seventeen; Legislative Assembly, twenty-seven; Convention, forty-nine; Restoration, twelve; Louis Philippe, twenty-eight; 1848, forty-nine; 1849, thirty-four; and 1851, eleven).

There are a number of factors which might have facilitated this political choice for the physician of the period. He was often a son of the lower middle class, which in general supported these parties. His own existence resembled that of the artisan in many ways. The average physician at the time was not wealthy. His individualism, his patriotism, and his distrust of the state put him in opposition to socialism, on the one hand; on the other, his own economic and social situation, and his reverence for science instead of church organizations, separated him from the conservative forces and gave him considerable impetus to oppose the old order. It is thus not surprising that doctors were often political leaders in a period where radical democracy was a great political force. This held true not only for France, but for all other European countries during the nineteenth century.[5]

There was one political problem which concerned doctors above all others: medical reform. Though French medical men were far better off than their German or Italian or British counterparts in certain respects (national unity, unification of medicine and surgery), enough unsolved problems remained to produce a considerable medical-reform movement in France too.[6]

The reform movement seems to have started right after the fall of Napoleon. In 1816, Paris hospital physicians protested against the *patente* (a tax for tradesmen, from which lawyers but not doctors were exempt), and Prunelle submitted a number of interesting suggestions. Fournier de Pescay followed suit in 1817. In 1825, a proposal for the legal regulation of medicine was brought before parliament, which provoked, of course, a flood of discussion. Pamphlets were published by U. Trélat (1828), E. Lemaître de Rabochanges (1825), and many others. At this occasion, the physicians of Paris elected a committee. Since committees were usually named from above during our period, it is perhaps worthwhile to list the names of the fifteen men elected, —that is, those who apparently were the most popular with their colleagues in December, 1828: Desgenettes, Broussais, Rostan, L. Roche, Husson, Bourgeoise, Kapeler, Louyer-Villermay, Gendrin, Ducrotay de Blainville, Lagneau, Magendie, Biett, Delaberge, and Villeneuve.

The Faculty and the Academy had been asked their opinions in connection with this law. Jules Guérin answered in the name of the Faculty in 1830, and Double answered for the Academy in 1833. In 1834, the Association for the Protection of Paris Physicians was founded. In 1836, another commission was named,[7] and in 1837, another regulation proposal was submitted. In the same year, J. M. P. Munaret published his *Du médecin de campagne*. Buchez suggested the socialization of medicine; another utopian, Cabet, an ex-student of medicine, asked for women doctors, lay nurses, and the scientific recognition of specialties, including dentistry. In 1843, the psychiatrist Delasiauve started his forceful publications on medical reform with the book *On the General Organization of Medicine in France*.

In 1845, a general congress of French medical men, including veterinarians and pharmacists, convened in Paris to voice the discontent of the profession. Rayer was its president, Serres, its vice-president, and A. Latour its secretary and driving force. But its results were meager, and the government continued to oppose a general association of physicians until 1858.

A new proposed law was submitted by Salvandy in 1847. He wanted to at least abolish the *officiers de santé*. Cousin later published a book on this proposal and the parliamentary discussions surrounding it. But, like the many propositions of Latour and others in 1848, it never became law. The first new laws came out under the Third Republic, between 1878 and 1892.

Most of the reform propositions asked for the abolition of the *patente* and the *officiers de santé*. They asked for protection against quacks, apothecaries, and bureaucratic domination. They wanted maximum self-government for physicians in settling their own problems, as well as the closely related ones of medical care for the indigent and for rural districts. Some suggested a *numerus clausus*, some state-employed district physicians in the country. They wanted more faculties, and more independent faculties. They strove for the exertion of some influence by practitioners on the reform of the curriculum, on examinations, and on the nomination of professors. They all violently attacked *permutation* and *cumul*. Unfortunately, the success of this large movement was rather limited.

So-called medical ethics, a mixture of true ethics and etiquette, were usually discussed under the heading "the duties and necessary qualities of the doctor" in our period. Later (1845), Max Simon coined the expression "deontology" to refer to the rights and duties of the doctor. The duties of the physician were, of course, closely related to the problems of medical reform, which tried primarily to define the rights of the doctor in society.

The pronouncements on medical ethics during our period brought out nothing essentially new. They usually contained the rules of the ancients, as revived after the sixteenth century, and the important additions made, especially by British physicians, during the eighteenth century. Cabanis' demands not to abandon incurables, to use self-criticism, and to treat rich and poor alike[8] can all be found in J. Gregory, *Duties and Qualities of the Physician* (1770). The same holds true of Monfalcon's admonitions[9] not to split fees with apothecaries, not to flee in case of epidemics, not to automatically prefer old physicians, and not to use publicity aids ("*compères*"). His urging that doctors should keep out of politics is original. Berthier (1821) felt that the dying should never be told the truth and that incurables should never be abandoned. Cruveilhier, in his famous commencement speech of 1836, concentrated on the duty to know, the professional secret, and the interdiction of fleeing. Trousseau[10] condemned experimentation on the sick and preached respect for the poor—two rules apparently not always obeyed.

It is noteworthy that the older physicians (for example, Marc, Bretonneau, and Pugnet) still refused to submit bills. They relied entirely on voluntary payments. A problem apparently not yet existing in our period was that of "conspicuous consumption." Dechambre wrote in 1882,[11] "I have known the apartments of Dupuytren, Marjolin, Lisfranc, Fouquier, Chomel, Andral, and Louis. They were sufficiently large, decorated decently, and arranged practically. They were 'sensible,' but today they would hardly be good enough for an average practitioner."

XVI. FOREIGN STUDENTS AND DOCTORS

It is well known that the Paris school had a tremendous effect on world medicine. Stimulated by it, brilliant centers of "hospital medicine" arose in other places like Dublin, London, and Vienna. This influence was to a large extent transmitted by the printed word, especially by the many review journals, but a considerable number of foreign medical students and doctors absorbed Paris ideas and techniques on the spot. It is impossible to give any detailed account of the external and internal problems posed by this "migration," which could be easily made the subject of a separate book. But our picture would be incomplete if we did not at least mention a few aspects of it.

These men came at different points in their careers and the length of time they devoted to Paris studies varied. Only few graduated at Paris (like Waller); most of them were what we today call graduate students. Some stayed only a few months, many a year or two, some (like Carswell) many years—and some forever.

There had always been medical travelers coming to Paris; in the eighteenth century they were mostly anatomists and surgeons[1] (for example, Haller, Voitus, and Heim). But never before had foreign medical students been as numerous as in the decades following the peace of 1815. This was reflected in the very great number of books reporting on medical Paris trips or on preparations for them. Laennec spoke of his 300 foreign disciples. In 1836 Muehry reported an association of foreign medical men presided over by the "foreigner" P. Ricord.[2] In 1837, J. H. Bennett of Edinburgh and Oliffe of Dublin founded the Paris Medical Society, which seems to have embraced Germans as well as Anglo-Saxons till the former founded their own society in 1844, with Stromeyer, Szokalski, Feldmann, Kolle, Schuster, Lebert, and Otterburg. In 1845, the following were also reported as members: K. Vogt, M. Schiff, J. von Gerlach, Luschka, Chelius, and Frerichs. Its board in 1853 consisted of Meding, Heyfelder, Panum, Rahn, and Schaible. This society, which also attracted Scandinavians, Swiss, and Poles, had its seat at 24 Rue de l'École de Médecine and flourished till 1870.

The Germans were, for several reasons, the strongest group numerically. We can mention only some of the most prominent Paris-trained German physicians and surgeons here. Among the latter, P. von Walther and Osiander came before 1815; in the twenties, it was the turn of Dieffenbach, Stromeyer, J. von Heine, Michaelis, Ammon, Pagenstecher, and Heyfelder. The latter continued to act as a link between French and German medicine. The 1830's saw Langenbeck, Roser, Demme, and Berend in the city on the Seine; in the 1840's, Thiersch, Wilms, G. Löffler, Middeldorpf, and A. von Graefe arrived.

Contacts during war service (1814–1815) made Heusinger a transmitter of French medical ideas. Ringseis came in 1812; Basedow, Casper, Kopp, Froriep, Pieper, Narr, and Spiess in the twenties; and Canstatt, Hasse, Lebert, Griesinger, Wunderlich, Schill, Staberoh, Oesterlen, Pruner Bey, Nöggerath, and Rinecker in the thirties. Pienitz and Damerow studied with Esquirol.

Not only clinicians but medical scientists too went to Paris, which, it is true, then excelled in comparative anatomy. During the first two decades of the century J. F. Meckel, Tiedemann, Wilbrand, C. A. Rudolphi, C. G. Jung the elder, and C. F. Nasse made their pilgrimages to Paris. A. A. Berthold, R. Wagner, Fechner, and Burdach followed in the 1820's; in the 1830's, Phöbus, Carus, and A. Ecker came; and in the 1840's, Karl Vogt, Robert Mayer, C. Eckhard, J. von Gerlach, and Küchenmeister.

Those familiar with the work of these men realize that the effect of Paris on foreigners varied very much. Some assimilated little or nothing, some became slavish imitators, and the best, like the great surgeons or Wunderlich and Griesinger, developed something new out of Paris suggestions. The subjective reaction varied too. Blind admiration was relatively rare, critical recognition the key note. Often the personalities of the great Paris doctors, "men of the world," impressed students used to the provincial German professors as much as the ideas of these French physicians.

A few German students distilled their nationalistic inferiority complexes into grotesque utterances full of metaphysical conceit. As an example, we quote P. von Walther: "The philosophical nullity [of the French] leads unavoidably to nullity in every branch of the natural sciences." He spoke of the "total failure of French medical schools" and of "medical practice being but a caricature" (because not enough drugs were used!)[3]—and this at a moment when, under the ministrations of Schelling and company the nullity and failure of German medicine had reached such proportions that for decades its youth had had to go to Paris in order to obtain a complete medical education.[4] When the Viennese Skoda, Rokitansky, Schuh, and Sigmund came to Paris in the 1840's, they had actually absorbed French influences long ago, and the trip could only serve as a check on impressions gained much earlier from the literature.

The quantity and quality of British Paris students during our period was quite impressive. While Astley Cooper attached himself to Desault and Chopart, Spencer Wells followed Malgaigne. Hodgkin and J. Clark were pupils of Laennec; Forbes, Budd, Farr, W. H. Walshe, and Carswell were all disciples of P. Louis, who was also closely connected with Marshall Hall. Hope studied with Andral, A. V. Waller with Piorry, and J. H. Bennett with Donné. W. A. F. Brown and A. Morison worked under Esquirol. E. H. Sieveking and W. Bowman were other old Paris students. The clinical supremacy that Great Britain had held for two centuries had clearly passed to France.

The best-known group of foreign students were, due to the labors of Sir William Osler, those coming from the United States. They abandoned Great Britain in favor of Paris after 1812. Gardner reported fifty of them in 1844. In 1851, they had a society of their own at 47 Rue St. André des Arts. We mention here only such eminent figures as O. W. Holmes, J. Jackson, Jr., H. I. Bowditch, E. Bartlett, Lemuel Shattuck, Alonzo Clark, A. Stewart, A. Stillé, W. W. Gerhardt, S. G. Morton, and J. C. Nott.

Most of them were pupils of Pierre Louis. Their great difficulty was that, returning to the United States, most of them failed to find either the tech-nological (large hospitals) or the spiritual climate for practicing "Paris medicine."[5] As Muellener has shown,[6] the same problem beset those brilliant Geneva students like Marc d'Espine, T. Maunoir, Lombard, Senn, and Rilliet, who formed Louis' inner circle. Earlier prominent Swiss students at Paris were Matthey, L. A. Gosse, J. L. Prévost, Mayor, and R. Schiferli; later came Horner and W. His, Jr.

Eminent Swedish physicians like F. T. Berg and A. Retzius, Danes like S. Trier, C. E. Fenger, and Panum, and Dutchmen like D. Tilanus, Broers, P. Fremery, H. van Hall, and De Man were also Paris trained. Burgersdijk[7] mentions the Café Hollandais-Américain at the Palais Royal as the meeting point of these students in 1823.

There were those who eventually stayed and thus became part of French medical history rather than of that of their own countries. The most prom-inent of them was the Spaniard Orfila. We might also mention the Germans M. Friedländer, Sichel, Meding, L. Bornitz, Gall, and Hahnemann; the Austrian M. Krishaber; the Swiss Kapeler and Kuentzli; the Hungarians Gruby and Mandl; the Greek Panas; and the Irishman Oliffe. It is sometimes difficult to decide to what extent political or racial reasons played a role in this transplantation. This was the period when fugitives from the absolutist countries of the Holy Alliance found asylum in Paris—when H. Heine, L. Boerne, Karl Marx, and Richard Wagner lived there as political refugees. Italian doctors like Coste, Rognetta, Fossati, and Cerisi (Cérise) and Poles like Raciborski, Grabowski, and Szokalski were clearly refugees.

Parallels with later medical migrations are so obvious that they need not be belabored here. The memories of these migrations have given the notion of our common Western medical heritage its flavor and concreteness.

XVII. LITERATURE AND MEDICINE The

most elementary connections between medicine and literature in our period were famous doctor-patient relationships. Except for the indestructible Victor Hugo, a man extraordinary in so many ways, the writers of our period needed doctors badly. Stendhal seems to have been particularly afflicted, since he was treated by Portal, Richerand, Bayle, Cullerier *oncle*, J. L. Prévost, Chomel, Gall, and Koreff. Balzac consulted, beside Nacquart, A. Dubois, Roux, and Louis. Lamartine was a patient of Bouillaud; Chateaubriand of Cruveilhier and Laennec; and De Vigny of Cruveilhier and Evrat. Evrat also treated Mickiewicz and George Sand, who also consulted Broussais and Rostan. Benjamin Constant and Saint-Simon were attended by Broussais, and the latter by Gall, Burdin, and Bailly as well. Madame de Staël had Portal and Laennec as doctors, Maine de Biran had Moreau and Laennec, A. Dumas had Piorry, Flora Tristan had Récamier, and Lamennais relied on Laennec, Rostan, and Bretonneau. Bretonneau also took care of De Tocqueville and Flaubert and was a friend of Béranger and Mérimée. Mérimée was also treated by Robin, Koreff, Bixio, Trousseau, and Royer-Collard, Sainte-Beuve was treated by Ricord, Philipps, and Peogey, and Comte by Esquirol and Robinet. Heinrich Heine's doctors were Sichel, Wertheimer, and Gruby. In 1820, Dr. Esprit Blanche (1796–1852) found a private institution at Montmartre, which was later transferred to Passy, continued by his son Emil, and kept open till 1893. Numerous writers from Nerval to Maupassant spent some time there.[1] There is no particular pattern discernible in the choice of physicians, except that political conservatives had a tendency to consult Cruveilhier or Laennec, while liberals chose Broussais or Gall.

A second, far more significant relation between literature and medicine in our period was the indebtedness of writers to medical theorists—especially to Cabanis and Gall, both of whom we have discussed earlier. Apparently, in a situation where the storms of revolution and war had torn down all traditional guideposts, scientific theories gave literary men suffering from the *mal de siècle* a much-needed feeling of orientation and certainty. This attitude also showed that medicine again enjoyed the respect of large portions of society.

Echoes of Cabanis can be found in, for example, Constant, Stendhal, Sainte-Beuve (who had himself studied medicine), De Vigny, and Flaubert. Gall visibly influenced Balzac, George Sand, De Vigny, Baudelaire, Flaubert, and Sainte-Beuve. Significant in this context was the fashion of publishing literary monographs on the "physiology" of this and that, for example, the *Physiology of Marriage* (Balzac), *The Physiology of Taste* (Brillat-Savarin), *The Physiology of Passions* (Alibert), *The Physiology of the Doctor* (L. Huart), of the employee (Balzac), the concierge (J. Rousseau), the newspaperman (L. Huart), the provincial (P. Durand), the bachelor and the spinster (L. Conailhac), the *rentier* (Balzac and Frémy), the bluestocking (F. Soulié), the National Guardsman (L. Huart), and so on. It is remarkable and rather surprising that so much scientific theorizing did not spoil the admirable creativity and spontaneity of French literature. Clinical case histories of the period are sometimes good literature, and literary descriptions often offer the precision and detachment of good case histories.

When the heroes of Balzac, De Staël, George Sand, Dumas, and Mérimée fell sick or died through the influence of emotions and passions, this idea could, as we have seen above, very well have been derived from contemporary medical literature, which did not ignore psychogenic disease.[2] The emotionally caused disease strikes us in this context as a typically romantic idea. But does this entitle us to baptize our medicine "romantic medicine"? This was, of course, the period of Anglomania and romanticism, and romantic traits could be found in Broussais, Laennec, Piorry, and others. But I definitely feel that nothing would be gained but confusion by characterizing the medicine of the period by a term applying essentially to literature, art, and music— and by uniting what was separated in reality, while separating what was united.

The third and most important connection between literature and medicine is the latter's description in the literature of the period. Most of the time this portrait is rather flattering, and one could argue that the "man in white" fashion of the twentieth century is a direct descendant of the literature of our period. The favorable reflection of medicine in literature is another piece of evidence of the latter's importance and impressiveness. It is an expression of the rehabilitation of medicine and, in turn, furthered this rehabilitation.

References to medicine are best known in the work of Balzac. On these more than 100 books and articles have now been produced.[3] We have already mentioned his continual use of the surgeon Desplein and the physician Bianchon, who clearly bore the traits of Dupuytren and Bouillaud. Balzac was not only a friend of the latter, but also of Prosper Menière and Nacquart. The names of Velpeau, Alibert, and Dubois, among others, appear in his works. The famous consultation in *Peau de Chagrin* unites Brisset, Cameristus, and Mangredie (Broussais, Récamier, and Magendie). Their ideas, their personal appearance, and their detachment are superbly described. That

Balzac had an excellent understanding of medical life is also revealed in his remark on Desplein: "The glory of surgeons resembles that of actors, who exist only during their lifetimes and whose talent can no longer be appreciated once they have disappeared." Paradoxically, Balzac's *Médecin de Campagne* is primarily a political book and contains very little on medicine proper. Balzac's world was a strange world composed almost exclusively of extreme characters—of geniuses, saints, scoundrels, and criminals, like the famous collection of plaster casts brought together by the phrenologists Gall and Dumoutier and now housed at the Musée de l'Homme.[4] But if this world was fantastic, its elements were, like those of the Gall collection, as true to nature as possible.

Balzac was by no means the only writer of the period in whose work doctors and their activities played a prominent role.[5] Jules Sandeau, Eugène Sue (who had been a surgeon for eight years), Alfred de Vigny, Claude Tillier, Maxime du Camp, Jules Janin, not to speak of later writers like Flaubert, Zola, and the Goncourts, were similarly inclined. Not all literary portraits of physicians were laudatory. Some were caricatures, like that of Alibert in Jong's *Deux Médecins* or that of Laennec (Dr. Lasinec) by Eusébe de Salles.

It is quite possible that these contemporary descriptions of Paris medicine will never be equaled by historians' attempts to recreate the medical past— and that these descriptions will still live on when medicine has developed so far beyond the Paris model that, without them, the latter would be com- pletely forgotten.

POSTSCRIPT I was trained as a clinician in the 1920's in Germany. When, in the 1930's, I lived in Paris, I was greatly impressed by the practicality and directness of French medicine. In the 1940's, I migrated to the United States. When I began delving into the history of the Paris School there, I was still a rather uncritical admirer of "hospital medicine." Under the influence of my studies and other circumstances, my point of view slowly changed. I came to see the rather severe limitations of "hospital medicine" more and more clearly, especially in medical education and research. I am still a fervent admirer of "classic" Paris medicine, but I think the foregoing shows that I am no longer an uncritical one.

Our period, like all periods in medical history, contains elements that should be preserved, for instance, certain of its attitudes in therapeutics and hygiene. Excellence in the latter field was due to the fact that Paris medicine showed an unusual awareness of the society in which it was embedded.

One of the most striking traits of this medicine was its concreteness. Perhaps never before or since has medicine been so free of abstractions. Our own medicine has, due to its marriage with the exact sciences, grown very abstract, so much so that one could almost speak of "abstract medicine." Laboratory data and figures have to a large extent replaced sense impressions; statistics, direct experience. This was unavoidable and, as a whole, quite salutary. Yet, it can be exaggerated, and it has been and is exaggerated. Perusal of the history of classic Paris medicine might preserve or revive some of the concreteness which is necessary in medicine, and without which it is incomplete and not entirely able to fulfill its task.

ABBREVIATIONS

The following abbreviations are frequently used.

AG	*Archives générales de Médecine*
Am. J. Hosp. Pharm.	*American Journal of Hospital Pharmacy*
Annales d'hyg. publ.	*Annales d' hygiène publique et de médecine légale*
Arch. Inst. Cl. Bernard	*Archives Internationales Claude Bernard*
Arch. Int. Hist. Sc.	*Archives Internationales d'Histoire des Sciences*
Bull. Hist. Med.	*Bulletin of the History of Medicine*
Bull. Johns Hopkins Hosp.	*Bulletin of The Johns Hopkins Hospital*
Bull. Soc. Anthr.	*Bulletin de la Société d'Anthropologie de Paris*
Bull. Soc. Fr. Hist. Méd.	*Bulletin de la Société Française d'histoire de la médecine*
Cert.	*Cabanis: Du degré de certitude de la médecine*
Chron. méd.	*La chronique médicale*
Dict. méd.	*Dictionnaire de médecine ou répetoire général des sciences médicales*
Dict. sc. méd.; DSM	*Dictionnaire des sciences médicales*
Fr. Hist. Stud.	*French Historical Studies*
Deut. Med. Wschr.	*Deutsche Medizinische Wochenschrift*
Gaz. d'hôp.	*Gazette des hôpitaux civils et militaires, Paris*
Hist. de la Méd.	*Histoire de la Médecine*
Jahrb. d. Med. als. Wissch.	*Jahrbücher der Medizin als Wissenschaft*
Journ. Hist. Med.	*Journal of the History of Medicine and Allied Sciences*
Journ. Med. Ed.	*Journal of Medical Education*
Mém. acad. méd.	*Mémoires de l'Académie royale de médecine de Paris*
Mitt. Gesch. Med. Natur.	*Mitteilungen zur Geschichte der Medizin und der Naturwissenschaften*
Nouv. Rev. Fr. d'Hématologie	*Nouvelle Revue Francaise d'Hématologie*
PM	*Cabanis: Rapports du physique et du morale de l'homme*
Presse méd.	*La presse médicale, Paris*
Progrès méd.	*Le progrès médical, Paris*
Rev	*Cabanis: Coup d'oeil sur les révolutions et sur la réforme de la médecine*
RM	*Revue des sociétés médicales de France et de l'étranger*
Schw. m. Wochschr.	*Schweizerische medizinische Wochenschrift*
Sudh. Arch.	*Sudhoffs Archiv für Geschichte der Medizin und der Naturwissenschaften*
Wiener Med. Wschr.	*Wiener Medizinische Wochenschrift*

NOTES

Chapter I

1. See Picavet; Temkin 1946; Rosen 1947; Ackerknecht 1950; Lesky 1954.
2. RM 1830, 3:153.
3. PM 1:38.
4. Cert. 53.
5. Rev. 77.
6. Rev. 189.
7. Rev. 308.
8. Rev. 358.
9. Rev. 286.
10. PM 1:159.
11. PM 1:132.
12. PM 1:351.
13. PM 2:431.
14. Rev. 23.
15. PM 1:7.
16. Rev. 25.
17. PM 1:412.
18. Rev. 421.
19. *Ibid.*
20. Rev. 369.
21. Rev. 371.
22. PM 1:329 ff.
23. Rev. 241.
24. Cert. 107.
25. PM 1:371.
26. Rev. 154.
27. Rev. 320.
28. Cert. 140.
29. Rev. 278.
30. Rev. 383.
31. Cert. 25; Rev. 325.
32. PM 1:xxx.
33. Rev. 271.
34. Cert. 7.
35. Rev. 237.
36. Rev. 167.
37. PM 1:xxviii.
38. Cert. 58.
39. Cert. 89.
40. Rev. 12.
41. Cert. 119.
42. Foucault 1963, 16, 39.
43. *Ibid.*, 49.

44. Fodéré 4:420.
45. Cert. 135.
46. Rev. 18.
47. Rev. 185.
48. Rev. 219.
49. PM 2:251, 253.
50. PM 1:436.
51. PM 1:285, 287, 293.
52. Gerdy iv.
53. Pinel, 1818, v.
54. *Idem*, 1809, ix.
55. *Idem*, 1818, 77; 1804, 397, 460, 462; 1809, ii.
56. Rostan 39, 51.
57. Bichat 1800, 51.
58. Corvisart 1818, iii.
59. *Idem*, 1929.
60. G. L. Bayle xiii.
61. Laennec 1826, 1:xxv.
62. *Ibid.*, 1:280.
63. *Idem*, AG 1:xv.
64. *Idem* 1826, 1:278.
65. Chomel 1848, x, 435, 441.
66. Louis xxiii.
67. *Ibid.*, 65, 68.
68. *Idem*, AG 1837, 44:205.
69. *Idem*, 1836, 76, 81, 55.
70. AG 1824, 4:497.
71. Bouillaud 161–176.
72. *Ibid.*, 126.
73. *Ibid.*, 38, 101.
74. Trousseau 1:1.
75. *Ibid.*, 3.
76. *Ibid.*, 33.
77. *Ibid.*, 139.
78. *Ibid.*, 29.
79. Alibert 370.
80. See D. G. Charlton.

Chapter II

1. Raige-Delorme, in *Dict. méd.* 1837, 15:375; see also Ackerknecht 1959.
2. Wunderlich 1841, 16.
3. Bibliographies of this literature in Kratzmann; Muehry.
4. Coste 1817, 490.
5. Ackerknecht 1950, 50.
6. Corlieu 324; Pinel 1818, 1:xxxviii; Héchemann 26; Brodier 14; G. L. Bayle 1810, xii; Laennec 1826, 1:13; Rostan 1826, 47; Bouillaud 1836, 114.

7. Tenon, as quoted in Meding 58.
8. Rosen 1956, 147; Rochaix 71.
9. Meding 48.
10. Wardenburg 2:229; Casper; Bouchardat 1853, 29; Guiart 178; Rostan 1864, 75.
11. Chaptal.
12. Pigeir 222–235.
13. Alhoy vi.
14. Coste 1817, 492.
15. Muehry 5 ff.
16. Bouchardat 1853, 18.
17. For example, the Beaujon hospital had 80 beds in 1795, 120 in 1804, and 140 in 1815. The Charité had 208 beds in 1786, and in 1793, it was decided to extend the number of beds to 500. The Pitié had 400 beds in 1809, 600 in 1816.
18. Kopp 28.
19. Durand-Fardel 7.
20. AG 1827, 14:162.
21. *Ibid.*, 1839, 50:114.
22. Otterburg 1841, 47.
23. *Dict. méd.* 1837, 15:372.
24. Wardenburg 2:231.
25. E.g., Raige-Delorme, in *Dict. méd.* 1837, 15:370.
26. RM 1838, 451.
27. Wardenburg 2:320.
28. See Meding; valléry-Radot.
29. Raige-Delorme, in *Dict. méd.* 1837, 15:369. For an interesting list of improvements by Dupuytren himself, see Ratier 1825, 19; also Maygrier 194.
30. Mac-Auliffe 75 ff.
31. Stewart 103.
32. Concerning this artificial disease concept, see Bianchetti; Wyss.
33. E.g., RM 1824, 2:1, 3:18, 4:329, 161; RM 1836, 1:63; Meding 119.

Chapter III

1. Wunderlich 1859, 244.
2. Pinel 1818, 2:3; Broussais 1829, 1:2.
3. Ackerknecht 1960, 137.
4. Rochard 3.
5. Delaunay 1906.
6. Portal 1813, x.
7. "*L'anatomie seule puisse dévoiler les signes des maux qui nous affligent.*"
8. Coste 1775.
9. Rev. 357.
10. Pinel 1813, 367.
11. Coste 1817.
12. Pinel 1818, cxi.
13. See Rossi.

Chapter IV

1. Regnault; Bouillaud 26; Cuvier 360; Richerand 297; Prunelle 59.
2. Wardenburg 198; Mac-Auliffe; Desault 1:42.
3. Richerand 302 ff.
4. Corlieu 2 ff.
5. Bouillaud 245; see also the Trousseau quotation above.
6. G. L. Bayle 519.
7. Rev. 332.
8. Pinel 1813, 369.
9. Smeaton.
10. Frank 147 ff.; Wardenburg.
11. Frank 136; Wardenburg 507.
12. Wardenburg 440.
13. Corlieu 55; Prévost 12; P. Sue was succeeded as librarian by Moreau de la Sarthe (1808–1826), the protégé and physician of Pasquier; MacMahon (1826–1835); and Dezeimeris (1836–1852).
14. Wardenburg 297; see also Poumiès de la Siboutie 88.
15. Fayet 196 ff.
16. They are rather extensively reported in Corlieu and Auffray.
17. Prévost 114.
18. Prévost 12.
19. Durand-Fardel.
20. Roland 11.
21. Delaunay 1931, 6.
22. 1864, 1:148; Rochard 280.
23. Haindorf 59.
24. Williams, 369.
25. See also Prunelle, P. Delaunay 1949.
26. Rochard 132.
27. Sachaile 501.
28. Corlieu 243.
29. Otto 30.
30. Daremberg 2:1015.
31. Maygrier 73.
32. Horn 755.
33. Muehry.
34. Otterburg 16.
35. Meding 349.
36. Auffray 64.
37. Stewart 122.

Chapter V

1. *Dict. méd.* 1839, 19:292.
2. For the biography of Pinel, see Semelaigne and Lechler.
3. Pinel 1818, 1:xxiii.

4. *Ibid.*, xlii.
5. *Ibid.*, viii.
6. Pariset 1:250; see also his inaugural address of 1806.
7. Cuvier 339.
8. Pinel 1818, 1:ciii.
9. The theory of the "epidemic constitution" (of the atmosphere) stems from Hippocrates. The Greeks, lacking the notion of contagion, attributed epidemics to unknown atmospheric or cosmic conditions which affected the entire population of a given area simultaneously. The "epidemic constitution" was the name given to the sum of these unknown conditions.
10. *Ibid.*, 363; *idem*, 1804, 386.
11. "Expectative" or "expectant" medicine, another Hippocratic idea, was medicine which did not engage in active therapy (for example, drugging, bleeding, or purging), but rather relied on nature's healing power to cure disease.
12. *Idem*, 1818, 1:xxxviii.
13. *Ibid.*, xxxix.
14. E.g., *ibid.*, lxxiii; *idem*, 1804, 397, 460, 462; *idem*, 1809, vi.
15. *Idem*, 1804, 466.
16. *Idem*, 1818, 1:xiv.
17. *Ibid.*, 7.
18. *Ibid.*, xc.
19. *Ibid.*, 2:11; Bichat 1802, 4.
20. Pinel 1818, 2:520 ff.; 2:75; 1:131.
21. For details, see Schneider 12–18.
22. See Geller.
23. The notebooks of both courses, written by Louis Nicholas Jusserandot, Bichat's disciple, friend, and later physician at Lons Le Saulnier, are in the library of the Zurich Institute of Medical History. Bichat as a pathologist and therapist will be discussed in Chapters XVI and XII.
24. Miquel 58.
25. It is significant that nobody has accused Bichat of cruelty, while Le Gallois and Magendie were much censured for the same type of experimentation.
26. Bichat 1802, 30.
27. *Ibid.*, 57.
28. *Ibid.*, 152, 64, 158.
29. *Ibid.*, 86.
30. See Weidmann.
31. Ackerknecht 1953, *Rudolph Virchow*, 71.
32. *Ibid.*, 102.
33. Regnault 18.
34. PM 1:xv.
35. *Dict. méd.* 1839, 19:293.
36. For lists, see Miquel; Bouillaud 1836, 43; Dufour, Pinel, Béclard, and Laennec prepared a Bichat edition in 1818 which never materialized.
37. Haindorf 57.
38. Petit; G. L. Bayle 1802, reprint 1856, 505.

Chapter VI

1. Letter in the Library of the Faculté de Médecine in Paris, Carton 402 (5154).
2. A very lively description of Broussais as an army physician in Spain is given in the *Souvenirs* of the pharmacist Fée.
3. Laennec 1826, xxvii; the book has nevertheless received enthusiastic praise even from anti-Broussaisists like the Louis pupil E. Bartlett (p. 208).
4. Dechambre (ed.), *Dictionnaire encyclopédique des sciences médicales*, 1869, 1:16.
5. Muehry 60.
6. Wunderlich 1859, 299.
7. Kratzmann 52.
8. Le Pelletier 399.
9. Temkin 1947, 21:298.
10. Trousseau 2:483.
11. Rochard 114 ff.
12. Charcot 7:vii.
13. Bouchut 2:208.
14. *Ibid.*, 210.
15. *Ibid.*, 227.
16. Bernard 1947, 119.
17. *Ibid.*, 19, 95, 150.
18. Wunderlich 1850, 1:31.
19. *Ibid.*, 68.
20. Virchow 35.
21. Bouchut 211, 224, 226, 381; see also Ackerknecht 1953, *Rudolf Virchow*, 58, 93, 95, 151.
22. Since military men played a preponderant role in the French hygiene movement of this time, we also encounter most of these men in this sphere; see Ackerknecht 1948, "Hygiene."
23. Réveillé-Parise 2:250.
24. Ackerknecht 1948, "Hygiene," 125. See also Leroux, F. M., *L'Expérience médicale objectée aux illusions d'une nouvelle secte*, Paris 1818, 120.
25. AG 1824, 5:307, 625.
26. RM 1825, iv, 189.
27. AG 1823, 1:73.
28. *Ibid.*, 1824, 6:140.
29. *Ibid.*, 1825, 7:153.
30. Corlieu 231.
31. Temkin 1947, 292; Ackerknecht 1948, "Hygiene," 138.
32. Broussais 1828, 490.
33. Reis 119.
34. Ackerknecht 1956, *Gall* (Eng. trans.), 32.
35. Ackerknecht 1948, "Anticontagionism," 578.
36. Reis 5; it is interesting that Reis does not mention P. C. A. Louis in this context.
37. Lee 19.
38. Holmes 429; this episode is told also by Le Pelletier 230–231, and by Beaugrand in Dechambre's *Dictionnaire* 1870, 11:160; see also Muehry 40.

39. Temkin (1947, 29e ff.) has given a splendid description of this process and the role Comte played in it. He is certainly correct in pointing out that Broussais' final acceptance of phrenology represented "a logical historical development from the point of view of his physiological premises." On the other hand, I feel that this does not exclude an interpreta-tion of B.'s phrenological activities as a political maneuver to regain popularity. He became, by the way, no orthodox phrenologist. As he said in the Academy discussion of 1836 (AG 1836, 41:112–124), he accepted "the spirit, not the letter, of Gall."

40. Peisse 1837, 2:396.

41. Lemay, *Progrès méd.* 1938, 1049.

42. Like other French materialists before (e.g., Cabanis and Georget) and after him, Broussais, in the shadow of death, felt compelled to leave a rather surprising written *profession de foi* in favor of deism.

43. Broussais 1829, 1:cxvii.

44. *Ibid.*, 1xxi.

45. AG 1824, 5:161 ff. See also Richaud des Brus, *De la non-existence du virus vénérien*, Paris 1826.

46. Ratier 1827; AG 1827, 15:247; Rosen 1951, 98.

47. Broussais 1829–1834, 4: 103; *idem*, 1822, 106.

48. Bousquet, AG 1823, 2:110; Le Pelletier 297, 309.

49. Laennec 1826, xxi.

50. Broussais 1829–1834, 4: 123.

51. *Ibid.*, 138.

52. Monfalcon 54; extensive bibliography on Broussais discussion, *ibid.*, 323–336.

53. C. Daremberg 1865, 319.

54. See Ackerknecht 1950, 49 ff.

55. Kratzmann 79.

56. Corvisart 1855, 5.

57. Le Pelletier 416.

58. Regnault 32.

59. AG 1839, 49:262.

60. E.g., Peisse 1827, 35; Kratzmann 55, 63; Le Pelletier 379.

61. AG 1829, 20:164.

62. C. Daremberg 1870, 1155.

63. Broussais 1829, 1:v.

64. Reis 30.

65. Broussais 1829, 2:222.

66. Peisse 1827, 35; Kratzmann 63.

67. Ratier, AG 1827, 14:165; Peisse 1827, 198.

68. Velpeau (Triaire 1892, 1:339) says in a letter to Bretonneau: "*Partout il en meurt (de la fièvre entéromésentérique), moins cependant, je pense, chez M. Broussais qu'ailleurs.*" Trousseau calls Broussais a good observer (*ibid.*, 484) and states (*ibid.*, 544): "*Rendez justice à Broussais en croyant que, si comme théoricien c'est un animal, comme médecin dans les maladies graves il gouverne bien ses malades.*"

69. AG 1839, 51:510.

70. E.g., Maljean.

71. Yet the label "romantic" was also applied by contemporaries to the medical writings of Rostan, an anti-Broussaisian. For the problematic character of this label, see Rosen 1961.

72. This was clear to many contemporary observers (Peisse 1827, 398; Kratzmann 64). It has been restated by Triaire (1899, 137). P. Delaunay has shown us the phenomenon admirably in its total context in his excellent political history of French medicine under the Restoration (1931, 57). To the latter author we are also indebted for an excellent case history of an average Broussaisian ("Un médecin Broussaisien: le Dr. Beunaiche de la Corbière," *Bull. Soc. Fr. Hist. Méd.* 1926, 20:397–428) which again brings clearly into focus the political element of Broussaisism.

73. Broussais was also "Napoleonic" in another sense. He, like many of his contemporaries (e.g., Dupuytren, who became the Napoleon of surgery, Balzac who wanted to be the Napoleon of literature, etc.), was infected by the megalomania of the little dictator and could build on the conditioning to a leader that his generation had undergone. Thus he became the Napoleon of medicine.

74. Le Pelletier 366; Ackerknecht 1948, 139.

75. Auber 139.

76. Rush 2:767, 906.

77. And many of his pupils blew, of course, the same horn. See, e.g., the disgusting parody of Laennec as "Dr. Lasinec" by Eusèbe de Salles (Malpart 29 ff.).

78. Broussais 1829, 2:243.

79. *Ibid.*, 4:163.

80. *Ibid.*, 366.

81. Peisse 1827, 392.

82. C. Daremberg 152.

83. Wardenburg 1:105.

84. "Inflammation is not the only cause of cancer." RM 1825, 2:177.

85. RM 1826, 2:28.

Chapter VII

1. G. L. Bayle 519–520.

2. J. Frank 44.

3. Wardenburg 2:407.

4. Héchemann 40.

5. Corvisart 1855, 5, 7, 13, 141.

6. *Ibid.*, 161.

7. Otto 2:48.

8. Corvisart 1855, 4, 290.

9. *Ibid.*, 218.

10. *Ibid.*, 260.

11. *Ibid.*, 222.

12. Corvisart 1929, Aphorism LV.

13. Corvisart 1855, 139.

14. Corvisart 1929, Aphorism I.

15. Corvisart 1855, 9, 246–250.

16. *Ibid.*, 13:254.

17. Pariset 1:124.

18. "Think of our Laennec so forbearing as to himself but so ready to resent offense when physiologism dares to touch Bayle, his most regretted teacher and friend." (Bretonneau; see also Laennec's eulogy of Bayle, 1826, 2:341–342).

19. Grandmaison 1889.
20. G. L. Bayle, in A. L. Bayle and Thillaye 2:888.
21. G. L. Bayle 1802, 506.
22. *Ibid.*, 507, 363, 493.
23. *Ibid.*, 510.
24. *Ibid.*, 510, 490.
25. Corvisart 1929, Aphorisms XXX–XXXVI; Bayle 1802, 519.
26. *Ibid.*, 358.
27. G. L. Bayle 1810, 363.
28. *Ibid.*, 478.
29. *Ibid.*, 377.
30. *Ibid.*, 487, 387.
31. *Ibid.*, 489.
32. *Ibid.*, 394.
33. *Ibid.*, 479, 393, 481.
34. DSM 1812, 671, 675.
35. Rouxeau's volumes are still the best biography of Laennec.
36. The only monograph on Guillaume Laennec is the 1964 Zurich thesis of B. Wigdorowits.
37. Manuscript of pathological anatomy course of 1803.
38. Bichat 1827.
39. Laennec 1826, 1:7.
40. *Ibid.*, 64.
41. *Hist. de la Méd.*, May 1964, 9; Kopp 101.
42. Morel de Rubempré 1825.
43. Triaire 1899, 137.
44. Cousin 172; Ratier 1827.
45. Laennec 1804, 31.
46. See Cayol, RM 1830, 2:1; on obsolescence of the concept, see Kratzmann 206; Dechambre's *Dictionnaire* 19:758.
47. *Ibid.*, 346.
48. Ackerknecht 1953, *Rudolph Virchow*, 100.
49. 1:xxv.
50. 1:133.
51. 1:183.
52. 1:280.
53. *Ibid.*, 494, 182.
54. *Ibid.*, 501.
55. Ed. of 1819, 1:21.
56. Ed. of 1826, 1:537 ff.
57. *Ibid.*, 555 ff.
58. 2:769.
59. 1:646.
60. *Ibid.*, 649.
61. *Ibid.*, 696.
62. 2:93.
63. *Ibid.*, 97.
64. *Ibid.*, 196.

65. *Ibid.*, 481.
66. For a more detailed discussion of these manuscripts, see Ackerknecht 1964.
67. RM 1833, 1:359.
68. See his *aggrégation* thesis of 1823.
69. For a more detailed discussion, see Ackerknecht 1962.
70. It shows him personally far more aggressive and argumentative than his printed work.
71. See Isler.
72. See Florkin.
73. See Triaire 1899.
74. 323.
75. See Ratier, AG 1827, 14:557.
76. A detailed report on Cayol by Ratier, RM 1829, 1:68 ff.

Chapter VIII

1. RM 1830, 1:270.
2. Peisse 1837, 2:305.
3. 90.
4. Triaire 1899, 355; Dubois d'Amiens 2:383 ff.
5. 1:415.
6. Ratier 1827, 49.
7. Chomel 1834, 318 ff.
8. Schneider 38.
9. for Grisolles psychosomatics, *Ibid.*, 40.
10. Gardner 157; Ratier 1827, 29 ff., x. 63.
11. Wunderlich 1841, 121.
12. Peisse 1837, 1:134.
13. Delaunay 1953, 330; on Louis, see also Shryock 1936.
14. Schiller.
15. Holmes 431; Wunderlich 1841, 121; Muehry 81; Isensee 2:642; Otterburg.
16. Andral 1823–1827, vi.
17. Astruc 1935.
18. Kratzmann 108.
19. Wunderlich 1841, 139; Pariset Vol. 2.
20. Sachaile 441.
21. Jaccoud 56 ff.; Béclard and Axenfeld 5.
22. Ackerknecht 1953, *Rudolph Virchow*, ii.
23. Caveribert.
24. See Dejeant 1930.
25. 1841, 121.
26. Luteaud.
27. Piorry 1837, xi.
28. *Idem*, 1839, 359.
29. *Ibid.*, 526.
30. Schneider 42.
31. Piorry 1837, 417.
32. *Idem*, 1867, 500; 1839, 51.

33. *Idem*, 1867, 260.
34. *Idem*, 1839, 427, 450.
35. *Ibid.*, 369.
36. See his *Traité* of 1840, and Semadeni.
37. Corlieu, 502.
38. 1841, 122.
39. Rostan 1826, 13.
40. See Corlieu 471 for extensive discussion of their relationship.
41. Rostan 1826, 30.
42. Schneider 34.
43. For more on Trousseau's personality, see Labarthe; Helme.
44. 1:427, 645, 874.
45. Schneider 47, 50.
46. 1:155, 43, 879; 2:204.
47. 3:819 ff.

Chapter IX

1. Delaunay 1949, 34; see also Huard 1962.
2. Schultes 2:181.
3. Maygrier 215 ff.
4. Meding 262.
5. See lists in Corlieu; Maygrier; Stewart; Sachaile, etc.
6. Véron 1:341.
7. 411.
8. 43.
9. Mutzner.

Chapter X

1. 202.
2. *Gazette médicale*, Jan. 4, 1841, 17.
3. 22.
4. 324 ff.
5. For an example, see Cranefield; for the whole complex, see Ackerknecht 1957.
6. Le Gendre 77.
7. Charcot 1:xxxii.
8. Reprinted in Pasteur's *Oeuvres*, Paris 1939, Vol. 7.
9. Laennec 1826, 2:233.
10. See Chapter I.
11. Ackerknecht 1949.
12. Poumiès de la Siboutie 91.
13. AG 1824, 4:479.
14. Holmes 422; Haberling 41.
15. See Liard; Williams; d'Irsay; Puschmann; Flexner.
16. 10, 14–15.
17. Pasteur 1939, 36.
18. Cert. 94.

19. Trousseau 36.
20. Fayet 476.
21. Olmsted; Arnold.
22. Lichtenthaeler.
23. Otto 2: 129; Gardner 70.
24. Wunderlich 1859, 319 ff.; Kratzmann 79, 85.
25. Trousseau, in Triaire 1892.
26. AG 1824, 4:256.
27. AG 1845, 4:8.
28. Berman 1963.
29. On Dutrochet, see Rich; on Raspail, Weiner; on Donné, Dreyfus; on Dujardin and Davaine, Théodoridès 1960, 1961.
30. AG 1839, 3:154.
31. Nordenskjöld.
32. Merz 2:230.
33. Corlieu 204, 319; RM 1831, 1:322.
34. Astruc 23.
35. Corlieu 255.
36. Ibid.
37. AG 1826, 10:146 ff.

Chapter XI

1. Cless, AG 1840, 52:377; Kratzmann 115 ff.; Muehry 86 ff.;Casper 85; Wunderlich 1841, 16; idem, 1859, 318. For the whole complex, see Ackerknecht 1958.
2. A. L. Bayle, Préface; Cayol; J. L. Brachet, De l'emploi de l'opium, Lyon 1828; Küntzli 16; Rilliet and Barthez; Bouchut, in Petersen 181; Trousseau 1:827; Regnault 29.
3. Hecht, Dechambre's Dictionnaire 1876, 18:136.
4. Rostan 1864, 75, 375.
5. Delaunay 1906.
6. PM 2:92.
7. Frank 31.
8. Cert. 118.
9. Ratier 1825, 58.
10. Pinel 1818, 1xxvi.
11. Idem, 1804, 441.
12. Idem, 1818, 276, 314.
13. Idem, 1804, xxii.
14. Ibid., 15.
15. Ibid., 425.
16. Idem, 1818, 334.
17. Idem, 1804, 400.
18. Ibid., 148.
19. RM 1830, 4:109.
20. DSM, Vol. 60, "Therapie."
21. 1811, 105.
22. Dufour 253.

CHAPTER IX

23. Ratier, RM 1829, 4:33.
24. Ratier 1825, 26.
25. *Bibl. méd.*, Vol. 10, Paris 1805, p. 290.
26. *Dict. méd.* 1844, Vol. 29, "Therapeutique."
27. Trousseau 1:100; Pidoux 2:485, 714.
28. For details, see Mac-Auliffe 1904; Grasset 1911; Delaunay 1949.
29. Translation of Auenbrugger 243.
30. 610.
31. 607.
32. 393.
33. 609, 608.
34. 517.
35. Laennec 1826, 1:703.
36. Ackerknecht 1962, 95.
37. Laennec 1826, 1:499.
38. 193.
39. Delaunay 1949, 78.
40. Wunderlich 1841, 123.
41. Olmsted 155.
42. Trousseau 1:709.
43. Ratier 1827, 97–98.
44. Petersen 1877, 184–210; E. Lesky, *Wiener Med. Wschr.* 1956, 68:728, 1965, 146 ff.
45. Peisse 1:160.
46. 1844, 286.
47. 203.
48. Ackerknecht 1962, 395.
49. Kremers and Urdang 471; Bouillet 333; Julia Fontenelle, AG 1824, 6:152.
50. Olmsted 152.
51. Ackerknecht 1945, 104.
52. *Idem*, 1962, 412.
53. *Ibid.*, 409.
54. Buess.
55. Olmsted 130.
56. Ackerknecht 1962, 404 ff.
57. Baptiste; A. L. Bayle 1:407–507.
58. Delaunay 1949, 75; Walser.
59. Avignon 1776, 30.
60. See also the thesis of J. T. Poussel, Paris 1820; Chomel, *Gaz. d'hôp.* 1846, 8:498.

Chapter XII

1. Rochard; Delaunay 1906; Ackerknecht 1960.
2. Ammon 39.
3. Desault 1:28.
4. C. Daremberg 2:1296.
5. 74.
6. Casper 186; Muehry 44.

7. Delaunay 1931, 91.
8. Also noted in his competitor Lisfranc, Horn 262.
9. See Amussat; Lesky 1961.
10. 1859, 305.
11. 151.
12. 324.
13. 2:58.
14. 139.
15. Casper 140.
16. 324.
17. 125.
18. He is the Dr. Desplein of the *Comédie humaine*.
19. In Pilastre 153.
20. Wardenburg 2:35, 196; 2: 295; Andrée 72; Rochard; Marx..
21. Dufour.
22. Sigerist 316.
23. Regnault 23.
24. 379.
25. 1:86–87.
26. *Discours d'ouverture*, Collège de France 1824.
27. 2:138.
28. RM 1835, 2:329.
29. Pauly, in Lisfranc; Pilastre 183.
30. RM 1825, 4:393.
31. Richerand 129.
32. Otterburg 129.
33. Denonvillers *et al.* 623.
34. Rochard 267.
35. xiii.

Chapter XIII

1. For "hygiene" as a method of treatment, see Chapter XI.
2. Rosen 1958, 131 ff.
3. Ackerknecht 1948, "Hygiene," 118.
4. 259.
5. 713.
6. Bernard 1865, 35.
7. Dubois d'Amiens 1: 219 ff.
8. Véron 308.
9. Delaunay 1931.
10. Bouchardat 1867, 5.
11. Pariset 1:150–154.
12. Meding 219–251.
13. Rayer 1826, xxii.
14. See Ackerknecht 1952, "Villermé"; Astruc
15. Ackerknecht 1953, "Virchow, "46.

16. 14.
17. *Annales d'hyg. publ.* 1:v.
18. 5.
19. Cert. 28.
20. 6.
21. Brodier 239–240.
22. ix.
23. xiii.
24. Villermé 1833.
25. PM 2:240–242.
26. *Dict. med.* 1834, 8:503.
27. Ackerknecht 1952, "Maladies."
28. *Idem,* 1959.
29. See also Rosen 1951.
30. Charcot 8:144.
31. Delaunay 1949, 55, 68.
32. Weiner 154.

Chapter XIV

1. 1841, 17.
2. 192.
3. Guardia 482.
4. Bichat 1800, 138.
5. 1944, 16.
6. 1:305 ff.
7. Auffray 7.
8. For a list, see Casper.
9. Rev. 323; see also Daremberg 1201 and Rayer 1818, 99.
10. More extensive lecture notes exist in the Zurich Institute and in Grenoble (see Monteil).
11. Bichat 1827, 211.
12. *Ibid.,* 247.
13. *Ibid.,* 301, 304.
14. Miquel 84.
15. Dubois 1838, 383.
16. Ackerknecht 1964, "Laennec," 150.
17. Ratier 1827, 21.
18. Delhoume 1937, 47 ff.
19. Mérat, "Lesions organiques," DSM 27:490, 18.
20. Corlieu 324.
21. Delhoume 1937, 165.
22. Andral 1829 1:537, 541.
23. For details, see Ackerknecht 1958, *Nervenärzte;* 1959, *Short History.*
24. Rosen 1963; Foucault 1961.
25. See the description by his son Scipio, *Mém. acad. méd.* 1836, 5:31.
26. For an eyewitness report, see Frank 84 ff.
27. For Daquin, see Nyfeller.

28. Casper.
29. Muellener 1964, *Sud. Arch.*
30. For an eyewitness report, see Horn 699 ff., 722 ff.
31. Esquirol 1:49.
32. *Mém. acad. méd.* 1840, 9:229.
33. Kratzmann 255.
34. For details, see Müller.
35. Rev. 422.
36. PM 1:356–357.
37. *Ibid.*, 145.
38. *Ibid.*, 60, 95:319.
39. PM 2:409, 359.
40. Cert. 149.
41. PM 1:149.
42. 250–254.
43. 254.
44. 246.
45. 560.
46. 123, 217, 242, 248.
47. See Ackerknecht and Vallois; Ackerknecht 1956, "Dumoutier."
48. For the history of pediatrics, see Peiper.
49. Wyss.
50. Muellener 1965.
51. Bianchetti.
52. Grmek.
53. Geller; Charcot 7:4 ff.
54. Ackerknecht 1948, "Hygiene," 122.
55. Ebneter.
56. Häfliger; Haller.
57. Mantel.
58. For details concerning ophthalmology, see Hirschberg.
59. Bass.

Chapter XV

1. Saucerotte; Chevalier.
2. Delaunay 1931.
3. Astruc.
4. Ackerknecht 1952, "Villermé," 328.
5. *Idem*, 1932, 74 ff.
6. For elements of a bibliography of the very extensive literature, see Ackerknecht 1932; *idem* 1947, 136; Delaunay 1931, 72.
7. Muehry 225 ff.
8. Cert. 127, 154.
9. DSM 1819, 31:293, 307, 331, 345.
10. 13, 21.
11. Dechambre's *Dictionnaire* 1882, 27:500.

Chapter XVI

1. Bayer.
2. 15.
3. 147, 163, 153.
4. Echoes of this in Baas 650.
5. Ackerknecht 1950.
6. Muellener 1964; Ackerknecht 1964, "La médecine à Gèneve."
7. Knegtel.

Chapter XVII

1. Le Breton.
2. Le Yaouanc 31–39.
3. Ibid., 510–516; see also Cruchet 234 ff.
4. Ackerknecht and Vallois; Ackerknecht 1956, "Dumoutier."
5. Ackerknecht 1955, 36.

BIBLIOGRAPHY

Ackerknecht, E. H.   *Beiträge zur Geschichte der Medizinalreform*. Leipzig 1932 (also *Sudh. Arch.* 1932, 61–183).

Ackerknecht, E. H.   "Hygiene in France, 1815–1848," *Bull. Hist. Med.* 1948, 22:117–155.

Ackerknecht, E. H.   "Anticontagionism between 1821 and 1867," *Bull. Hist. Med.* 1948, 22:562–593.

Ackerknecht, E. H.   "Recurrent Themes in Medical Thought," *Scientific Monthly* 1949, 69:80–83.

Ackerknecht, E. H.   "Elisha Bartlett and the Philosophy of the Paris Clinical School," *Bull. Hist. Med.* 1950, 24:34–60.

Ackerknecht, E. H.   "Villermé and Quetelet," *Bull. Hist. Med.* 1952, 26:317–329.

Ackerknecht, E. H.   "Maladies et Sociétés," *Arch. Internat. Hist. Sc.* 1952, 309–319.

Ackerknecht, E. H.   "Broussais or a Forgotten Medical Revolution," *Bull. Hist. Med.* 1953, 27:320–343.

Ackerknecht, E. H.   *Rudolf Virchow: Doctor, Statesman, Anthropologist*. Madison, Wisc. 1953.

Ackerknecht, E. H., and Vallois, Henri V.   *François Joseph Gall et sa collection*. Paris 1955.

Ackerknecht, E. H., and Vallois, Henri V.   *Franz Joseph Gall, Inventor of Phrenology and His Collection*. Trans. Claire St. Léon. ("Wisconsin Studies in Medical History," No. 1.) Madison, Wisc. 1956.

Ackerknecht, E. H.   "P. M. A. Dumoutier et la collection phrénologique du Musée de l'Homme," *Bull. Soc. Anthr.* (Paris) 1956, I, VII, X series, 289–308.

Ackerknecht, E. H.   "Medical Education in 19th Century France," *Journ. Med. Ed.* 1957, 32:148–152.

Ackerknecht, E. H.   "Typen der medizinischen Ausbildung im 19. Jahrhundert," *Schw. M. Wochschr.* 1957, 45:1361–1366.

Ackerknecht, E. H.   *La médecine à Paris entre 1800 et 1850*. ("Les Conférences du Palais de la découverte," Series D, No. 58.) Paris 1958.

Ackerknecht, E. H.   "Zur Geschichte der Lehr- and Forschungsstätter für Psychiatrie und Neurologie in Europa," in Kolle, K. *Grosse Nervenärzte*, Vol. II. Stuttgart 1958, 223–230.

Ackerknecht, E. H.   "Die Therapie der Pariser Kliniker zwischen 1795 und 1840," *Gesnerus* 1958, 15:151–163.

Ackerknecht, E. H.   *A Short History of Psychiatry*. Trans. Sulammith Wolff. New York 1959.

Ackerknecht, E. H.   "Alexàndre de Humboldt," *Presse méd.* 1959, 67:1764.

Ackerknecht, E. H.   "Die Pariser Spitäler als Ausgangspunkt einer neuen Medizin," *Ciba Symposium* 1959, 7:98–105.

Ackerknecht, E. H.   "Pariser Chirurgie von 1794–1850," *Gesnerus* 1960, 17:137–144.

Ackerknecht, E. H.   "Laennec und die Psychiatrie," *Gesnerus* 1962, 19:93–100.

Ackerknecht, E. H.   "Aspects of the History of Therapeutics," *Bull. Hist. Med.* 1962, 36:387–419.

Ackerknecht, E. H.   "Laennec und sein Vorlesungsmanuskript von 1822," *Gesnerus* 1964, 21:142–154.

Ackerknecht, E. H.   "La médecine à Genève, surtout dans la première motié du 19e siècle," *Proceed. XIX. Int. Congr. Hist. Méd.* (Basel) 1964. Basel 1966, 420–425.

Alhoy, L. F. J.   *Promenades poétiques dans les hospices et hôpitaux de Paris.* Paris 1826.

Alibert, J. L.   *Éloges historiques, composés pour la Société médicale de Paris, suivis d'un Discours sur les rapports de la médecine avec les sciences physiques et morales.* Paris 1806.

Ammon, F. A. von.   *Parallele der französischen und deutschen Chirurgie: nach Resultaten einer in den Jahren 1821 und 1822 gemachten Reise.* Leipzig 1823.

Amussat, J. Z.   *Recherches sur l'introduction accidentelle de l'air dans les veines.* Paris 1839.

Andral, Gabriel.   *Clinique médicale; ou, Choix d'observations recueillies à la Clinique de M. Lerminier.* 4 vols. 1823–1827.

Andral, Gabriel.   *Traité d'anatomie pathologique.* 3 vols. Paris 1829.

Andral, Gabriel.   *Essai d'hématologie pathologique.* Paris 1843.

Andrée, C. M.   *Neuester Zustand der vorzüglichsten Spitäler und Armenstalten in einigen Hauptorten des In- und Auslandes.* Leipzig 1810.

Archives générales de Médecine.   Ed. Raige-Delorme. Paris 1823–1879.

Arnold, K.   *Die Geschichte der französischen Physiologie 1750–1850.* Munster 1959.

Astruc, Pierre.   *L.-R. Villermé.* Paris 1933.

Astruc, Pierre.   *Gabriel Andral.* Paris 1935.

Astruc, Pierre.   "1848 et la Médecine," *Progrès méd.* 1946, Nos. 12–13.

Astruc, Pierre.   "La médecine au 19e siècle," *Progrès méd.* 1957, Nos. 15–18.

Auber, T. C. E.   *Philosophie de la médecine.* Paris 1865.

Auenbrugger, Leopold.   *Nouvelle méthode pour reconnaître les maladies internes de la poitrine traduit et commenté par Jean Nicholas Corvisart.* Paris 1808; reprint Paris 1855.

Auffray, Y.   *L'enseignement de la médecine au XIXe siècle.* Rennes 1963.

Baas, J. H.   *Grundriss der Geschichte der Medizin und des heilenden Standes.* Stuttgart 1876.

Baptiste, Roger.   *L'acupuncture et son histoire; avantages et inconvénients d'une thérapeutique millenaire.* Paris 1962.

Bartlett, Elisha.   *An Essay on the Philosophy of Medical Science.* Philadelphia 1844.

Bass, G.   *Die Gerichtsmedizin als Spezialfach in Paris von 1800 bis 1850.* Zurich 1964.

Bayle, A. L.   *Bibliothèque de thérapeutique; ou, Recueil de mémoires originaux et des travaux anciens et modernes sur le traitement des maladies et l'emploi des medicamens.* 4 vols. Paris 1828–1837.

Bayle, A. L., and Thillaye, Auguste.   *Biographie médicale, par ordre chronologique d'après Daniel le Clerc, Eloy ... .* 2 vols. Paris 1855.

Bayle, G. L.   *Idée générale de la thérapeutique.* Paris 1805; reprint Paris 1855.

Bayle, G. L.   *Recherches sur la phthisie pulmonaire ... .* Paris 1810; reprint, Paris 1855.

Bayer, F. W.   *Reisen deutscher Aerzte im Ausland (1750–1850).* Berlin 1937.

Béclard, P. A., and Axenfeld, [?].   *Rapport sur les progrès de la médecine en France par MM. Béclard and Axenfeld.* Paris 1867.

Béclard, J. A.   *Notices et portraits. Éloges lus a l'Académie de Médecine.* Paris 1878.

Berman, A.   "Conflict and Anomaly in the Scientific Orientation of French Pharmacy 1800–1873," *Bull. Hist. Med.* 1963, 37:440–462.

Berman, A.   "The Scientific Tradition in French Hospital Pharmacy," *Am. J. Hosp. Pharm.* 1961, 18:110.

Bernard, Claude.   *Introduction à l'étude de la médecine expérimentale.* Paris 1865.

Bernard, Claude.   *Rapport sur les progrès de la marche de la physiologie générale en France.* Paris 1867.

Bernard, Claude.   *Principes de la médecine experimentale.* Paris 1947.

Berthier, Ferdinand.   *Considérations physiologiques et médicales sur le plaisir.* Paris 1821.

Bianchetti, B.   *Charles-Michel Billard und sein traité des maladies des enfants nouveau-nés.* Zurich 1963.

Bichat, M.-F.-X.   *Recherches physiologiques sur la vie et la mort.* Paris 1800.

Bichat, M.-F.-X.   *Traité des membranes en général, et de diverse membranes en particulier ... .* Paris 1802.

Bichat, M.-F.-X.   *Anatomie pathologique.* German trans., Leipzig 1827.

Bichat, M.-F.-X.   *Anatomie générale, appliquée à la physiologie et à la médecine ... .* Paris 1830.

Binet, Léon, and Vallery-Radot, Pierre.   *La Faculté de Médecine de Paris: Cinq siècles d'art et d'histoire.* Paris 1952.

Bouchardat, Apollinaire.   *Nouveau formulaire magistral ... .* Paris 1853.

Bouchardat, Apollinaire.   *Rapport sur les progrès de l'hygiène en France.* Paris 1867.

Bouchut, Eugène.   *Histoire de la médecine et des doctrines médicales.* 2 vols. Paris 1873.

Bouillaud, J. B.   *Essai sur la philosophie médicale et sur les généralités de la clinique médicale ... .* Paris 1836

Bouillet, J.   *Précis d'histoire de la médecine.* Paris 1883.

Brodier, Léon.   *J.-L. Alibert, médecin de l'Hôpital Saint-Louis (1768–1837).* Paris 1923.

Broussais, F. J. V.   *De l'irritation et de la folie.* Paris 1828.

Broussais, F. J. V.   *Examen des doctrines médicales et des systèmes de nosologie.* 4 vols. Paris 1829–1834.

Broussais, F. J. V.   *Histoire des phlegmasies ou inflammations chroniques.* 2 vols. Paris 1822.

Buchez, P. J. B.   *Introduction à l'étude de sciences médicales ... .* Paris 1838.

Buess, H.   "Die Injektion," *Ciba Zeitschrift* No. 100, March 1946.

Burgener, P.   *Die Einflüsse des zeitgenössischen Denkens in Morels Begriff der Dégenerescence.* Zurich 1964.

Cabanis, P. J. G.   *Coup d'oeil sur les révolutions et sur la réforme de la médecine.* Paris 1804.

Cabanis, P. J. G.   *Du dégré de certitude de la médecine.* 3d ed. Paris 1819.

Cabanis, P. J. G.   *Rapports du physique et du moral de l'homme.* 2 vols. Paris 1824.

Casper, J. L.   *Charakteristik der französischen medicin, mit vergleichenden Hinblicken auf die englische.* Leipzig 1822.

Cattet, J. J. F., and Gardet, J. B. J.   *Essai sur la contagion.* Paris 1802.

Caveribert, Raoul.   *La vie et l'oeuvre de Rayer (1793–1867).* Paris 1931.

Cayol, J. B.   *Clinique médicale, suivie d'un traité des maladies cancereuses.* Paris 1833.

Chaptal, A.   *Mes souvenirs sur Napoléon.* Paris 1893.

Charcot, J. M.   *Oeuvres complètes, recueilliés et publiées par Bourneville.* 9 vols. Paris 1886–1890.

Charlton, D. G.   *Positivist Thought in France during the Second Empire, 1852–1870.* Oxford 1959.

Chevalier, A.   "Aerzte der französischen Revolution," *Ciba Zeitschrift* 1938, No. 60.

Chomel, A. F.   *Leçons de clinique médicale, faites à l'Hôtel-Dieu de Paris par le professeur A. F. Chomel ... .* Vol. I: *Fièvre typhoide.* Paris 1834.

Chomel, A. F.   *Elements of General Pathology.* Trans. F. E. Oliver, M.D., and W. W. Morland, M.D. 3d ed., enlarged. Boston 1848.

Corlieu, Auguste.   *Le centenaire de la Faculté de Médecine de Paris (1794–1894) ... .* Paris 1896.

Corvisart, J. N.   *Essai sur les maladies et les lésions organiques du coeur et des gros vaisseaux.* Paris 1818; reprint Paris 1855.

Corvisart, J. N.   *Aphorismes de médecine clinique, par le baron Corvisart. Recueillis par F. V. Merat.* Paris 1929.

Coste, J. F.   *Du genre de philosophie propre à l'étude et à la pratique de la médecine.* Nancy 1775.

Coste, J. F.   "Hôpital," *Dict. sc. méd.* 21:367–544. Paris 1817.

Cousin, V.   *De l'enseignement et de l'exercise de la médecine et de la pharmacie.* Paris 1850.

Cranefield, P. F.   "Charles E. Morgan's *Electro-Physiology and Therapeutics:* An Unknown English Version of DuBois-Raymond's *Thierische Elektricität,*" *Bull. Hist. Med.* 1957, 31:176.

Cruchet, René.   *La médecine dans la littérature française.* Baton Rouge, La. 1939.

Cruveilhier, Jean.   *Essai sur l'anatomie pathologique en général, et sur les transformations et productions organiques en particulier.* Paris 1816.

Cuvier, Georges.   *Rapport historique sur les progrès des sciences naturelles depuis 1789, et sur leur état actuel ... .* Paris 1810.

Daremberg, C. V.   *La médecine. Histoire et doctrines.* Paris 1869.

Daremberg, C. V.   *Histoire des sciences médicales, comprenant l'anatomie, la physiologie, la médecine, la chirurgie et les doctrines de pathologie générale.* Paris 1870.

Daremberg, Georges.   *Les grands médecins du XIXᵉ siècle.* Paris 1907.

Dejeant, H. G.   *La vie et l'oeuvre de Bouillaud.* Paris 1930.

Delaunay, Paul.   *Le monde médical parisien au dix-huitième siècle.* 2d ed. Paris 1906.

Delaunay, Paul.   "La médecine et les idéologues: L.-J. Moreau de la Sarthe," *Bull. Soc. Fr. Hist. Med.* 1920, 14:24.

Delaunay, Paul.   *Les médecins, la Restauration et la Révolution de 1830.* Tours 1931.

Delaunay, Paul.   *D'une révolution à l'autre 1789–1848.* Paris 1949.

Delaunay, Paul.   *Louis and the Numerical Method in Science, Medicine, and History.* London 1953, 321–330.

Delhoume, Léon.   *Dupuytren.* 3d ed. Paris 1935.

Delhoume, Léon.   *Cruveilhier.* Paris 1937.

Denonvilliers, C. P., Nélaton, Velpeau, Guyon, Félix, and Labbé, Léon.   *Rapport sur les progrès de la chirurgie.* Paris 1867.

Desault, P. J.   *Oeuvres chirurgicales de P. J. Desault.* Ed. Xavier Bichat. 2 vols. Paris 1789.

Dictionnaire de médecine ou répetoire général des sciences médicales ... . Ed. Adelon et al. 30 vols. 2d ed. Paris 1832–1849.

Dictionnaire des sciences médicales.   Ed. Adelon, Aland, Alibert et al. 60 vols. Paris 1812–22.

Dictionnaire encyclopédique des sciences médicales, publié sous la direction de MM. les docteurs Raige-Delorme et A. Dechambre, par MM. les docteurs Axenfeld, Baillarger ... .   100 vols. Paris 1864–1889.

Double, F. J.   *Séméiologie générale ou, traité des signes et de leur valeur dans les maladies.* 3 vols. Paris 1811–1822.

Dreyfus, C.   "Alfred Donné, "*Nouv. Rev. Fr. d'Hématologie,* 1962, 2:241–255.

Dubois, Frédéric.   *Traité des études médicales, ou de la manière d'étudier et d'enseigner la médecine.* Paris 1838.

Dubois, Frédéric.   *Éloges de l'Académie de Médecine.* 2 vols. Paris 1864.

Dufour, J. M. L.   *A travers un siècle, 1780–1865, science et histoire.* Paris 1888.

Dupic, Antoine.   *Antoine Dubois, chirurgien et accoucheur*. Paris 1907.
Durand-Fardel, Raymond.   *L'internat en médecine et en chirurgie des hôpitaux et hospices civils de Paris. Centenaire de l'internat, 1802–1902*. Paris 1903.

Ebneter, F.   *Die Dermatologie in Paris 1800–1850*. Zurich 1964.
Erez, Ruth.   *Marshall Hall 1797–1857*. Zurich 1963.

Faber, R.   *Nosography*. New York 1923.
Fayet, Joseph.   *La Révolution Française et la science, 1789–1795*. Paris 1960.
Fée, A. L. A.   *Souvenirs*. Paris 1856.
Fiaux, F. L.   *L'enseignement de la médecine en Allemagne*. Paris 1877.
Fischer, P.   *Der Traité clinique des maladies des enfants von Rilliet und Barthez*. Zurich 1960.
Flexner, Abraham.   *Medical Education: A Comparative Study*. New York 1925.
Florkin, Marcel.   *Naissance et déviation de la théorie cellulaire dans l'oeuvre de Théodore Schwann*. Paris 1960.
Fodéré, F. E.   *Traité de médecine légale et d'hygiène publique; ou, De police de santé, adapté aux codes de l'Empire français ... .* 3 vols. Paris 1799.
Foucault, M. J. P.   *Histoire de la folie à l'âge classique; folie et déraison*. Paris 1961.
Foucault, M. J. P.   *Naissance de clinique*. Paris 1963.
Frank, Joseph.   *Reise nach Paris, London, und einem grossen Theile des übrigen Englands und Schottlands in Beziehung auf Spitäler ... .* Vienna 1804–1805.

Gadient, A.   *Die Anfänge der Urologie als Spezialfach in Paris*. Zurich 1963.
Ganière, P.   *Corvisart*. Paris 1951.
Gardner, A. K.   *Old Wine in New Bottles; or Spare Hours of a Student in Paris*. New York 1848.
Geller, G.   *Die Geriatrie an der Salpêtrière von Pinel bis Charcot*. Zurich 1965.
Georget, E. J.   *De la physiologie du système nerveux*. Paris 1821.
Gerdy, P. N.   *Physiologie philosophique*. Paris 1846.
Goris, A.   *Centenaire de l'internat en pharmacie des hôpitaux de Paris*. Paris 1920.
Grandmaison, G. de.   *La Congrégation*. Paris 1889.
Grasset, Hector.   *Histoire de la physiothérapie*. Paris 1911.
Grmek, M. D.   *On Ageing and Old Age; Basic Problems and Historic Aspects of Gerontology and Geriatrics*. The Hague 1958.
Guardia, J. M. M.   *Histoire de la médecine*. Paris 1884.
Guiart, J.   *Histoire de la médecine française*. Lyons 1947.
Guillier, O.   *Histoire de l'Hôpital Nôtre-Dame de Pitié 1618–1882*. Paris 1882.

Haberling, Wilhelm.   *Johannes Mueller*. Leipzig 1924.
Häfliger, Eduard.   *Die Orthopädie in Paris von 1800–1850*. Zurich 1965.
Haindorf, Alexander.   *Beiträge z. Culturgeschichte der Medizin und Chirurgie Frankreichs, und vorzüglich seiner Hauptstadt ... .* Göttingen 1815.
Haller, F. W.   *Vertebragene Erkrankungen in medizinhistorischer Sicht*. Bonn 1962.
Héchemann, L.   *Corvisart*. Paris 1906.
Helme, François.   *Les jardins de la médecine*. Paris 1907.
Hirschberg, Julius.   "Frankreichs Augenärzte 1800–1850," in Graefe-Saemisch, *Handbuch der ges. Augenheilkunde*, Vol. XIV, Div. 3. Leipzig 1912.

Hoffmann, L. F.   *La peste à Barcelone.* Paris 1964.

Holmes, O. W.   *Medical Essays, 1842–1882.* Boston 1891.

Horn, Wilhelm.   *Reise durch Deutschland, Ungarn, Holland, Italien, Frankreich, Grossbritannien und Irland ... .* 4 vols. Berlin 1831–1833.

Huard, P. A.   "Jean Civiale," *88 Congr. des Soc. Sav.* 1963, 3:109–115.

Huard, P. A.   "La fortune des médecins français au XIX siècle," *Concours Médical* 1962, 6274–6283, 6427–6430.

Ingrand, H.   *Le Comité de Salubrité de l'Assemblée Nationale Constituante.* Paris 1934.

Irsay, Stephen d'.   *Histoire des universités françaises et étrangères des origines à nos jours.* 2 vols. Paris 1933–35.

Isensee, Emil.   *Die Geschichte der Medizin und ihrer Hulfwissenschaften.* 2 vols. Berlin 1840.

Isler, H. R.   *Thomas Willis.* Stuttgart 1965.

Jaccoud, Sigismond.   *De l'humorisme ancien comparé à l'humorisme moderne.* Paris 1863.

Knegtel, M. M.   "Médecins Neerlandais à Paris 1818–1842," *Hist. de la Méd.* May 1964, 3–11.

Kopp, J. H.   *Aerztliche Bemerkungen, veranlasst durch eine Reise in Deutschland und Frankreich im Frühjahr und Sommer 1824.* Frankfurt a. M. 1825.

Kratzmann, Emil.   *Die neuere Medizin in Frankreich, nach Theorie und Praxis.* Leipzig 1846.

Kremers, Edward, and Urdang, George.   *History of Pharmacy: A Guide and a Survey.* 2d ed. rev. Philadelphia 1951.

Künzli, M.   *État de la médecine. Plan d'organisation médicale.* Paris 1846.

Labarthe, Paul.   *Nos médecins contemporains.* Paris 1868.

Laennec, R. T. H.   *Propositions sur la doctrine d'Hippocrate.* Paris 1804.

Laennec, R. T. H.   *Traité de l'auscultation médiate et des maladies des poumons et du coeur.* Paris 1826.

Lain Entralgo, P.   "Sensualism and Vitalism in Bichat's *Anatomie générale*," *Journ. Hist. Med.* 1948, 3:47 ff.

Le Breton, Eugène.   *La maison de santé du Dr. Blanche.* Paris 1937.

Lechler, W. H.   *Philippe Pinel; seine Familie, seine Jugend- und Studienjahre, 1745–1778 ... .* Munich 1959.

Lee, Edwin.   *Observations on the Principal Medical Institutions and Practice of France, Italy, and Germany. With Notices of the Universities, and Cases from Hospital Practice.* Philadelphia 1837.

Le Gendre, Paul.   *Un médecin philosophe, Charles Bouchard; son oeuvre et son temps.* Paris 1924.

Lepage, Gabriel.   *L'Association Générale de Médecins de France 1858–1908.* Paris 1908.

Le Pelletier de la Sarthe, A.   *Histoire de la révolution médicale du XIXᵉ siècle.* Paris 1854.

Lesky, Erna.   "Cabanis und die Gewissheit de Heilkunde," *Gesnerus* 1954, 11:152.

Lesky, Erna.   "Notes on the History of Air Embolism," *Germ. Med. Monthly* 1961, 6:159–161.

Lesky, Erna.   *Die Wiener Medizinische Schule im 19. Jahrhundert.* Graz and Cologne 1965.

Le Yaouanc, M.   *Nosographie de l'humanité Balzacienne.* Paris 1959.

Liard, L.   *L'enseignement supérieur en France 1789–1889.* Paris 1888.

228

Lichtenthaeler, Charles. "Les dates de la renaissance médicale," *Gesnerus* 1952, 9: 8–30.
Lisfranc, Jacques. *Maladies de l'utérus, d'après les leçons cliniques de Lisfranc, faites à l'Hôpital de la Pitié, par H. Pauly*. Paris 1836.
Louis, P. C. A. *Researches on the Effect of Bloodletting*. Boston 1836.
Lutaud, A. "Les médecins dans Balzac: Bianchon-Bouillaud," *Bull. Soc. Fr. Hist. Méd.* 1925, 19: 145.

Mac-Auliffe, Léon. *La Révolution et les hôpitaux de Paris*. Paris 1901.
Mac-Auliffe, Léon. *La thérapeutique physique d'autrefois*. Paris 1904.
Maljean, [?]. "Le romantisme médical: Broussais," *Chron. méd.* 1927, 34: 99 ff.
Malpart, M. *Un médecin romantique: Eusèbe de Salles (1796–1873)*. Paris 1928.
Mantel, I. *L'otologie à Paris 1800–1850*. Zurich 1965.
Marandel, [?], *Essai sur les irritations*. Paris 1807.
Marc, C. C. H. "Introduction," *Ann. d'hyg. publ.* vol. I, pp. i–xxxvi, 1829.
Maygrier, J. P. *Annuaire médical*. Paris 1810.
Meding, K. H. *Manuel du Paris médical; recueil des renseignements historiques, statistiques, administratifs et scientifiques sur les hôpitaux et hospices civils et militaires ... .* Paris 1853.
Menière, Prosper. *Journal*. Paris 1903.
Merz, T. *History of European Thought in the 19th Century*. 4 vols. Edinburgh and London 1897–1904.
Miquel, Antoine. *Éloge de Xavier Bichat*. Paris 1823.
Monteil, J. J. *Le cours d'anatomie pathologique de Bichat: un nouveau manuscrit*. Grenoble n. d. [1964].
Monfalcon, J. B. *Précis de bibliographie médicale, contenant l'indication et la classification des ouvrages les meilleurs ... .* Paris 1827.
Morel de Rubempré, J. *Les médecins de Paris*. Paris 1825.
Muehry, Adolf. *Darstellungen und Ansichten zur Vergleichung der Medizin in Frankreich, England und Deutschland ... .* Hanover 1836.
Muellener, E. R. "Die Entstehung des Kleptomaniebegriffs," *Sudh. Arch.* 1964, 48: 216–239.
Muellener, E. R. "Genfer Medizinalstatistik in der ersten Haelfte des 19. Jahrhunderts," *Gesnerus* 1964, 21: 154–192.
Muellener, E. R. "Six Geneva Physicians on Meningitis," *Journ. Hist. Med.* 1965, 20: 1–26.
Müller, Stefan. *Antoine Laurent Bayle*. Zurich 1965.
Mutzner, U. *P. Bretonneau*. Zurich 1965.

Nordenskjöld, Erik. *The History of Biology: A Survey*. Trans. B. Eyre. New York 1946.
Nyffeler, J. R. *Joseph Daquin und seine Philosophie de la Folie*. Zurich 1961.

Olmsted, J. M. D. *François Magendie; Pioneer in Experimental Physiology and Scientific Medicine in XIX Century France*. New York 1944.
Osler, William. *An Alabama Student*. Oxford 1909.
Otterburg, S. J. *Das medizinische Paris, ein Beitrag zur Geschichte der Medizin und ein Wegweiser für deutsche Aerzte*. Carlsruhe 1841.
Otto, Carl. *Reise durch die Schweiz, Italien, Frankreich, Grossbritannien und Holland ... .* Hamburg 1825.

Pagenstecher, C. H. A. "Pariser Kliniken und Professoren 1819–1820," *Mitt. Gesch. Med. Natur.* 1912, 19: 321.

Pariset, Étienne.   *Histoire des membres de l'Académie royale de médecine; ou, Recueil des éloges lus dans les séances publiques de l'Académie royale de médecine.* 2 vols. Paris 1845.

Pasteur, Louis.   *Quelques reflexions sur la science en France.* Paris 1871. (Reprinted in *Oeuvres*, Vol. VII, Paris 1939.)

Peiper, Albrecht.   *Chronik der Kinderheilkunde.* Leipzig 1958.

Peisse, Louis.   *Les médecins français contemporains.* Paris 1827.

Peisse, Louis.   *La médecine et les médecins.* Paris 1837.

Petersen, Julius.   *Haupmomente in der geschichtlichen Entwickelung der medizinischen Therapie.* Copenhagen 1877.

Petit, M. A., and Serres, E. R. A.   *Traité de la fièvre enteromesentérique.* Paris 1813.

Picavet, F.   *Les idéologues.* Paris 1891.

Pigeire, J.   *La vie et l'oeuvre de Chaptal.* Paris 1932.

Pilastre, E.   *Malgaigne, 1806–1865; étude sur sa vie et ses idées d'après ses écrits, des papiers de famille et des souvenirs particuliers.* Paris 1905.

Pinel, Philippe.   *La médecine clinique.* Paris 1804.

Pinel, Philippe.   *Traité médico-philosophique sur l'alienation mentale.* 2nd ed. Paris 1809.

Pinel, Philippe.   "Clinique," *Dict. sc. méd.* 5:364–371, Paris 1813.

Pinel, Philippe.   *Nosographie philosophique.* 3 vols. Paris 1818.

Piorry, P. A.   *Traité de diagnostic et de séméilogie.* 2d ed. Brussels 1837.

Piorry, P. A.   *Hämopathologie.* Leipzig 1839.

Piorry, P. A.   *Ueber die Erblichkeit bei Krankheiten.* Weimar 1841.

Piorry, P. A.   *La médecine du bon sens; de l'emploi des petits moyens en médecine et en thérapeutique.* Paris 1867.

Portal, Antoine.   *Observations sur la nature et le traitement des maladies du foie.* Paris 1813.

Poumiès de la Siboutie, F. L.   *Souvenirs d'un médecin de Paris.* 2d ed. Paris 1910.

Prevost, F. L.   *La Faculté de Médecine de Paris; ses chaires, ses annexes et son personnel enseignant de 1794 à 1900.* Paris 1900.

Prost, P. A.   *La médecine éclairée par l'observation et l'ouverture des corps.* Paris 1804.

Prunelle, C. V. F.   *Des études du médecin, de leurs connexions et leur méthodologie ... .* Paris 1816.

Puschmann, Theodor.   *A History of Medical Education.* London 1891.

Rameaux, J. F.   *Appréciations des progrès de l'hygiène publique depuis la commencement du 19e siècle.* Strasbourg 1839.

Ratier, F. S.   *Formulaire pratique des hôpitaux civils de Paris.* 2d ed. Paris 1825.

Ratier, F. S.   *Coup d'oeuil sur les cliniques médicales de la Faculté et des hôpitaux civils de Paris.* Paris 1827.

Rayer, P. F. O.   *Sommaire d'une histoire abrégée de l'anatomie pathologique.* Paris 1818.

Rayer, P. F. O.   *Traité théoretique et pratique des maladies de la peau, fondé sur de nouvelles recherches d'anatomie et de physiologie pathologique.* Paris 1826–27.

Regnault, J. B.   *Considérations sur l'état de la médecine en France depuis la révolution jusqu'à nos jours.* Paris 1819.

Reis, P. H. L.   *Étude sur Broussais et sur son oeuvre.* Paris 1869.

Réveillé-Parise, J. H.   *Études de l'homme dans l'état de santé et dans l'état de maladie.* 2 vols. Paris 1845.

Revue des sociétés médicales de France et de l'étranger.   Ed. A. Dupau and others. Paris 1822–1886.

Rich. A. R. "The Place of Dutrochet in the Development of Cellular Theory," *Bull. Johns Hopkins Hosp.* 1926, 39:330–365.

Richerand, A. *Histoire des progrès récents de la chirurgie.* Paris 1825.

Rilliet, Frédéric, and Barthez, A. C. E. *Traité clinique et pratique des maladies des enfants.* 3 vols. Paris 1853.

Rochaix, Maurice. *Essai sur l'évolution des questions hospitalières de la fin de l'ancien régime à nos jours.* Dijon 1959.

Rochard, J. E. *Histoire de la chirurgie française au XIXe siècle; étude historique et critique sur les progrès faits en chirurgie et dans les sciences ....* Paris 1875.

Roland, R. *Les médecins et la loi du 19 Ventôse an XI.* Paris 1883.

Rosen, George. *The Specialization of Medicine.* New York 1944.

Rosen, George. "The Philosophy of Ideology and the Emergence of Modern Medicine in France," *Bull. Hist. Med.* 1946, 20:328–339.

Rosen, George. "An American Doctor in Paris in 1828," *Journ. Hist. Med.* 1951, 6:64–116.

Rosen, George. "Hospitals, Medical Care and Social Policy in the French Revolution," *Bull. Hist. Med.* 1956, 30:124–149.

Rosen, George. *A History of Public Health.* New York 1958.

Rosen, George. "Romantic Medicine: A Problem in Historical Periodization," *Bull. Hist. Med.* 1961, 25:149–158.

Rosen, George. "Social Attitudes toward Madness in 17th and 18th Century Europe," *Journ. Hist. Med.* 1963, 18:220–240.

Rossi, Ennio. "Giovanni Rasori (1766–1837) or Italian Medicine in Transition," *Bull. Hist. Med.* 1955, 29:116–133.

Rostan, L. L. *Traité élémentaire de diagnostic, de prognostic, d'indications thérapeutiques ....* Paris 1826.

Rostan, L. L. *De l'organicisme.* Paris 1864.

Roux, P. J. *Relation d'un voyage fait à Londres en 1814; ou, Parallèle de la chirurgie anglaise avec la chirurgie française ....* Paris 1815.

Roux, P. J. *Quarante années de pratique chirurgicale.* Paris 1854–1855.

Rouxeau, Alfred. *Laennec avant 1806.* Paris 1912.

Rouxeau, Alfred. *Laennec après 1806, 1806–1826 d'après des documents inédits.* Paris 1920.

Ruin, J. G. G. *Essai sur J. B. G. Barbier.* Amiens 1939.

Rush, Benjamin. *Letters.* Ed. L. H. Butterfield. Philadelphia 1951.

Sachaile de la Barre, C. (pseud. for Lachaise, Claude). *Les médecins de Paris jugés par leurs oeuvres.* Paris 1845.

Saucerotte, Constant. *Les médecins pendant la révolution, 1789–1799.* Paris 1887.

Schiller, J. "Claude Bernard et la statistique," *Arch. Int. Hist. Sc.* 1963, 16:405–418.

Schneider, D. *Psychosomatik in der Pariser Klinik von Pinel bis Trousseau.* Zurich 1964.

Schultes, I. A. *Briefe über Frankreich.* 2 vols. Leipzig 1815.

Schweigger, A. F. *Ueber Krankenanstalten zu Paris.* Bayreuth 1809.

Sédillot, C. E. *Recherches sur le cancer.* Strasbourg 1846.

Semadeni, Helmut. *Die Erbkrankheiten um 1850.* Zurich 1960.

Semelaigne, René. *Les grands aliénistes français.* Paris 1894.

Shryock, R. H. *The Development of Modern Medicine.* Philadelphia 1936.

Sigerist, H. E. *Einführung in die Medizin.* Leipzig 1931.

Smeaton, W. A. *Fourcroy, Chemist and Revolutionary.* Cambridge 1962.

Stewart, F. C.   *The Hospitals and Surgeons of Paris.* New York and Philadelphia 1843.

Stromeyer, G. F. L.   *Erinnerungen eines deutschen Artzes.* 2 vols. Hanover 1875.

Temkin, Owsei.   "The Philosophical Background of Magendie's Physiology," *Bull. Hist. Med.* 1946, 20: 10–35.

Temkin, Owsei.   "Gall and the Phrenological Movement," *Bull. Hist. Med.* 1947, 21: 275–321.

Temkin, Owsei.   "The Role of Surgery in the Rise of Modern Medical Thought," *Bull. Hist. Med.* 1951, 25: 248–259.

Théodoridès, J.   "Le rôle novateur de Davaine en biologie et médecine," *Arch. Inst. Cl. Bernard* 1961, Vol. I.

Théodoridès, J.   "Quelques parasitologistes microscopistes français du 19e siècle (Dujardin, Donne, Gruby, Davaine)," *85 Congrès Soc. Sav.* 1960, 625–632.

Thouvenel, O. S.   *Sur les devoirs publics du médecin.* Paris 1806.

Trélat, Ulysse.   *De la constitution du corps des médecins.* Paris 1828.

Triaire, Paul.   *Bretonneau et ses correspondants; ouvrage comprenant la correspondence de Trousseau et de Velpeau avec Bretonneau.* Paris 1892.

Triaire, Paul.   *Récamier et ses contemporains, 1774–1852. Étude d'histoire de la médecine aux XVIIIe et XIXe siècles.* Paris 1899.

Trousseau, Armand.   *Clinique médicale de l'Hôtel-Dieu de Paris.* 3 vols. Paris 1873; trans. J. R. Cormack and P. V. Bazire, Philadelphia 1873.

Valléry-Radot, P.   *Deux siècles d'histoire hospitalière.* Paris 1947.

Véron, L. D.   *Mémoires d'un bourgeois de Paris, comprenant: la fin de l'Empire, la Restauration, la Monarchie de Juillet, et la République jusqu'au rétablissement de l'Empire.* 6 vols. Paris 1853–1855.

Villermé, L. R.   *Population, Hygiène.* Paris 1829.

Villermé, L. R.   *Des Épidémies.* Paris 1833.

Virchow, Rudolph.   *Gesammelte Abhandlungen zur wissenschaftlichen Medizin.* Frankfurt a. M. 1856.

Virey, J. J.   *Hygiene philosophique.* Paris 1828.

Voullonne, [?].   *Mémorie sur la médecine agissante et la médecine expectante.* Avignon 1776.

Walser, H.   "L'école hypnologique de Nancy: Berceau de la psychothérapie moderne," *Médecine et hygiène* Apr. 28, 1965, 685: 443.

Walther, P. von.   "Historische Umrisse von Frankreichs naturwiss. Kultur in näherer Beziehung auf Medizin und Chirurgie," *Jahrb. d. Med. als Wissch.* 1806, 1: 143.

Wardenburg, J.   *Briefe eines Arztes.* Gottingen 1799.

Weidmann, Peter.   *Venereologie in Paris 1800–1850.* Zurich 1965.

Weiner, D.   "François Vincent Raspail," *Fr. Hist. Stud.* 1959, 1: 149–171.

Wigdorovits, B.   *Guillaume Laennec.* Zurich 1965.

Williams, L. P.   "Science, Education and Napoleon," *Isis* 1956, 47: 369 ff.

Wolfe, D. E.   "Sydenham and Locke on the Limits of Anatomy," *Bull. Hist. Med.* 1961, 35: 193–220.

Wunderlich, K. R. A.   *Wien und Paris.* Stuttgart 1841.

Wunderlich, K. R. A.   *Handbuch der Pathologie und Therapie.* Stuttgart 1850.

Wunderlich, K. R. A.   *Geschichte der Medizin.* Stuttgart 1859.

Wyss, H. E.   *Johann Ferdinand Heyfelder (1798–1869) und seine Beobachtungen über die Krankheiten der Neugeborenen.* Zurich 1964.

"X."   *Biographie des médecins français vivants.* Paris 1826.

INDEX

See St Louis Hosp. 240

Medicine at the Paris Hospital, 1794–1848
by Erwin H. Ackerknecht, M.D.

designer: *Gerard Valerio*
typesetter: *Baltimore Type and Composition Corporation*
typefaces: *Kennerley text and display*
printer: *Universal Lithographers, Inc.*
paper: *P&S R*
binder: *Maple Press*
cover material: *G.S.B. S/535 Black #9 and Curtis Tweedweave text*